In Search of
Beauty in Music

A SCIENTIFIC APPROACH TO MUSICAL ESTHETICS

by

CARL E. SEASHORE

PROFESSOR OF PSYCHOLOGY AND DEAN EMERITUS OF THE
GRADUATE SCHOOL, THE STATE UNIVERSITY OF IOWA

THE RONALD PRESS COMPANY · NEW YORK

Library of Congress Catalog Card Number: 47-3744

PRINTED IN THE UNITED STATES OF AMERICA

This volume is affectionately and gratefully inscribed
for my comrades in research in the psychological laboratory
which has been dedicated to the pursuit of
Insight into the Nature of Mental Life,
Appreciation of its Beauty, and
Wisdom in its Control
Development of Personality, Scientific Integrity,
and the Art of Deliberate and Adequate Statement of Fact
Center for Fundamental Science and Service to Mankind
Memorial to the Pioneers in Psychology
Hearth for Comrades in Research

PREFACE

MORE HAS BEEN ACHIEVED in the laying of foundations for science in music in the present century than in all preceding centuries. The chief reason for this is that the applied science of music has had to await the development of such underlying sciences as acoustics, physiology, electrical engineering, anthropology, experimental education, and experimental psychology. In all these fields phenomenal progress has been made in the instrumentation and standardizing of techniques of measurement. Naturally to these should be added the development of a body of science-minded musical artists who welcome such scientific approaches. The progress has been facilitated and rushed at phenomenal speed by the practical aspects of radio, phonophotography, phonography, industrial acoustics, and the increasing demands for the psychology of music in these fields, as well as in education.

During this period of extraordinary expansion in the basic sciences which contribute to the scientific foundations of music, it has been my great fortune to be associated with scientists and musicians who have been interested in cultivating a closer affiliation between science and music through teaching, lecturing, writing, and the direction of research.

This volume is designed as an introduction to the science of music for advanced students of music and psychology, music teachers, educators, professional musicians, and general readers interested in the scientific approach to the understanding and appreciation of beauty in music. It is an attempt to integrate my interpretive and popular articles on research in the psychology of music which have more or less direct bearing on the problem of esthetics. Each chapter has appeared in whole or in part in some leading musical, scientific, or educational journal.

Since the book opens a large variety of new fields of thought and investigation, the reader is advised to turn to the table of contents for a preliminary orientation by deliberate examination of the listings of specific topics where he can identify familiar items and new items in which he may be interested.

In collecting this material I have aimed to organize these articles into a unified series while retaining as far as possible the original form and setting, whether used in whole or in part or assembled under a single group heading. This has the advantage of presenting each topic in readable and newsy style, generally in direct address to some specific audience or reading constituency. The need of this becomes evident when it is seen that each of the 35 chapters virtually opens a new avenue of approach to the psychology of music and esthetics and presents masses of research findings which are new to the majority of readers. Each article or unit of an article opens up a new vista for discovery and exploration which must be grasped as a more or less new idea, each in its individual field, and yet with due regard for the unity in the theme of the book as a whole. This explains the apparent repetition which is carried for the purpose of a progressive establishment of relationships. In other words, the book aims to reduce laboratory technicalities to a minimum and reveal the natural possibilities and relationships in this virgin field by presenting cold illustrative facts from the laboratory and from technical publications in warm highlights. It is not a comprehensive treatise, but rather a series of examples of the material which might appear in a complete treatment of the subject. To indicate the original sources for these contributions from the Iowa psychological laboratory, the following footnote is appended.[1]

---

[1] *Elementary Experiments in Psychology.* New York: Henry Holt & Co., 1908. 218 pp. Revised edition, with Robert H. Seashore, 1930.

Psychology in Daily Life. New York: D. Appleton & Co., 1914. xvii, 226 pp.

The Psychology of Musical Talent. New York: Silver Burdett Co., 1919. xvi, 288 pp.

The Psychology of the Vibrato in Voice and Instrument. Iowa City, Iowa: University of Iowa Press, 1936. 159 pp.

The Psychology of Music. New York: McGraw-Hill Book Co., Inc., 1937. 408 pp.

Why We Love Music. Philadelphia: Oliver Ditson Co., 1940. 82 pp. (A Swedish translation was published in Sweden in 1947.)

Revision of the *Seashore Measures of Musical Talents.* Iowa City, Iowa: University of Iowa Press, 1940. (With Joseph G. Saetveit and Don Lewis.)

Pioneering in Psychology. Iowa City, Iowa: University of Iowa Press, 1942. vii, 232 pp.

The University of Iowa studies in the psychology of music have appeared in four volumes published by the University Press as follows: Vol. I, *The Vibrato,*

In this emphasis upon the present status of current musical achievements, I am not unmindful of the contributions made from the time of the appearance of Helmholtz' monumental volume, *Sensations of Tone*; the extensive investigations in the field of musical anthropology; the historical, creative and theoretical contributions by the great musicians; as well as the work of contemporary scientists.

It is a pleasure to acknowledge the generous support given our project by the administration of the University of Iowa; the foundations which have contributed generously toward stipends for investigators, and the late Mr. George Eastman in particular for his aid in furthering the project; and, above all, the long list of my comrades in research, to whom I bow in profound gratitude for the share that each has had in pursuit of the common task for which it has been my privilege to act as mentor and spokesman.

CARL E. SEASHORE

Iowa City, Iowa
November 18, 1946

1932, 382 pp. (out of print) ; Vol. II, *The Measurement of Musical Talent*, 1935, 144 pp.; Vol. III, *The Vibrato in Voice and Instrument* (a textbook, see above) ; Vol. IV, *Objective Analysis of Musical Performance*, 1937, 379 pp.

Most of our original articles from 1900 to 1932 appeared in the *University of Iowa Studies in Psychology* (now in its 27th volume) published in the Psychological Review Monograph Series.

Since the principles investigated in the psychology of music during this period have many common elements with other related inceptive sciences, a considerable number of publications emanating from this laboratory have appeared from the pens of my associates in child welfare, speech, education, graphic and plastic arts, psychology, otology, and acoustics.

CONTENTS

PART ONE

SCIENTIFIC APPROACHES TO MUSICAL ESTHETICS

PART TWO

EXAMPLES OF SCIENTIFIC FOUNDATIONS FOR MUSICAL ESTHETICS

PART THREE

EXAMPLES OF SOME SUBJECTIVE VARIABLES

PART FOUR

HISTORICAL BACKGROUND AND EDUCATIONAL APPROACHES

PART FIVE

SOME SCIENTIFIC SPECULATIONS AND CONCLUSIONS

FIGURES

PART ONE

SCIENTIFIC APPROACHES TO MUSICAL ESTHETICS

Chapter 1

SCIENCE IN MUSIC

MUSIC DRAWS UPON a number of basic sciences—such as mathematics, physics, physiology, anatomy, genetics, anthropology, and general psychology—in the light of prevailing musical theory and practice. It has become the function of the new applied science, the psychology of music, to integrate all these contributions and fit them, as a unified function, into the theory and practice of music, and to initiate specifically designed experiments for solving musical problems. The initiative has been taken by psychologists; but, as knowledge of the scientific aspects becomes a part of artistic creation and skill, this work of integration will be taken over more and more by musicians, and the distinction between the scientist and the artist will tend to disappear.

On the occasion of a football game at the University of Oklahoma in 1939, I saw seventy-seven marching bands on parade. This represented only a section of the state—and a dust-bowl state at that. It meant that music is being taught in the public schools of that state on a surprisingly large scale. Out of these popular bands in showy uniform will come a host of musicians of all kinds and degrees of ability. Music is in the public schools to stay—on a large scale. Music in America is in the air, literally and figuratively.

In the last ten years, the State University of Iowa, as one of the American universities that have taken cognizance of this problem, has conferred twenty doctor of philosophy degrees and two hundred and fifty-five master of arts degrees in music. The master of arts is coming to be required of all high-school music teachers. From kindergarten up to the graduate school,

From *Science*, 1942, 1417–1422, implementing the article "The Musical Mind," *Atlantic Monthly*, 1928, *141*, 358–367.

music has been taken in with the three R's and their derivatives. As a result, we have such relatively new terms as *music educator* and *musicology*.

For a certificate to teach music, the candidate must ordinarily be certified for courses in general psychology and educational psychology; a third requirement, the specific psychology of music, is fast coming in through our training schools for teachers. Next will come musical esthetics!

In recent years the development of the Acoustical Society of America has brought about a revolution in musical thinking. Research in musical acoustics is being put on a rigidly scientific basis and is making great progress. There is an awakening interest in what is called musicology, the science of music. This science has many branches, one of the most active of which is the psychology of music.

In view of this new demand for and the new possibilities of a scientific approach to music and scientific foundations for musical education and musical theory in preparation for the teaching and study of music, it is time to inquire, *"What can psychology do for music?"* [1]

From the time of Aristoxenus and Pythagoras, there have been two basic attitudes toward music: one the impressionistic attitude of the musician who is not interested in explanations but merely in results which are judged by his unaided ear and speculative mind; the other that of the scientific inquirer, like Pythagoras, who asked, for example, "What are the reasons for the musical scale, and what are its limitations?" The first is the easy, *laissez faire* attitude; the second is a critical and scientific attitude which made no great progress until the beginning of the renaissance. Its first prominent organizer, Helmholtz, digested material accumulated from all sources, and made funda-

---

[1] When I was completing a series of thirty consecutive articles on the Psychology of Music for *Music Educators Journal*, the editor, recognizing that each of these articles had been an actual contribution to music from the psychological laboratory in the attempt to show what psychology is doing for music, asked me to generalize the series by answering the above question. My answer was in twelve statements, which are repeated here in italics. These statements do not mean that psychology has accomplished all these things, but rather that the way has been paved. Nor does it mean that these are the only things psychology can do, but the items listed necessarily are limited to those which I personally have had firsthand experience in the psychological laboratory.

mental contributions through laboratory researches discussed in his epoch-making volume, *Die Tonempfindungen* (1862).

Psychology as an experimental science had its beginning only seventy years ago, and, in the first half of that period, showed no interest in music. Thus the scientific approach to the understanding and mastery of music is relatively new, and antiscientific musicians are still with us in large numbers.

Psychology gives us a workable insight into the nature of the musical mind and thus lays foundations for the classification of events in musical experience and behavior and for the development of a scientific musical terminology. The psychology of music is the science of musical experience and behavior. A general knowledge of the structure and function of the musical organism is therefore one of the first requirements in a scientific approach to the study and mastery of music. It helps the student to understand the specific features with which he is dealing in learning and performing, and it furnishes the essential basis for the orderly arrangement of observed facts. For example, we learn that the sound wave as the exclusive source of musical tones has only four basic variables: frequency, intensity, duration, and wave form. On the basis of that, it has been found that the musical organism must have four corresponding capacities for hearing all music: the sense of pitch, the sense of loudness, the sense of time, and the sense of timbre. This conception simplifies the understanding of the nature and function of the musical mind in that each of these four basic functions appears in such complex musical forms as harmony, melody, dynamics, rhythm, volume, and tone quality. It has been shown that all of our musical memory, musical action, and musical composition may be expressed in these four terms. Thus the classification vastly simplifies the task of the musician and makes the problems of appreciation and performance concrete and specific. The understanding and description of musical design in composition, of all the forms of musical expression of feeling, all the techniques in ear-training, all the analyses of musical appreciation, all deviations from the true and regular in artistic forms, and all descriptions of types of musicianship and of music in general, hinge upon a clear insight into the nature of the functioning of this type of classification. Yet this is but one aspect of the classification that the psychology of music contributes to the understanding and description of the musical mind in action.

Psychology organizes the scientific description of musical tones and the means for producing them. Psychology enables the musician to think in orderly, specific, describable, repeatable, and verifiable terms. All this is new to the traditional nonscientific musician. For example, he is interested in tone quality. But what is tone quality? What is its relation to other attributes of tone? What are its determinants? What are the limits, possibilities, and means for its mastery? Which, if any, of the accretions of scores of fantastic names for tone quality are significant, definable, and usable? These are all psychological questions with a musical meaning which may be taken into the laboratory.

One element of tone quality is timbre, but, until recently, no music book revealed an adequate understanding of this concept. Definitions were often meaningless, and the waste of time and efficiency in teaching the mastery of timbre has been prodigious, largely because neither teacher nor pupil knew what was to be developed and had no objective standards for orientation. The French pronunciation added to the mystery.

Another element of tone quality is sonance. We had no name in music for this vital concept of tone quality until about twenty years ago.

Now, tone quality can be explained in terms of timbre and sonance so that the members of the Acoustical Society of America, the musicologists, the intelligent teachers and students of music, and scientists in general are satisfied. Discriminative hearing, appreciation, and mastery in the control of tone quality rest upon a correct terminology and insight into the nature of the concept.

The musician can now look at the graphic picture of the tone spectrum of his violin and the graphic performance score as recorded with a camera, and he can see in minute detail exactly how he performed in a given rendition. In analyzing the results, psychology accepts the physicist's account of tone production as exemplified in various instruments, the physiologist's account of the vocal mechanism and the human ear, the geneticist's theory of inheritance and development, the anthropologist's account of evolution in the human race, and the psychologist's account of the principles of hearing. Each of these contributions thus helps the musician to know and to describe a certain characteristic of voice or instrument and to analyze and specify the best means for artistic tone control and the acquisition of musical skills. To facilitate this for experimental purposes, there are available at present tone generators which enable us to produce any kind of tone desired according to specifications and to describe such tones quantitatively. Applied science can now improve the violin or any other instrument, create entirely new models, and effect new ensembles of instruments.

Psychology gives us an orderly insight into the nature, scope, and limitations of musical hearing and appreciation. The child says with satisfaction, "I see with my eyes and hear with my ears." That attitude, until recently, satisfied many a student and teacher of music. But there is now an elaborate and serviceable experimental psychology of hearing, both pure and applied, for which we find countless applications in the hearing, appreciation, and performance of music. The musician is now becoming interested in knowing and in being able to state exactly what in the musical tone it is that he hears, appreciates, tries to perform, and intends that the listener shall hear. He finds available an elaborate and technical system of laws of hearing, the most important of which are the laws of illusion in hearing. He finds that, if it were not for the operation of law in illusion, there could hardly be any real music. He finds that the relation between the physical sound and the sound as it is heard is not 1:1 and that a series of conversion tables for this relationship are of vital importance in hearing. He finds that acoustic principles determine the carrying power and the pleasantness or unpleasantness of his tone. His understanding and artistic rendition rest upon observance of these laws. The composer and the performer must be guided by definite laws of phonetics and acoustics. Musical hearing and musical criticism must take them into account. In other words, the insight, interpretation, description, and mastery of music hinge upon the command of principles of hearing; and the musician finds that musical education is, in large part, a systematic training of a discriminating ear.

Psychology enables us to analyze and to evaluate musical talents as a basis for guidance in musical education, vocational and avocational. Musical talent of various kinds and in varying degrees is inherited. There is not one, but a hierarchy, of musical talents, many of which can now be analyzed clearly and measured with precision. In this equipment, nature is prolific. Education and refinement build upon selected native capacities, but, most frequently, a large part of this inherited endowment is lost for want of cultivation.

The magnitude of individual differences is conspicuous in music. Yet the problem in music education is to deal with each individual difference with proper recognition of the total personality in the total situation. One of the unfortunate fallacies promulgated by many music teachers is the idea that, while not all children inherit musical minds, it is their function to devote as much effort to those children who have little or no such inheritance as to those who have much. The public-school music teacher now faces stubborn facts when he makes a survey of musical talent in the school and finds that, of two equally intelligent pupils, one has more than a hundred times as fine a sense of pitch, sense of rhythm, sense of time, or sense of timbre as the other, knowing that these are relatively independent variables and that a pupil may stand high in one and low in another. These are facts which the teacher cannot ignore in selecting instruments, registering pupils for training, and interpreting success or failure and laying foundations for praise and blame.

It has been found that, in the human races of the world today and at the various culture levels of civilized people, there is little difference in the average of the elemental capacities for musical hearing. But, within any such group, there is an extraordinary range of difference among individuals. There is as wide a distribution of the gift of music among the primitive South Sea Islanders as there is in the families of the social register, and in both groups the highly gifted are relatively rare and the nongifted are in abundance. When we find that these differences in capacity are fairly independent of age, intelligence, training, and cultural or racial origin, we face new problems in music. Native talent is the capital which it is the business of the music educator to invest. He must therefore know what talent is and how to make the best investment. Psychology is furnishing the methods and the means for such measurement, not only at the sensory and motor levels but also at the higher, creative levels.

Psychology furnishes the technique for the measurement of musical achievement by the analysis and the objectifying of goals as a means of motivation in training. The techniques developed for the measurement of musical talent are now carried into the field of analysis and measurement of musical achievement. It has become possible to set up definite musical objectives as specific goals of achievement in various stages of training and to measure progressive achievement in the work toward these goals. Thus a pupil is furnished a check list of specific concepts, skills, and critical judgments which are to be acquired, and he may enjoy the privilege of knowing, in specific terms, what progress he is making from time to time. This is a powerful element in motivation and in attainment of efficiency through instruction. This organization of scientific measurement of musical achievement is going to revolutionize the musical curriculum. There will be a general housecleaning for discarding the nonessential, the undefinable, and the incongruous; music educators are now joining in co-operative movements to determine the minimum essentials and the order of their development in terms of scientifically defined concepts.

Psychology enables us to organize musical training in terms of a growing body of principles in educational psychology. Educational psychology has revolutionized teaching in all other public-school subjects. Music educators and psychologists now are attempting to glean nuggets from current literature on the various aspects of the psychology of learning in order to select and to organize those general facts in educational psychology which have a bearing on the art of instruction in music. Music teachers are fast joining the ranks of those who conduct psychological experiments in the actual musical situation. It has been the function of psychology to stimulate and to facilitate this movement.

Psychology paves the way at all levels for principles of musical criticism and for a logical award of praise or criticism. Historically, musical criticism has generally been impressionistic and unscholarly. But it is no longer satisfactory to fill the music columns with laudatory or condemnatory slush which is popularly conventional, prejudiced, and often subsidized. The psychology of music has begun to pave the way toward intelligent appraisal by furnishing the means for logical criticism and discriminating judgment, expressed in terminology standardized for the art. Considerate and judicious criticism is one of the most promising means for motivating (or rightfully discouraging) anyone— from the child in the elementary grades to the professional on the stage. It is not only pedagogical but humanitarian to recognize individual differences in the degree and kind of musical capacity at all levels in the award of praise or criticism. We cannot expect equal achievement from all the children in a given grade in school; and, in awarding credit for work, the modern teacher faces a new problem: the attainment of a fair balance in giving credit or discredit for achievement in relation to capacity for achievement and specific outstanding fortes and faults.

Psychology makes possible the use of performance scores for the detailed analysis and the quantifying of artistic elements in musical performance. The greatest single contribution made in the recent advances of the psychology of music lies in the development of musical phonophotography and the invention of the graphic musical performance score, both of which are based upon the objective recording of individual sound waves in the musical tone. The phonographic recording had to be supplemented by a series of phonophotographic processes. The musician can now perform with voice or instrument in the recording studio where, in addition to a permanent phonographic record, a series of synchronized cameras will reproduce every aspect of each sound wave, so that each note can be reconstructed in minute detail much finer than the ear can hear. This recording may be done in a dead room, which eliminates from the musical performance all characteristics that are due to extraneous sounds and the acoustic characteristics of the music room. Thus in the time that it takes to sing a song, whether it is sung on the stage or in the radio studio or in the laboratory, we obtain a motion-picture record which contains thousands of items of musical significance.

But the mastery of this type of recording revealed the necessity of a new type of language for musical performance. This has taken the form of what is known as the performance score, in which the actual rendition of each note is graphed in such detail as may be desired, in terms of clearly defined characteristics. This graphic performance score is a brand-new language with a systematized series of symbols. These symbols represent defined concepts for musical performance, and they are analogous in significance to the language and symbols of mathematics or biology. In terms of such a performance score, any specific element in the character of the performance can be isolated for analysis and measurement. The musician can see revealed in the score an astonishing number of features of which he otherwise would not be aware. The interpretations given by various artists can be compared and criticized, and new features in the phonographic record for the ear can be recognized when they have been revealed by the cameras. For the preservation of primitive music, for the criticism of great artists, and for educational purposes, the resources of the performance score are inexhaustible; it opens a new area of interest and proficiency in music.

Individuality in the art of musical interpretation lies largely in artistic deviation from the true, the rigid, and the uniform as represented by the musical score. The performance score represents precision measurements of all forms and degrees of artistic deviation or license, judgment, and skill.

Psychology enables us to set up norms of prevailing musical achievement and to show by experiment how these norms for attainment could and should be refined. We do not have and do not desire fixed standards or norms in any element of musical excellence. There must be room for artistic individuality, and there are countless elements that may contribute to the goodness or badness of a voice or an instrument. But the psychology of music has introduced techniques, especially through the use of the performance score, for showing the style, the tendencies, the limits of variability, and any other characteristic in any element of the best musical performance of today. There is a recognizable limit or tolerance within which the artist must be restrained. For example, when we take such a debatable and often unbearable feature as the vibrato of a singer, norms can be established to show that every good singer sings with a vibrato on practically every note intoned, whether he hears it or intends it or not. It is an inalienable element of goodness in voice. On an average, the twenty-five best-recognized singers of today have a pitch pulsation of approximately a half tone; this seems unbelievable, because it is not heard as such. They have an average rate of pulsation of about six and one half per second; this tends to take the form of a smooth sine curve and may occur in pitch, intensity, or timbre, and frequently occurs in all three. Excellent but untutored primitive singers have approximately the same kind and degree of vibrato as do recognized musicians.

But these norms of prevailing excellence in voice can readily be refined. Norms of average performance for violin and other instruments have been established. For example, if we assume that the violin vibrato is more musically acceptable than the prevailing voice vibrato, as is generally conceded, we can take the best violin vibrato as a model for the establishment of a more ideal norm. We can proceed, in a short time, to refine the vibrato of a singer to something like the violin norm, which is barely half as conspicuous as the prevailing vocal norms. Psychologists have shown how this can be done for any pupil and for any artist now on the stage. It is difficult to imagine what a tremendous advance in the art of singing such a modulation of the prevailing vibrato among singers would be if such reformation of the stage were attempted seriously. It would ban the tremolo (which is simply a bad vibrato) and would contribute vastly to the beauty in flexibility, tenderness, and richness of tone. It took psychologists to show what the vibrato is, how bad the prevailing vibrato can be and how it can be improved.

Psychology prescribes instruments and techniques which shorten the time of musical training and yield a higher precision and mastery than is ordinarily obtained. Thanks to the extraordinary development in the recording and transmission of sound by electronics, we are now in a position to equip the music studio (both public and private) with training instruments. Skill in pitch intonation is gained by training in front of an instrument which shows instantly, to a hundredth of a whole-tone step, the precision, the artistic deviation, or the degree of error in singing or playing in pitch. The pianist can practice various principles of artistic dynamics in phrasing by keeping his eye on a dial which registers all dynamic changes in terms of defined units of intensity of tone. The student who has difficulty with rhythm can go through rigorous exercises on model patterns and see how he conforms to these patterns, either in terms of time as measured in hundredths of a second, or in terms of stress as measured in decibels. The most difficult feature that both vocal and instrumental students have to master is that of tone quality. And here again the student can have the advantage of an instrument which shows the wave form of his tone the instant it is sounded; the wave form can be presented in such a way that he can compare it with the desired norm, and can thus practice with his visual aid to extraordinary advantage. In short, music is falling in line with industry in turning to mechanized features such as instrumental aids. It can be said conservatively that where this is done there can be expected an extraordinary shortening of the time of training for a specific skill, and a hitherto unattainable degree of precision may be obtained.

Psychology has contributed toward enabling us to record, preserve, and interpret music in all forms of historical interest. The musical anthropologist now has at hand unlimited facilities for accumulating a wealth of historical material in music. The phonograph recordings are now good, and the acoustic recordings with motion pictures now have sufficient fidelity for exacting scientific purposes. Portable motion-picture machines are now at work in all parts of the world, and the producers and newsgathering interests are glad to co-operate with scientists. Hollywood producers have under consideration a plan for sending musical and linguistic anthropologists into primitive fields a year or two in advance of proposed filmings. Such an expert could thus make a preliminary scientific survey of the prevailing types of music and the performers, which would be available both for the filming industry and for purely scientific purposes. The field camera would be at the free disposal of the musical anthropologist for recording such scientific and artistic features as he may have found significant for the science of music. The sound tracks may be accompanied by significant motion pictures of dancing and other forms of dramatic action essential for vitalizing the music. In short, the problem of how to record primitive music is solved.

The problem now before us is to find workers who can analyze and utilize that material for the history, the science, and the art of music. The best phonographic and film recordings of music today are of such high quality that any artist should be glad to be immortalized by the faithful preservation of his music through recordings. Here, again, we already have unlimited source material for scientific analysis—a gold mine for musicologists. One who was at work on the collection and preservation of music three or four decades ago is in a position to appreciate the fabulous advantages which the collector of today has over the collector of twenty years ago.

Psychology furnishes the groundwork for a future science and philosophy of musical esthetics. Musical esthetics of the past has been largely a speculative armchair product. With the coming in of facilities for measuring musical values that should constitute the groundwork of esthetics, we enter upon a radically new era in this field. Armchair theories can now be put to experiment to be verified or discarded, modified or simplified. This applies particularly to all aspects of the nature and significance of scales and every other aspect of intervals, to all studies of the evolution of musical feeling, to all aspects of the evolution of musical values, to the fundamental concepts of the power of music, and to theories of goals to be attained. The study of such total problems can now be fractionated in the scientific attitude of dealing with one specific element at a time, such as some particular phase of harmony, balance, symmetry, resolution, or musical license. For this purpose, a radical revision of terminology for the scientific and philosophical discussion of musical esthetics must be introduced.

The scientific procedure in a new and unlimited field of this kind is a slow and arduous process, and in any generation mere beginnings can be made. But, as in the introduction of scientific methods in the classification of plants and animals and the interpretation of their complete life histories, once the scientific attitude is made possible, the purely speculative will gradually become less and less acceptable as a final solution. More progress toward a scientific approach to musical esthetics has been made in the last twenty years than in all preceding history.

Coda. There is, of course, a large body of scientific principles and means of progress developed by musicians themselves in creative experimentation and thinking within the art. That is taken for granted. The features here discussed are drawn from contributions in current science that have a bearing on music. For the purpose of concrete illustrations, they are limited to features with which the author has had firsthand acquaintance. Many other scientific approaches deserve mention. The aim has been to present a point of view and a comparatively new frame of reference for scientific thinking in music.

What is indicated here for music applies in principle to the other fine arts, especially to dramatic art, poetry, and dancing. The more we rise into a consideration of the common elements of all artistic creative power and the assimilation of art in daily life and philosophical thought, the more we become aware of a common ground of interest, appreciation, and cultivation of the scientific spirit in all arts, both pure and applied.

Chapter 2

SCIENCE IN MUSICAL ESTHETICS

IN A RECENT NUMBER of the *British Journal of Psychology,* James Mainwaring gives a comprehensive criticism of empirical approaches to esthetics.[1] It is a clear presentation of a point of view often voiced, and it should be reviewed critically by the various interests concerned.[2] Instead of an attempt at formal criticism, let me set out a single constructive illustration of one empiricist's point of view in defense. In this I shall limit myself to a single concrete case dealing with the significance of a tonal spectrum in musical esthetics from the laboratory point of view, and, for the sake of clarity and brevity, I shall limit myself to a few categorical statements which any competent investigator in the field of psychological acoustics can verify and evaluate.

Science can clarify and define essential concepts in esthetics. The term *tonal quality* represents one of the large categories of musical esthetics. It has two components, namely, timbre and sonance. Timbre is a cross-section of a tone as represented by a single sound wave in terms of its harmonic structure, fundamental frequency, and total intensity. Sonance represents the quality of a tone as determined by the harmonic structure of the successive waves in the tone as a whole. Thus, timbre is a case of simultaneous fusion of partials at a given moment in the tone, whereas sonance is a case of successive fusions of changing harmonic structures during the maintenance of a

---

[1] *British Journal of Psychology,* 1941, *32,* 114.

[2] He uses the term *empirical* broadly as including laboratory experiment, systematic observation, and uncontrolled observation. In the uncontrolled observation he finds most of his material and rightly discourages it. But, in a few cases of systematic observation and laboratory experiment, he treads with uncertainty and leaves them unreasonably open to suspicion.

From *British Journal of Psychology* (General Section), 1942, *32,* 287–294.

musical note. The present illustration will deal only with timbre, a term which, when understood in musical esthetics, should be as useful as the terms pitch or rhythm. A parallel case could easily be made for sonance, thus covering the entire concept of tonal quality.

As a result of recent extraordinary developments in acoustical techniques, the investigator can now select a fair sample of a note in its actual musical setting and take a highly detailed motion picture of every sound wave in that tone as it is generated. Realizing that everything that is conveyed from the performer to the listener is conveyed on sound waves, he has here the material basis for the analysis and clarification of all possible elements in the musical tone as an art object. The form of the sound wave is the physical basis of timbre. He can take as a fair sample any representative wave in the tone and run it through a harmonic analyzer which, in a single process, will determine the number of partials present, their distribution, their relative formant groupings, and the amount of energy represented in each. These readings, which appear on a series of dials, can be transferred into a table. The facts thus established can be represented in a single graph called a tonal spectrum.

He can convert this physical spectrum into a psychological or musical spectrum which, instead of showing the amount of energy in each partial, represents the audibility or loudness of each partial in terms of decibels. The art of making this transformation in accordance with the psychological and acoustic laws of hearing is a very recent contribution. Scientific esthetics must employ both physical and psychological spectra; however, for the present purpose we shall think only in terms of the physical spectrum. From a spectrum the investigator can derive a complete, detailed, verifiable description and definition of the tone in cross-section, and, in terms of the sequence of spectra, he can give an account of the qualitative character of the tone as a whole. An experience of beauty, of course, should be couched in psychological terms insofar as possible. Likewise, the description of a physical tone should be couched in the established terminology of acoustics. (See Chapters 7 and 8.)

One of the greatest causes of confusion in esthetics is abuse of language. In musical history we find scores of synonyms substituted for the term *tonal quality,* practically all of them loose and ill-defined. When once we understand the nature and significance of the tonal spectrum as the basis of timbre and sonance, we can scrap all inconsistent terms and thus establish a common usage among scientists, artists, and philosophers.

To the scientific worker, the tonal spectrum becomes a familiar tool for analyzing purposes. A single glance at the spectrum immediately gives him a clear concept of the quality of the tone represented in cross section. It may be as exact and as easily understood as a commonplace mathematical equation. As acoustic science develops such technical terminology, that terminology tends to become popular, so that the teacher or the artist as well as the composer can readily understand what a spectrum means. He can formulate descriptions and definitions in terms of it, he can criticize or instruct in tonal quality in terms of that picture, and he can think and speak with scientific precision about the beauty or ugliness of a specific tone. For this purpose it is not necessary for him to go through the process of deriving the tonal spectrum any more than it is necessary for the pleasure driver of an automobile to be an expert in automobile engineering. Such transition from the purely technical concepts to popular and practical spheres is one of the splendid examples of growth and spread of learning.

Current attempts to name tonal qualities have resulted in such crude terms as *rich* and *pure, smooth* and *rough, big* and *small;* but these are inadequate. We speak of the different vowel qualities, bearing in mind that the differences involved are differences in formant regions. Then, in desperation, we go one step farther and speak in terms of instruments—such as the *flute tone,* the *trombone tone,* or the *violin tone*—ignoring the fact that each of these instruments is capable of producing hundreds of differences in quality. All such terms are more or less beggarly. But, if we proceed on the assumption that all differences in tonal quality are representable in the spectrum, we should make great progress in laying foundations for a consistent, simplified, and permanent language of musical esthetics.

Students of esthetics, therefore, may fairly ask if it is not possible to discover or set up a consistent scale of tonal qualities named in terms of the variables of the tonal spectrum. We think this can be done when the facts are sufficiently in hand. For example, we could recognize as many types of spectra as there are letters in the alphabet, and name them alphabetically. Then, a person talking about tonal quality could refer, in established terms, to a spectrum as the A, B, or C type (on the analogy of names for vitamins) or to possible combinations of these, such as the A-K type. Finally, descriptive names might be assigned to each for a given scale of definable differences.

Science broadens the horizon for insight into the full nature of the esthetic situation. One of the objections recently made to the experimental method is that the laboratory experimenter raises more questions than he can answer. That is one of the great merits of the scientific method. The experimental psychologist would go beyond the prevailing adage that, if you ask one question of nature, nature will ask you ten, and say he can set up a sample experiment in esthetics that will raise a hundred other relevant questions not previously thought of. When Wundt was asked what he had learned from his experiments with reaction-time tests, he replied that it had given him an entirely new concept of the human mind. So I would say that, while the experimentalist in the laboratory can give a final and verifiable solution to only one minute problem at a time, one of the great merits of the experimental procedure lies in the fact that it forces upon the horizon a vast array of issues which come as corollaries to the situation solved. It is obvious that recent progress in experimental psychology has performed this very function for esthetics by generating a deeper insight into the nature of experience and expression of esthetic emotions, and into the nature of the relation between the esthetic object and one who creates or feels beauty or ugliness in it. Would it be unjust to say that the laboratory empiricist is to the non-empiricist in esthetics as the astronomer is to the stargazer? Both look into the starry heavens but they see entirely different worlds of beauty.

Science creates a feeling of confidence in the tangibility of esthetic issues. Many serious books on esthetics now in our libraries take the same attitude toward esthetic experiment that the forerunners of modern psychology took toward psychological experiment a hundred years ago: mind is so different from matter; beauty is such an ethereal and fleeting situation; a feeling of beauty is never constant; after all, beauty deals with subjective values, not objective facts; problems that can be solved in the laboratory are only an infinitesimal aspect of the esthetic situation; like the historical soul, which is not subject to experiment, beauty is a sort of ultimate reality in itself, intangible.

But when the theory of evolution came upon the horizon there was a sudden about-face in philosophical psychology, and experimental psychology became an inceptive science. Fechner and his followers in experimental esthetics committed many blunders, but they made progress through trial and error, which resulted in the gradual acceptance of the feasibility of scientific experiment in esthetics.

The critic must distinguish between the empirical and the experimental. Great discredit is rightly thrown upon esthetics by the publication of empirical studies of beauty which do not conform or measure up to the sanctions of scientific procedure. They bring discredit upon scientific method, as, for example, in the case of securing judgments about likes and dislikes of presumably beautiful objects without setting any experimental control to determine on which feature the esthetic judgment is based; in judgments that ignore the influence of the total situation in which the experience occurs; in questionnaires (which are certainly subversive of scientific procedure); and in the statistical treatment of uncountables.[3] But these are fumblings

---

[3] I have had a hand in combating this type of procedure in visual esthetics by introducing the Meier-Seashore Art Judgment Tests. (See the *Meier-Seashore Art Judgment Test*, University of Iowa Press, 1929, 125.)

Before this, it was common practice to test artistic tastes by asking a person to indicate, for example, which of two landscapes he prefers. Such procedures can never lead to a scientific judgment. They have no scientific value whatever. In the Meier-Seashore tests, we succeeded in fractionating the procedure by providing that the judgment in the comparison of two presumably beautiful objects should be based upon one specific feature at a time as seen in its true setting. For example, the tests consist of a booklet containing one hundred

not only in an inceptive applied psychology, but also in an inceptive art or philosophy of values.

However, none can dispute that a fundamental tool, such as the tonal spectrum, has objective validity. This the student of musical esthetics must admit, and, more important, he must develop a faith and confidence in objective and verifiable procedures. Twenty years ago, it did not seem at all likely that a relatively exact science of tonal quality would be developed in this generation. But modern acoustics has been revolutionary in its progress, and our present equipment in the laboratory now enables us to face that problem with enthusiasm and with feelings of certainty in findings.

Science aids in dealing systematically with esthetic problems. Take again the problem of the sources of beauty or ugliness in tonal quality as represented by the spectrum, and consider one of the elements, such as the formant, that is, the character of the grouping of dominant partials. Analysis of this problem shows that the principal variables in the formant are the number of formants present, the position of the formant, the width of the formant, and the relative prominence of the formant. These are indisputable facts which must be taken into account when making esthetic judgments about tonal quality. And the subdivision of factors involved must be carried further. Thus the element of dominance of formant regions in musical tones can be fractionated to determine what qualitative characteristics of tone are due to specific types of distribution of formant regions. This is now illustrated in acoustical studies of speech, where vowels are defined in terms of characteristic formant regions. This method is now employed in comparative studies of musical instruments. Progress is slow, but it is in firm step, so that any one who teaches, thinks, or creates intelligently in terms of tonal quality should understand the structure and function

---

pairs of reproductions of famous paintings. One is the true copy of the original; the other is like it except that one feature is changed within reasonable limits of tolerance, but so that it modifies some esthetic principle in the composition. For example, the esthetic judgment is the answer to the question, "In which of these two pictures do you prefer the position of the moon?" To complete the comparison, as many artistic principles as may be significant may be segregated. It is this requirement, that the judgment be based upon one specific, clearly defined, artistic feature at a time, that makes for science.

of formants. Leading composers are becoming alarmed at their growing responsibility for formants, both objective and subjective.

The method of natural sciences is applicable in musical esthetics. In a virgin territory, the botanist collects as many varieties of specimens as he can find; then he takes them into his laboratory, examines each in detail, and names and classifies them. So the student of esthetics may collect specimen features of beauty or ugliness in actual musical situations, and examine, name, and classify them. Take again our problem of timbre: each specimen is represented by a spectrum. No botanist has collected and classified all plants. No one will ever collect samples of all varieties of beauty in the quality of musical tones, but each investigator and each generation will go as far as possible under the limitations of time and the extent of facilities. Preceding science has given him the tools, such as the art of determining the spectrum, as well as insight into the nature and ramifications of its significance.

The method of physical sciences is also applicable in musical esthetics. The sustained illustration which I am carrying through is an example of the use of physical method insofar as we are dealing with the nature and significance of musical sounds. (See Chapter 6.) Not only can we make physical analysis of specimen sounds taken from actual music, but we can reverse the process and build synthetic tones on the specifications for any harmonic structure. (See Chapter 8.) We now have in the laboratory a tone generator which is capable of sounding tones of any desired harmonic structure composed of the first sixteen partials (or fewer). The operator at the panel can determine how many partials shall be present, the character of their distribution, the amount of energy to be assigned to each, and the phase relationships of partials. Then he presses the button and out comes the tone of the structure specified. With so many variables, the mathematician tells us we can produce more than a million varieties of tone, thus imitating voice, musical instruments, sounds in nature, or, theoretically, any other desired kind of tone. Thus we proceed in the opposite direction of the naturalist and produce tones synthetically in order to determine the range and types of recognizable and significant elements of musical beauty.

Science encourages co-operation with all other legitimate approaches. Under the preceding headlines, I have attempted to state the point of view represented by a psychologist in musical esthetics in his attempt to interpret scientific approaches. Other experimenters in this field might, or do, differ from this point of view; but I submit it as a fair sample in the light of which the validity of the assumptions and criticisms of Mainwaring might be reviewed.

There are many problems in esthetics, such as theories of esthetic value or the nature of beauty as reality, which should be approached mainly from the philosophical point of view. One also must take cognizance of the inspirations of the mystic. The splendid progress made in creative music has furnished the most basic groundwork we have for the determination of esthetic values, particularly those values which deal with problems and possibilities of designs in musical form. The artist's interpretation of the printed score is, of course, the commonest object of esthetic judgment. Music anthropology envisages the racial development of art principles. The history of music is a critique of unfolding art principles. Genetics traces the rise of esthetic judgments in the growth of the individual. Education develops methods for training in esthetic judgment. The experimental sciences unravel new facts and can put existing theories and practices to the acid test. The pursuit of beauty is fascinating, and it is profitable on each of these fronts.

Why not encourage all such approaches? Let the music historians, anthropologists, and critics enlarge their storehouses and submit to periodic housecleaning by separating the valid material from the invalid. Let the composer enlarge our conceptions of beauty by adding to our heritage of musical creations as art objects. Let the educationist put evolving theory into practice. Let the philosopher tell us from time to time what the greatest thinkers have thought about the nature of beauty and of esthetic values. Let the experimenter be ever ready and challenge all comers to verify and validate their facts and theories. Let us clarify the concept of beauty progressively by requiring each contributor to define beauty from his area, his purpose, and his point of view—but beware of the possible acid test in the musicological laboratory!

Chapter 3

A VISIT TO THE ACOUSTICAL
LABORATORY STUDIO

LET ME INVITE the reader to come with me for a visit to a branch of the psychological laboratory. Like the visit to a world's fair museum, such an inspection can be only superficial and fragmentary, calling attention here and there to outstanding problems which have been worked on in the laboratory and to typical apparatus employed in laying foundations for this inceptive science of the psychology of music and speech. Insofar as possible, I will introduce each exhibit by stating the general purpose and field in which it is used.

While all the instruments and techniques to be mentioned in this section were designed primarily for the purpose of the psychology of music, they are of such fundamental nature for the study of sound that practically all of them are used now in a number of specialized divisions of the laboratory, especially those divisions which are concerned with hearing, tone production, and phonetic theory. The designing of instruments has been a matter of co-operation on the part of staff members, students, and specialists in underlying fields—notably, physics, physiology, and electrical engineering. Instead of reporting contributions to the psychology of music made possible by these inventions, I shall speak mainly with reference to the instruments that we see as we pass through the laboratory.

PHONOPHOTOGRAPHY

The recording unit of the laboratory which we now enter, has been in a long process of development. It has taken advan-

---

Extracts from the author's *Pioneering in Psychology,* University of Iowa Press, 1942, Chapter V, 51–68.

tage, from time to time, of new inventions coming into the market, of the recognition of new specific needs, and of the improvement of sound-conditioned rooms. Microphones, for example, have been improved every year for thirty years, and it is desirable to have the latest and best of these. New vistas for acoustic measurements are continually being discovered and adapted for specific purposes.

Speaking in terms of singing, let me describe a typical procedure in recording the performance of a singer or player.[1] This acoustically treated and musically acceptable studio laboratory looks very much like a radio studio. The singer is alone in the room, standing before a microphone. There are no surrounding disturbances, and he is aware of the fact that his voice will reach a large and critical audience. He sings in his best artistic mood, inspired not only by his audience at the time of recording, but also by his future phonograph record audience, and aware of all the objective facts to be revealed by the camera.

In the adjoining room, there is equipment for the recording by phonograph and camera; several machines may record simultaneously. Thus a permanent phonograph record is made, and a battery of cameras simultaneously record pitch, loudness, time, and timbre of every note on motion-picture films, in terms of frequency, intensity, duration, and wave form. These films contain the complete and highly detailed permanent record of every significant element in the musical sounds, namely, the tonal, the dynamic, the temporal, and the qualitative. This record becomes the research material for measurement, reconstruction, and interpretation.

The studio is built in the manner to which musicians and listeners are accustomed. The record contains not alone the singer's voice, pure and simple, but also modifications by various acoustical characteristics of the room and possibly modifications from outside sources as well. To eliminate such room and environmental characteristics from the recorded voice, the singer may repeat, as nearly as possible, the same rendition in

---

[1] See Joseph Tiffin's article in the University of Iowa *Studies in the Psychology of Music*, Vol. I, 1932, 118–133.

an adjoining dead room. A dead room for this purpose is a room that has been built and treated acoustically so as to eliminate practically all reverberation from the walls, ceiling, and floor, and from any of its necessary contents. It is proofed also against sounds from the outside. By repeating the original rendition in this room, we have the record of the sound of the voice in ordinary concert environment for comparison with the sound of the voice by itself in the dead room.

In such recording, we have a choice of various types of cameras, the most convenient of which is the stroboscopic type which automatically furnishes on a single film a chart or picture of all the intonational, tonal, temporal, and dynamic modulations of the sound. This is an extraordinary timesaver, because it takes only a fraction of the time required for reading the more detailed films which show the measurement of pitch, loudness, and time. This camera, which records the form of the sound wave, selects "fair samples" of tonal timbre and records them on a separate film at very high speed; this is essential for the harmonic analysis that is to follow. Thus, in the time that it takes to sing a song, the more or less automatic outfit furnishes a complete record of the performance. The record is permanent and can be analyzed in great detail. From it we can construct a performance score and make quantitative tabulations for any feature measured.

Bearing in mind that the interception of those sound waves which constitute music, and the faithful reproduction of those waves for both the eye and the ear, by phonograph record and film, are almost universal requirements for the study of any singer, musical instrument, or other tonal performance for measurement, we realize at once that this recording studio is, by all odds, the busiest part of the laboratory. It is utilized for scores of different purposes, often unrelated, but all calling for a faithful record of sound.

In these recording devices, the human element of the experimenter must be eliminated so that all the recording is done automatically with far higher precision than could be produced through the control by eye, ear, or hand. The sound wave must speak for itself, so that it can be faithfully interpreted, whether it represents varieties of sound in nature or in art, regardless of whether generated through voice or instrument.

The microphone that feeds into the camera is connected with a phonographic recording machine, so that a high-quality, permanent record of what was actually rendered is preserved for the ear. Thus the investigator has at hand the means of comparing what is heard with what is seen in the motion picture, item for item.

A PERFORMANCE SCORE

Produced on a special type of motion-picture film, the photographic record of a five-minute song may contain thousands of specific facts bearing on the tonal, dynamic, temporal, and qualitative aspects of every note of the song, each of which is measurable and exactly definable. We were baffled at first by the accumulation of such masses of data and had no simple way of sorting and representing them. A solution was found in the design of what we now call the "performance score." In its simplest form, it is somewhat like the ordinary musical score. (See Figures in Chapters 5 and 24.)

In such a score, we can see as much detail as may be significant. It is customary to record pitch, loudness, and time in this manner. Then, because of the great complexity of the timbre, it is customary to represent fair samplings of tone spectra separately. Having once adopted this idea of representing four elements of the song graphically, that scheme may be applied to any particular feature of music or speech sound which it is desired to study in detail. For example, there are such features as phrasing scores, rhythmic patterns, the vibrato, or the harmonic structure of the tone. All elements of the sound are represented graphically to the eye.

This recognition is analogous to the fact that a picture of an object can be represented adequately in three dimensions of space and color. The painter has the means of representing, in a single picture, all desired degrees of variation in these three dimensions of space and a vast selection of variants in color. Imagine for a moment how helpless we would be if it had not occurred to someone that all types of objects and situations could be represented in pictures. That would be analogous to the situation in which we found ourselves in music. The performance score is a unified picture in three or four dimensions of music as it is actually performed. Of course, the means for making such pictures were discovered only recently, through the invention of sound photography.

Just as the recognition of the fact that every feature of a musical rendition can be represented in terms of four elements brought order out of chaos in the laboratory measurement, so now the adoption of various types of performance scores representing each of these four elements complements this by enabling us to assemble and interpret great masses of facts in terms of a fairly simple picture. Without such language and pictorial interpretation, most of the findings of the camera would have been lost. One can get some conception of the mass of material contained in a performance score if one realizes that for each note in the original musical score there is a graph showing exactly the form of attack and release and all the minute changes in pitch and loudness during the body of a tone, with the time and rhythmic value of each element of change during the tone. Every element in the actual phrasing is shown; yet the score is so compact that it may not occupy more than twice the space occupied by the original musical score.

To the musician, it seems almost incomprehensible that so much (for example, media for the expression of musical feeling) can be represented in simple, accurate, and definable language and pictures. Before we realized the full significance of this, we in the laboratory were quite as helpless as the musician in attempting to represent what seems to be a chaotic mass of detail.

It may seem like straining a point to say that the device for throwing the hundreds of findings in a musical selection into a comparatively simple picture, which we call the performance score, is analogous to the adoption of terminology in the biological and physical sciences, or in mathematics. But it may seem stranger still to assert that the performance score representing the world of music is to what we can hear as the painting or photographing of objects in color and relief is to what we can see in nature or art.

HARMONIC ANALYSIS

Let us go to another room, which has facilities for the complete analysis of tone quality. We find that tone quality consists of two factors, namely, timbre and sonance. Timbre denotes the character of a tone in cross-section, the tone being represented by a single vibration. Sonance represents the changes in timbre, pitch, and loudness which take place during the duration of a tone as a whole. The technique used here is known as harmonic analysis.

The theory of this has been known for a long time, but it is only recently that accurate and convenient instruments for the analysis have become available in various forms. Thus with the Henrici analyzer [2] we can take an adequately photographed sound wave, run it through the analyzer, and can see on a series of dials a quantitative statement of the number and distribution of overtones or partials present, plus an indication of the percentage of energy in each. This can be converted into a graphic tonal spectrum in which we can see at a glance a true profile representing the timbre of the tone at a particular moment in the tone, namely, for the duration of a single vibration. Such a spectrum may be used to show the actual percentage of physical energy in each of the partials, or it may be converted into a spectrum showing the actual role that each partial plays in musical hearing.

By fair sampling of individual vibrations within a tone or in a succession of tones, one can obtain a true picture of the constant fluctuation in the internal structure of a tone, that is, sonance, which together with timbre in cross section, gives a complete picture of the quality of the tone. The harmonic analyzer can determine the presence and the degree of prominence

[2] See frontispiece of author's *Psychology of Music,* McGraw-Hill, New York, 1938.

of as many as forty partials, that is, single pure tones, which may be present in a rich tone of voice or instrument.[3]

By this means we can record and describe any voice or solo instrument—indeed, any sound in nature or art—if the process is not too complicated by the presence of harmony or gross noise. For the first time such complete analysis of the quality of the tone gives a true quantitative and detailed kaleidoscopic picture of the hundreds of changes which take place within the tone during the singing or playing of a single note.[4] In terms of such revelations, the science of tone quality is becoming as tangible, exact, and objectively descriptive as pitch, loudness, and time have come to be. This new conquest of science will revolutionize music in many respects. It will enable us to write specifications for the reproduction of any desired tone quality; it will lay foundations for the classification and definition of tone quality; it will enable us to identify types of goodness or badness in musical tones.

Out of the laboratory will come a standardized series of names for the basic variants in tone quality; these names will be somewhat analogous to our speaking of the "ah" quality or the "ee" quality of a tone in terms of specific formants.[5] This will lead to the scrapping of the loose verbiage now used for the description of qualities of tone, and there will be a gradual development of a technical, definable, logical, and verifiable terminology in music. This development of course will be a slow process, but the goal, clearly indicated, is now in sight.

Out of this new knowledge will come new techniques of training the quality of voice or instrument. The time of instruction will be shortened, the training will be intelligent, and a hitherto unknown degree of precision in the discriminating control of the timbre and sonance of the tone will be reached. In practical music, the concept of tone quality is still in the dark ages, as zoology was before we had the concepts of genera, species, varieties, and types.

---

[3] Within the last few years new types of harmonic analyzers have become available for specific uses; these simplify the procedure, save time and expense.

[4] *Ibid.*, p. 107.

[5] *Ibid.*, p. 116 ff.

SYNTHETIC TONES

We now may logically turn from the analysis of tone quality to its reproduction and synthetic reconstruction with tone generators. Given, for example, the harmonic analysis of a violin tone or a singing voice, the question arises: Can such a tone be reproduced according to specifications? To this question we have found a happy affirmative answer in terms of the tone generator. Its use is described in Chapter 8.

THE PIANO PERFORMANCE SCORE

It will be observed that this piano camera works on entirely different principles from those described for the recording of other instruments or voices. (For an account of the camera and its performance scores, see Chapter 12, which gives illustrations of the structure of the camera, the character of the photographic record, and the piano performance score.)

MUSICAL ROBOTS

No musician can play the same note alike twice in succession. For this reason, when we undertake to study such instruments as the violin, the clarinet, and the oboe, it is necessary to set up exact conditions for automatic playing which can be maintained in steady tone as long as desired. Take, for example, the violin. If we wish to determine how much of the violin tone is due to the resonance of the room, it is necessary to play a given sustained note, first in the musically acceptable studio, and second in the dead room, where there are practically no reverberations. This, of course, could not be done by freehand bowing.

Dr. Arnold Small, starting from the technique developed by Abbot at Purdue University, built an adjustable holder for the violin; the holder was capable of maintaining the instrument in any desired position or any desired degree of rigidity, and it was made in such a way that one factor at a time could be varied. The bowing is done with a continuous belt, which is shaped like a hair bow and yields a comparable quality of tone.

This bow can be set up to control its relations to the string, the degree of pressure, and the speed of movement from the face or width of the bow band. The essential point in this setup is that the experimenter shall be able to maintain and repeat a tone of a fixed timbre and sonance as long as desired.

Beyond this stage the procedure is the same as in ordinary recording for voice or instrument; that is, oscillograms are taken at high speed to record with fidelity the form of the sound wave. The sound wave is then run through a harmonic analyzer which delivers the data from which we can construct the tone spectrum under a given condition. This harnessing of the violin is a way of putting this extraordinarily delicate and responsive instrument under exact control for a single note at a time. Given such control it can be made the job of a lifetime, or generations, to work out in minute detail the general characteristics of a given instrument, step after step, by varying one factor at a time.

Here is one example of a robot in the laboratory. (See Chapter 13.) Horne and Small wanted to determine the role of the mute in violin playing. Starting with a mechanically played violin, they took the standard mutes on the market and added to these a number of specially made mutes so as to get fair samplings of the effect of the weight, the size, the shape, the material of which they were constructed, and different ways of mounting. Each of these was varied in turn, and therefore the form of the sound wave that was recorded under each of these conditions revealed the effect of different mutes upon the tone. For complete analysis of the effect of the mute, many other factors, of course, would have to be taken into account. The cumulative findings would give us a progressively refined measure of what a given mute under a given condition actually contributes to the timbre of the tone, all other factors being kept constant.

Similar procedures have been followed in the study of the bridge; and, as these are progressively refined, another series must be made to determine the effect of a given bridge on a given mute, and vice versa. In this manner, hundreds of specific factors in the violin can be isolated and measured.

The same principle is applied to other instruments; for example, here is an oboe robot in which the human element is eliminated. It is energized mechanically from a constant pressure source, and every factor that enters into the character of the tone is under control. The same principle is applied to other families of instruments. It can readily be seen that the introduction of the robot into the experimental laboratory is one of the first essential conditions for the rigidly exact study of the character of instruments and the techniques of playing them. So in musicology as in war, the latest advance lies in the projection of a mechanized unit.

One can readily realize what a vast field of exploration is laid open by the techniques that are just beginning to come in; first, as a result of the high fidelity of the latest microphones; second, by the facilitation of harmonic analysis with new types of instruments; and third, by the possibility of putting the playing of an instrument under constant control. Developments of this kind attain their most vital significance when they operate for research in the school of music, as at Iowa, where research students in music have full access to the laboratory.

MEASUREMENT OF THE EXPRESSION OF EMOTION
IN MUSIC

The laboratory scientist is an explorer, always looking for new frontiers. Among his thrills are the discovery of some previously unknown important thing, the bringing of order out of chaos in a virgin field, and the actual achievement of something that supposedly could not be done. Such an achievement is the measurement of the expression of emotion through music. The problem has been nibbled at for half a century by measuring its effects on pulse rate, breathing, blood pressure, metabolism, distraction, and by the psychogalvanic reflex. But all of these are fragmentary and more or less accessory factors. However, all have one element in common, namely, the attempt to measure the intensity of mental activity in terms of some physical expression. They have revealed a great deal about the physiology of the expression of emotion, but none of them has attempted to measure the expression itself, that is, the actual musical form that the expression takes.

We have been fortunate in being able to isolate one element in the expression of musical emotion and to show exactly what form this expression takes in actual music. For a number of years we conducted experiments which led to exact analysis and description of this form of expression. For our purpose, we took what seemed, at the time, a comparatively insignificant factor, namely, one of the thirty or more musical ornaments, the vibrato. Relying upon the varied resources of the laboratory, we were able to make an exhaustive analysis of what types of vibrato exist, the frequency of their use, the role they play in musical emotion as a whole, norms for tolerance, and methods of development. The results of these experiments are reported in detail in two monographs, Volumes I and III of the University of Iowa *Studies in the Psychology of Music,* and in numerous scattered articles in the standard journals.

Instead of looking to the apparatus, let us simply recall what has been accomplished by rigorous experimental procedures. Some time ago, I analyzed all our findings, all of which were based rigidly and logically upon exact measurement, and found that we had answered in a significant way more than two hundred questions by measurement of the vibrato. In order to give a fair sample, here is a list of twenty-five of these:

(1) What is the vibrato?
(2) How can the vibrato be recorded and measured?
(3) What are the musical elements of the vibrato?
(4) What is a good vibrato?
(5) What is a bad vibrato?
(6) What is the relation of vibrato to tremolo?
(7) How general is the use of the vibrato in good music?
(8) What is the origin of the vibrato?
(9) How does the vibrato develop with experience and training?
(10) Is the vibrato desirable?
(11) What is the difference in the vibrato of voice and violin?
(12) How does the vibrato function in other instruments?
(13) How does the vibrato vary with musical mode and emotion?

(14) How does the vibrato vary with register, loudness, tempo, and timbre?

(15) What are the norms for pitch vibrato?

(16) What are the norms for intensity vibrato?

(17) What are the norms for rate of the vibrato?

(18) How does the timbre pulsate in the vibrato?

(19) What is the difference between the actual vibrato and what is heard?

(20) What are the normal illusions which make the vibrato tolerable?

(21) What is the difference between the scientific and musical hearing of the vibrato?

(22) What is the physiological theory of the vibrato?

(23) What can training in the vibrato accomplish?

(24) Should formal training in the vibrato be encouraged?

(25) Is there musical significance in this knowledge of the vibrato?

It took a long time to answer our first question: *What is the vibrato?* It will take some time before the definition and our answers to the numerous questions involved will penetrate musical literature, but it is gratifying to know that we are making rapid progress. Intelligent consideration of vibrato already has made its way into the textbooks, dictionaries, and the encyclopedias, and into common-sense conversation on the subject. The most progressive music teachers and the virtuosi now on the stage are becoming more conscious of the vibrato and are becoming greatly concerned about their exhibition of it. We have numerous cases in which the vibrato of a singer has been greatly improved by scientific findings, and there are other cases in which voice teachers have taken a radically new attitude in the development of its refinement. (For a summary of our scientific findings on the vibrato, see Chapter 5.)

THE VOCAL CORDS

The theory of the function of the vocal cords has been represented in armchair controversy for ages, but it has been only in the most recent years that we have been able to study the problem by means of adequate experiment, and this through the extraordinary developments by motion-picture photography.

We speak of three parts of the vocal apparatus: the vibrators, the generators, and the resonators. Air pressure acts as a generator upon the vocal cords; it sets them into vibration, and the tone thus generated is modified into significant and meaningful character through the action of the resonators in the oral cavities, controlled by movements of lips and tongue. Using an ordinary dentist's mirror, one can see the vocal cords in action. Motion pictures of their movement can be interpreted by interrupting the pictures—on the principle of stroboscopic vision.

The first work on this project in the Iowa laboratory was done by Koehler's first assistant, Dr. Metzger, who came here from Berlin for post-doctorate study and made a substantial contribution.[6] The work was taken up next by Tiffin and his associates, who made further improvements and who organized experiments, their primary objective being the determination of the extent to which the vocal cords vibrate in a single segment or in harmonic series of segments. In this they made fundamental contributions to theory.

There are now many forms of vocal-cord cameras, and we have standard films depicting the character of the movement of the cords. Recently two extraordinary achievements have been made in the Bell Telephone Laboratories: first, the utilizing of a lamp which secures brilliant illumination for the recording of detail, and second, the speeding up of the rate of motion pictures taken under this illumination to as high as 4,000 exposures per second. This achievement is an application of the principle developed in ballistic photography a few years ago.

When progress takes place at such pace, one can hardly begin to recite the discoveries, but one feels gratified to realize that we now have the means of verifying or disproving old theories and of discovering countless new elements in phonation through these new photographic techniques. It can be safely said that the long-standing controversy over the theories

---

[6] Wolfgang Metzger, "Mode of Vibration of Vocal Cords," University of Iowa *Studies in Psychology,* Vol. XI, 1918, 82–159.

of the function of the vocal cords is now settled. Through the photographic access to the cords, a new branch of science of acoustics and phonetics is developing.

What now interests us most, concerning the role of measurements of this kind in the psychology of music, is its variety of practical applications; in voice placement, for example, the mechanism of registers and the relation between vibration of the vocal cords and the countless factors that enter into the energizing and the resonating of vocal sounds.

EYE MOVEMENT IN READING A MUSICAL SCORE

Here is a bidimensional eye camera. A good deal of experimental work has been done on principles of sight reading.[7] Here, as in other fields, when one wants to do fundamental work, it is necessary to record and measure one factor at a time. One of the most fundamental questions with which we are concerned is the speed and direction of eye movements in reading a section of a new musical score at sight, because, from a psychological point of view, eye movement determines the course, the speed, and the integrating movements of attention. It is well known that, in all forms of reading, the eye behaves like a motion-picture camera in that it moves quickly from one point of observation to another. Nothing is seen during the movement; but what will be seen are the cumulative and fusing pictures taken at the moment of rest for each point of observation. The analogy of the eye to the motion-picture camera is clear. Much of this can be studied by various eye-movement cameras now available, which record the rate and character of movement in the horizontal direction.

But since, in reading an ordinary score, the eye makes movements in various directions, a two-dimensional camera is required to facilitate the analysis. This camera is built so that it actually charts every movement of the eye in two dimensions; thus one can see at a glance when and what features in the score were observed. This camera was built in the Iowa labora-

---

[7] Herman F. Brandt, "Ocular Patterns as an Index of the Attention Value of Size," *American Journal of Psychology*, 1940, *53*, 564–574.

tory by a graduate student, Dr. Herman F. Brandt, originally for the purpose of analysis of eye movement in reading, in the study of attention-values of advertisements, the analysis of the movement of attention in looking at a beautiful picture, and for motion studies in engineering. Indeed, it is a universal instrument for the measurement of bidimensional eye movement. For example, it is now used as the principal measuring instrument in time and motion studies in engineering.

In the field of music this opens avenues of investigation within the area of sight reading which will undoubtedly lead to a better understanding of the leaps and bounds, the selection of points of observation, preliminary skirmish, and consolidation of observations in sight reading. All of these may be measured objectively in terms of this camera, which records on a motion-picture film. For psychological and musical purposes, all may be interpreted in terms of the movement of attention.

This type of experiment, like all we have considered so far, is perhaps of greatest significance from the point of view of theoretical psychology in that it gives a true insight into what actually happens in the specific types of human ocular behavior in perception. As I have said before, the fact that we have a specific practical purpose in mind does not interfere with our search for fundamental psychological facts in so-called "pure psychology." Indeed, the exactly controlled formulation of an experimental situation for a practical purpose may greatly facilitate the procedure in the search for fundamental truths, in that the practical objective forces us to take into account factors that might otherwise have been overlooked.

One realizes the significance of this when one observes an expert pianist playing a complicated musical score at first sight. One may ask: How many elements in the musical score does he actually see individually, and how many are inferred from knowledge of musical structure? How does the eye move in a preliminary glance at the general character of the page as a whole? What role do exploratory anticipations play from stage to stage? How many elements in a chord or how many chords in a group can he grasp in a single point of observation? What is the relation between the individual note and the eye movement, or between the phrase and the eye movement? In what order does the pianist verify such preliminary impressions? What would happen if the composition violated musical sanctions by injection of irrelevant notes? How many eye movements does he make in reading a hundred successive chords at first sight? Are the rate and the direction of eye movements indices to efficiency in sight reading? What laws of movement for the reading of prose transfer to the reading of a complicated score? What fundamental changes in eye movement take place in learning by the method of the whole as compared with the method of the parts? How is it possible for the talented pianist to take a fully orchestrated score and render it in a normal tempo as a piano score at first sight? These and hundreds of other questions can now be answered by objective measurement under normal conditions of piano playing with a printed score in a conventional position for reading.

BRAIN WAVES

The psychology of music has gained much from the perfection of speaking films, phonographs, and radio. One is amazed by the realization of the fact that all space in and around us reverberates with magnetic waves which can be converted into sound—into music in all its intricate forms. One wonders what it is in the human mechanism that makes one responsive to all these forms of vibration so that they can be registered meaningfully through hearing.

On this tour through the laboratory, let us look into the brain-wave laboratory. Our reason for doing so is the fact that, primarily through the leadership of Dr. Lee Travis and a succession of his associates, Iowa was one of the pioneers in this field of investigation. The laboratory is one of the best-equipped in the country for this purpose.

In the laboratory, the man upon whom the experiment is to be made rests comfortably on a couch. Two or more electrodes are attached to different parts of the surface of his head. Elaborate electrical registering apparatus records on motion-picture film the presence of nerve impulses by means of the accompanying electrical deflection. It is fantastic to see these pictures of the nerve impulse revealing its rate and variation with location, complexity, intensity, and duration of the processes. Not only can we see action-current-waves, but we can convert them into sound which we can hear. This harnessing of brain waves in electrophysiology for nerve impulse is quite analogous to the harnessing of radio waves for the conduction and generation of musical sounds. The brain acts through alternating currents, much as an electric circuit.

There are certain basic rays—such as the alpha ray, which beats at about ten per second—and a series of other rays of higher frequency, which are designated by other Greek letters. The same principles that register the brain wave can also be used in tracing the course of the nerve impulse from the sense organ through various intricate centers to the brain or from the brain through various centers to the muscles. We now have the means of discovering the origin and course of the nerve impulse, whether it be incoming or outgoing. We may look upon the brain as a central station from which incoming and outgoing impulses are distributed through various centers in the spinal cord and other parts of the nervous system.

To give one illustration of the application of this to music, one of the problems in the study of the vibrato is to determine what elements of the nervous system control the pulsations of the vocal cords in the vibrato cycle, thereby affecting pitch, loudness, and time. The study of this problem leads to the discovery of fundamental biological principles almost infinitely complex, and yet frequently measurable and explainable. Here the musicologist is in a situation analogous to that of the astronomer who, with telescope and spectroscope, with intricate mathematical theories and untiring observation, reveals law and order in the system as a whole, although he can observe only one infinitesimally small part of it at a time.

HEARING LOSS

Let us enter this comparatively soundproof room where audiometers of various kinds with which we can measure hearing ability can be found. Hearing ability usually is called *acuity of hearing* or *sensitiveness to sound,* as distinguished from *discrimination for sound.* One exhibit is a record blank on which the curve of normal hearing is represented by a curve which shows in decibels the degree of hearing loss found at each pitch level. Defective hearing is not generally a flat loss of hearing; it shows up in various degrees at various points in the tonal register, depending ordinarily upon the character of the defect in the ear.

It is important to know whether a musician or a prospective student of music is hard of hearing, and if so, to what extent and of what nature. But acuity of hearing may not be regarded as a talent in line with the sense of loudness, pitch, etc., because, with inceptive or moderate hearing loss, the musician may have as keen musical discrimination for the sounds he can hear as is found in a person with good hearing. It is, of course, a notable fact that many distinguished musicians had to contend with deafness of various degrees, and did so with extraordinary success; in fact, some were totally deaf. The audiometer, however, always will be a key instrument in a studio for musicology. For a significant feature of hearing impairment measured by an audiometer, see the discussion of presbycousis in Chapter 22.

Our visit must come to an end. We have looked at technical exhibits, and we have spoken of their uses in music and speech. All of the exhibits find application both in allied fields and in such more remote fields as physiology, physics, eugenics, education, and anthropology. The laboratory is well equipped for many other fields of research; but, as in all research, we must fractionate the problem: the visitor must see only a few things at a time.

Chapter 4

PRINCIPLES OF MEASUREMENT
IN MUSICAL ESTHETICS

MOST OF OUR KNOWLEDGE is of the common-sense variety, gained in ordinary observation; very little is based upon experiment. Yet, where there is no experiment there can be no science. Furthermore, in a new applied science, such as the psychology of music, there is a vast amount of so-called "experimentation" that is neither scientific nor valid. In planning an experiment or in evaluating the results of an experiment in the psychology of music, we should check the procedure against such criteria as set forth in the following six paragraphs. Consider their application, for example, in an experiment to determine the carrying power of voice or instrument.

GENERAL PRINCIPLES OF SCIENCE IN MEASUREMENT

(1) The factor under consideration must be isolated in order that we may know exactly what it is that we are measuring. For example, we must take one factor, such as pitch, intensity, timbre, tempo, size of the room, or the acoustical treatment of the walls, and isolate and define it adequately.

(2) All other factors must be kept constant while the selected factor is varied under control. For example, if intensity is a selected factor in carrying power, we must vary that factor in graded steps while all other factors in the tone and in the total environment are kept constant.

(3) The observed facts must be recordable. For example, the intensity may be recorded in terms of the energy or power of the tone.

Adaptations from an article in the *Music Educators Journal*, May 1936; and Chapter III of the author's *Psychology of Music*, McGraw-Hill, New York, 1938.

(4) The situation must be repeatable for verification. It should be possible for any scientist with proper equipment to repeat the experiment under identical conditions.

(5) The conclusion must be validated in relation to the total personality and in the total musical situation.

(6) The conclusion must be limited to the factor under control. For example, we can say only that the most favorable intensity for carrying power here found holds for the conditions here controlled and that it must therefore be integrated with other factors in a series of experiments in which each of these is investigated in turn.

If the plan for an experiment fails on any one of these points, this may invalidate the conclusion to be drawn. If we wish to weigh the reliability of evidence from experiment, here is a fair scale. We should not maintain that every serious study in psychology should be scientific. There is nothing sacred about science. Science simply strives for accuracy and logical coherence of facts. In the interest of progress and practice, we must put up with a great many makeshifts, often of no scientific value but very useful in the process of trial and error at our present state of limited knowledge. The scientist makes a sacrifice in devoting time and energy to the study of one specific isolated factor at a time, regardless of how small a part it may be of the whole; but the reward for this sacrifice is adequate— the discovery of verifiable truth. The musician as a practical man must draw upon currently accepted truths through tradition, common-sense observation and general knowledge, and do the best he can in the practical situation; but as science progresses, he will be more and more open-minded and eager for the fragments of scientific facts that come in or that he may discover by his own experiments.

The criteria here set up represent the basic requirements of science. A survey of the experimental literature in psychology shows that experiments generally accepted as more or less scientific range from those which conform rigidly to these requirements to those which can scarcely be said to follow any of them. In this situation formative science can be tolerated on the ground that "doing the best we can" from time to time is often a stage preliminary to mastery. In all sciences we find such regions of exploratory effort. Therefore, while we should not be censorious about the criteria for pure experiment, we should always hold before ourselves a goal which must be approached in a stabilized science and temper, and we must evaluate our conclusions by the limitations set up in relation to this goal.

BASIC PRINCIPLES IN THE PSYCHOLOGY OF MUSIC

Laboratory experiments in the psychology of music have revealed progressively a number of principles which seem to facilitate experiment, introduce important elements of economy, insure exhaustive treatment, furnish criteria of validity, and form bases for the foundations of esthetic theories.

Some principles have emerged incidentally throughout the foregoing chapters. In the interest of a combined review and forecast, a selected number of these will be mentioned again. It has been suggested that we call these a duodecalogue for the psychology of music.

(1) Music, as it comes from the musician to the listener, is conveyed on sound waves. Countless other factors—dramatic action, gesture, grimaces, smiles and frowns, picture hats and jewelry, personal charm, environment, and audience—all contribute to the pleasure or displeasure in the musical situation, but they are not music. Recognition of this fact simplifies our problem.[1]

(2) The sound waves are measurable, and there are only four variables that have musical significance: frequency, intensity, duration, and form. Recognition of this is a forward step in that it brings order and simplicity out of chaos and despair. Physically, the infinite variety of musical sounds can be reduced to these four variables and measured in terms of them.

(3) The psychological equivalents, or correlates, of these characteristics of sound are pitch, loudness, time, and timbre.

---

[1] The reader will do the author the kindness to assume that qualifying phrases could be added for this and other direct and categorical statements which lack of space compels us to make without qualification. Such phrases as "other things being equal," "as a general principle," "subject to exceptions in minor detail," "in our present state of knowledge," etc., should be understood throughout.

Rhythm, harmony, volume, and tone quality are compounds of these; thought, feeling, action, memory, and imagination are in terms of them. We thus obtain a basic classification of all musical phenomena and give each its place in the family tree with its four large branches: the tonal, the dynamic, the temporal, and the qualitative.

(4) The correspondence between the physical fact and the mental fact is not entirely direct or constant; there are many illusions of hearing. While we describe, for example, the pitch of A conventionally and practically as having a frequency of 440 vibrations per second, which is an invariable factor, the experience of that pitch may vary under a large variety of conditions resulting in illusions of pitch; many of these illusions are interesting, and they are of practical significance in actual music. It is a triumph of science, however, that we can identify, measure, and explain each of these illusions. Thank God for illusions! Without illusions there could be no musical art.

(5) The medium of musical art lies primarily in artistic deviation from the fixed and regular; from rigid pitch, uniform intensity, fixed rhythm, pure tone, and perfect harmony. Therefore the quantitative measurement of performance may be expressed in terms of adherence to the fixed and so-called "true," or deviation from it in each of the four groups of musical attributes.

(6) In each of the four categories, we have a zero point for a scale of measures. Thus, for pitch we may start from a standard tone; for intensity, from silence; for duration, from zero duration; and for timbre, from the pure tone.

(7) On the basis of the above considerations, we may develop a definable, consistent, and verifiable musical terminology. For example, we shall be able to say exactly what timbre is and adopt adequate terminology for its variants. In the same way we shall be asked to scrap the hundreds of loose and synonymous terms used to designate timbre and shall be enabled to use the selected term correctly in the light of its new definition.

(8) All measurements may be represented graphically in what we have called the performance score, which symbolizes the language of scientific measurement in a graph that has musi-

cal meaning. This score carries the three factors—pitch, intensity, and time. Timbre must be represented graphically in a more detailed score.

(9) Norms of artistic performance may be set up in terms of objective measurement and for the analysis of superior or any other level of performance for the purpose of evaluating achievement and indicating goals of attainment.

(10) The best performance of today can be improved upon. We must therefore look forward to experimental procedures to determine ideal norms which will set up new standards of attainment, vastly increased resources, power, and beauty in music.

(11) In the future, musical esthetics will be built upon the bases of scientific measurement and experimental analysis. With modern means of measurement, any advocated theories may be put to the acid test.

(12) Where there is no experiment, direct or indirect, there is no science. Science, by virtue of its adherence to minute detail, is always fragmentary and incomplete. Its findings must always be supplemented by practical intuition, common sense, and sound philosophical theories of the art. Science deals with selected topics. The musician must deal with the situation as a whole with the means at his command.

There is an important scientific approach in the clinical field, for music may have marked therapeutic value. Clinical psychology of music will draw upon psychiatry, sociology, criminology, and education for scientific principles. The same is true of its application to industry.

(13) Musical talent may be measured and analyzed in terms of a hierarchy of talents as related to the total personality, the musical medium, the extent of proposed training, and the object to be served in the musical pursuit.

(14) For musical guidance on the basis of scientific measurement, the application must be restricted to the factors measured; but it should be supplemented by an adequate audition, case history, and consideration of personality traits and avenues for achievement. All musical guidance should be tempered by the recognition of the extraordinary resourcefulness of the

human organism and the vast variety of the possible musical outlets for self-expression.

(15) Successful performance rests upon the mastery of fundamental skills which may be isolated and acquired as specific habits; but, in artistic performance, these skills should be integrated so that in the musical mood there is no consciousness of habits, skills, or techniques as such.

(16) To facilitate the acquisition of musical skills, objective instrumental aids may be used to great advantage, for both economy of time and precision of achievement. Among such aids are visual projection or quantitative indication of pitch, intensity, time, and timbre at the moment the tone is produced.

(17) In the coming electrical organs, pianos, and other instruments, in view of the criticism to which all instruments will be subjected as a result of the possibilities of measurement, future progress will depend upon the adoption by their makers of the scientific point of view and the utilization of measurement. We are on the frontier of a new music. With the application of science, the composer will be given new tasks and new opportunities; the performer will constantly be facing new problems; the listener will always be expecting something new.

(18) If the pedagogy of music in the public schools is to keep pace with the pedagogy of all the other subjects, it must face frankly and adopt the scientific point of view. Practical music will have its first scientific approaches in the public schools rather than in the private studios or conservatories.

(19) The psychology of music is ultimately not a thing in itself. In employing a technique peculiar to that field, one must fall back upon a general grounding in psychology. After all, the laws of sensation, perception, learning, thinking, feeling, and action in general need be only specifically adapted to the demands of the musical situation.

(20) While the cold details of musical facts can be recorded and organized by a mere psychologist, validity and interpretation depend upon an intimate knowledge of music and feeling for it. The applied science will progress at its best when the musician can set the problem in compliance with the criteria enumerated above for scientific experiment.

TERMINOLOGY IN MUSIC ACOUSTICS

The physical aspect. Sound has a physical aspect and an approximately parallel mental aspect. For each of these we have standardized terminology, but in most situations in music and speech we refer to both the physical and the mental. We therefore have three series of correlates in acoustic phenomena: the physical, the mental, and the integrated or total references.

The terminology for the physical aspect is based objectively on the physical attributes of sound waves, namely, *frequency, amplitude, duration* of a sequence of waves, and *wave form.* Those represent the *tonal,* the *dynamic,* the *temporal,* and the *qualitative aspects* of the physical sound. Since all music exists directly or indirectly as sound waves, and since sound waves have no other primary attribute than those mentioned, every element of the physical aspect of musical sounds may be accounted for in these four categories or their complex forms or derivatives. By combination of the four basic elements, endless varieties of melody, harmony, rhythm, volume, and tone quality may be represented. Each of these is defined in terms of units of energy, physical or electrical. For each of the four basic attributes, the physicist has also devised terms available for specific purposes, such as frequency modulation, energy, power, harmonic composition, or spectrum.

The mental aspect. The terminology of the mental aspect roughly parallels the physical terminology in the naming of each category, namely, *pitch, loudness, time,* and *timbre* as representing the *tonal,* the *dynamic,* the *temporal,* and the *qualitative aspects* of tones. For many artistic and for most scientific purposes it is essential that the distinction between the physical and the mental aspects respectively be adhered to logically and consistently, and that there be no slipshod or dodging shift from one to the other in evading clarity in order to cover ignorance. The two are rarely exactly parallel. *Frequency,* for example, has many times the range of *pitch.* We seldom hear a tone as a true copy of the physical tone; the ratio of the physical to the mental is rarely 1 :1. The pitch for a standard physical frequency of 440 may vary under a variety of environmental, physiological, psychophysical, and psychological conditions. A tone of 60-decibel energy level may vary widely in loudness in hearing; a one-second duration may seem much longer or shorter; the timbre correlated with a specific structure of partials may vary widely in hearing. We recognize these divergencies as normal illusions; some are due to the limitations of the human organism or to the instrument, and others to artistic demands, conventions, or training. Without many of these illusions there could be no good music. In defining the mental terms, we relate them to the physical aspect, and, when necessary, we indicate essential deviations of the mental from the physical parallelism.

The total situation. But, in conventional treatment of musical sounds, we are most frequently thinking of the total or integrated situation which involves both objective and subjective factors and is concerned with physical, physiological, and mental aspects. That is what music is; and, for this, we have the well established usage of employing the mental terminology, as when we speak of *concert pitch, staccato* or *legato movements,* a *major key, poor phrasing, vibrato, accent, resolution,* or *harmony.* Thus, whenever we speak or think of actual music or speech, we have the total situation in mind. The very words *music* and *speech* are exhibits of this. Unfortunately, that necessitates our using the terms *pitch, intensity, time,* and *timbre* for two distinct purposes: to express the mental aspect specifically and to express the integrated situation in music and speech. We are here forced to depend upon the context or the universe of discourse to determine which of the two connotations is intended.

The Acoustical Society of America has a committee on terminology which publishes definitions from time to time in its *Journal,* as clarification develops through experiment. In these, emphasis is rightly laid on consistent distinction between the mental and physical terminology; but only slight attention is given to artistic and common-sense usage pertaining to what we have here distinguished as the total situation. But the history of music, criticism of music, and much of the psychology of music deals with this integrated situation without any reason for making the acoustic distinctions between the physical and the mental. Psychology is not ordinarily concerned with the historical "body and mind" situation, but rather with the functions of the integrated organism.

Psychological usage, in terms of which musical organization must be built, sometimes brings us into verbal conflicts. This is exemplified in the use of the terms *intensity* and *loudness*. *Loudness* is an appropriate synonym for *intensity*, but *intensity* is an attribute of all sensation; for example, *intensity of taste, odor, color, pressure, pain,* and *sound.* Therefore scientists have historically preferred the word *intensity* when the reference is dominantly to the total situation, and have favored the term *loudness* for a purely mental aspect of experience and behavior.

PART TWO

EXAMPLES OF SCIENTIFIC FOUNDATIONS FOR MUSICAL ESTHETICS

Chapter 5

A MUSICAL ORNAMENT: VIBRATO

IN A SERIES OF REPORTS, it is proposed here to answer three general questions about the vibrato in music: (1) What is it? (2) What makes it good or bad? (3) How can we improve it? The vibrato is the most important of all the musical ornaments because it occurs so frequently and because it contributes flexibility, tenderness, and richness of tone to tone quality.

There are several reasons why this aspect of music has not been properly understood, explained, or appraised by musicians. One obstacle has been that until recently there was no measuring instrument available for accurate recording and scientific analysis of the phenomenon. Another obstacle is the fact that the vibrato as we hear it is entirely different from the vibrato as it is performed. We now have the means by which it may be recorded and analyzed in the most minute detail, and by these means we have been able to isolate and explain the illusions that account for its tolerance.

On the basis of laboratory experiments, we are now in a position to offer a definition which is subject to critical examination and verification in the laboratory:

A good vibrato is a pulsation of pitch, usually accompanied by synchronous pulsations of loudness and timbre, of such

---

Based on the author's textbook *The Vibrato in Voice and Instrument,* University of Iowa Press, 1936, which was based mainly upon the monograph *The Vibrato,* Vol. I of the University of Iowa *Studies in the Psychology of Music.* The adaptation is drawn mainly from articles in the *Music Educators Journal,* February, March, and May 1937; an address before the International Congress of Psychology, 1935; *Acta Psychologica,* The Hague, 1935; and "The Natural History of a Musical Ornament," *Proceedings of the National Academy of Science,* 1930, 17.

extent and rate as to give a pleasing flexibility, tenderness, and richness to the tone.

This is a definition of a *good* vibrato; but vibratos may be good, bad, or indifferent. In general, we may say that a bad vibrato is any periodic pulsation of pitch, loudness, or timbre which, singly or in combination, fails to produce pleasing flexibility, tenderness, and richness of tone. Likewise, if we desire a generic definition of all vibratos, we might say that the vibrato in music is a periodic pulsation of pitch, loudness, or timbre, singly or in combination. This, it may be observed, is not differentiating in kind or in musical value.

This definition is a result of years of experimentation, and tells a long story. It identifies the media through which the vibrato may occur, and it shows that there are three distinct kinds of vibrato, namely, pitch vibrato, intensity vibrato, and timbre vibrato; each of these may occur singly or in combination. On the basis of the analysis of musical tones, we are in a position to say that these three can be isolated and demonstrated, and that they are the only kinds possible.

The second part of the definition describes its function, which is to give a pleasing flexibility, tenderness, and richness to the tone. These three aspects are universally recognized as desirable and fundamental in musical esthetics. Each holds a distinct and definable place in any psychological classification of the expression of feelings.

Figure 1 gives a good example of a performance score revealing the vibrato. The upper curve is the performance score for pitch; the lower for intensity. Time is indicated in tenths of seconds, by dots and dashes, and seconds are marked off by vertical bars. The notes from the score are interpolated as an aid in identification of the tone. The words are given at the bottom. The measures are separated by a short vertical bar under the words. The pitch is given in the staff. The space between a dotted and dashed line represents a semitone step. The reference letters at the left identify notes by a name, and the numbers at the left indicate the degree of difference in loudness in terms of decibels.

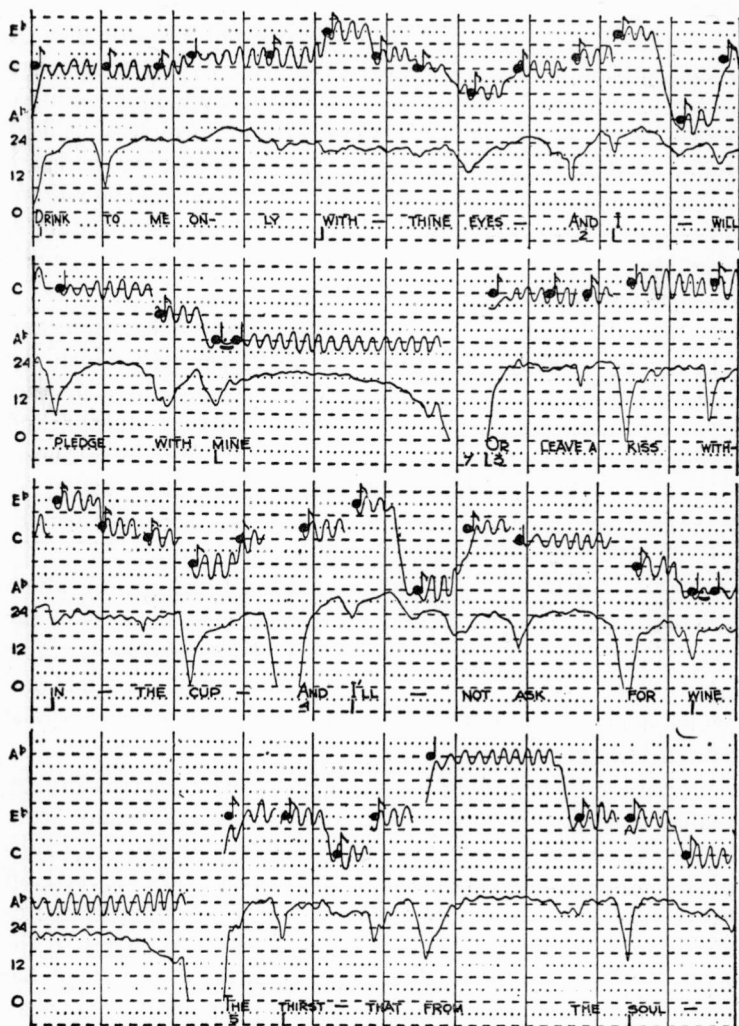

Figure 1a. *Drink to Me Only With Thine Eyes,* as sung by Kraft and recorded by Harold Seashore in the Laboratory Studio. The pitch of each note is represented by a graph.

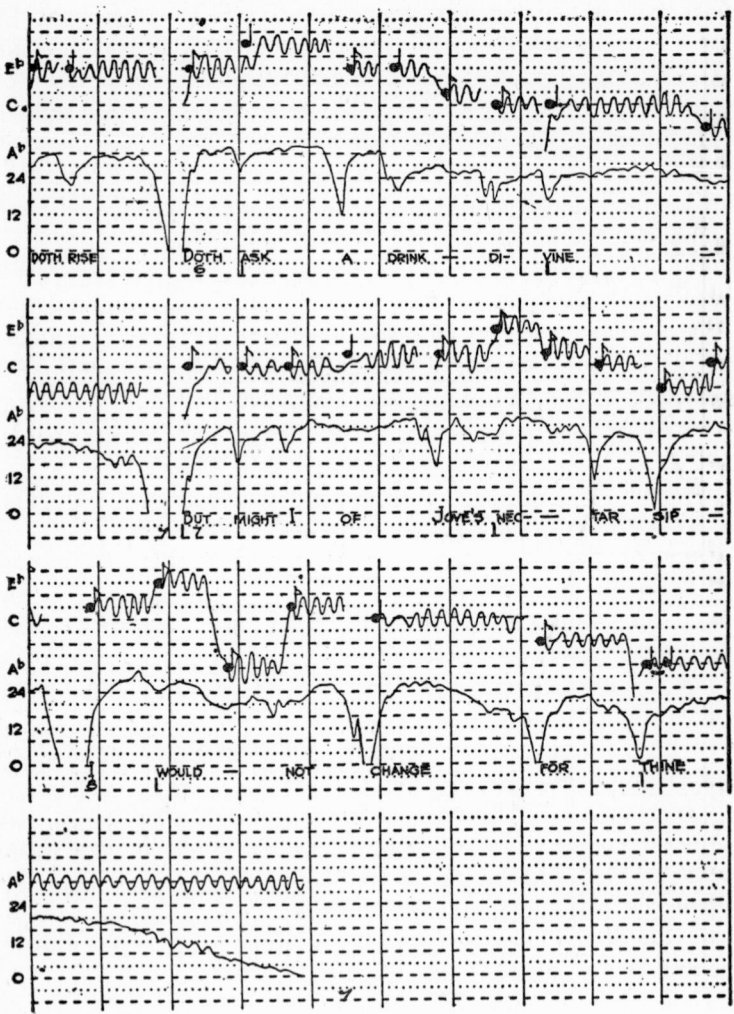

Figure 1b. *Drink to Me Only With Thine Eyes* (cont'd)

From this orientation, the reader may gather a large number of facts and the answers to questions. For example, we find in Figure 1 that Kraft averages a pitch pulsation of about 0.6 of a tone in extent at the rate of about 6 cycles per second. The average for all the best singers of today is about 0.5 of a whole-tone step in extent at the rate of 6.5 cycles per second. The intensity vibrato is present in parts of the tone, but it is not conspicuous. When it occurs, it is between 2 and 3 decibels of loudness and it tends to be at the same rate as for the pitch. The pitch vibrato is present in every tone, long or short, and in all the transitions.

By collecting performance scores for adequate samplings of singers under all sorts of conditions, we can build a veritable science of the vibrato, which, when it becomes a matter of popular knowledge among musicians, will probably be treated as common-sense knowledge. Here, I can mention only a few things about the occurrence of the vibrato and its true nature.

In singing, the pitch vibrato is practically universal. No good artist sings without it. It occurs not only in long tones but also in short tones: attack, release, and portamento. It comes in gradually in the voice of the child, just to the extent that the child sings with genuine feeling. It occurs in the most primitive races, wherever the intonation is of an emotional nature. It occurs in sustained emotional speech, and in hearty laughter of the adult. It is present in the vigorous crying of the newborn infant, in the singing of the canary, in the bark of the dog, in the cooing of the dove.

In short, it is present wherever sustained vocalization expresses genuine emotion. It is a basic phenomenon of nature, both in man and in higher animals. It rests fundamentally upon the periodic innervation of paired muscles under emotional tension. The canary bird in its simplest tour has a mere chatter in one pitch at the rate of six or seven pulsations per second; in fact, all the recognized tours of that bird may possibly be determined as embellishments upon this basic time pattern, through modulations of pitch and increasing complexity of rhythmic pattern in time and intensity.

The same principle applies to man. We are born with the

neuromuscular organism which has a number of natural periodicities. One of these is at the rate of from five to ten pulsations per second, and it is probably a phenomenon related to the refractory phase, which means the time after one nervous discharge into a muscle before the next discharge can become effective. The "ha-ha-ha" in hearty laughter at the rate of six or seven pulsations per second is a basic illustration of this phenomenon; the corresponding chatter may be heard in vigorous crying.

On this basic time pattern, the human vibrato, both of pitch and intensity, tends to take the form of a sine curve. This is partly because of the natural ease of this type of pulsation, and partly because that form is most pleasing to the musical ear. The vibrato present in that type of bodily tension which is characteristic of emotional expression is actually a form of trembling. In music this is modulated so that beauty is lent to the tone.

All instrumental vibrato is undoubtedly an imitation of the vocal. The violinist, for example, aims to give to the tone the richness, tenderness, and flexibility characteristic of the voice; but, in this imitation or voluntary production of the vibrato, he improves upon the vocal because he has a better control of the tone. He is, therefore, able to make it even more pleasing to the ear, usually by holding down the extent of the pulsation to a quarter tone as opposed to a semitone in voice. The vibrato occurs not only in the bowed stringed instruments, but possibly in all orchestral and band instruments, although not to the same degree of pulsation or so conspicuously. Sometimes it is a pitch vibrato, sometimes intensity, but usually both; and there is nearly always a timbre vibrato present. This timbre vibrato is a periodic change in the internal structure of the sustained tone in terms of pitch and intensity.

In certain instruments, a particular kind of vibrato is produced by mechanical devices, as, for example, the tremolo or the *voix celeste* in the organ. This tone characteristic is often spoken of as *tremolo,* but it is primarily an intensity vibrato. The word *tremolo* has no defined place in vocal music and should be scrapped. In fixed instruments such as the piano and organ there are various devices by which the vibrato may be produced through sympathetic vibrations and other means. The sympathetic vibration in the violin often results in a conspicuous intensity vibrato.

The significance of the conception here presented is of far-reaching consequence in music. It recognizes the organic basis for a trembling in tone production. This trembling is evidenced in the tonal, the dynamic, the temporal, and the qualitative aspects of the tone. The term vibrato is generic: scores of kinds of vibrato may be designated in terms of specific characteristics for which we now have names. To the singer it is not a question of whether or not he will use the vibrato; the question is: What kind is to be cultivated and tolerated?

In this brief description, I have attempted to define the phenomenon in such a way as to show what basic kinds of vibrato exist; what they accomplish in the way of tone quality; the frequency of occurrence; the purpose they serve; and the theories of causation. Although it has been a mere scratching of the surface on account of the limitations of space, I offer these statements as a challenge for criticism and interpretation in the musical world, for the revision of musical knowledge and for practice in dealing with the most universal and beautiful of musical ornaments.

WHAT IS THE NATURE OF BEAUTY IN THE VIBRATO?

Beauty in the vibrato is found in artistic deviation from the precise and uniform in all the attributes of tone.

The vibrato is the most natural and essential of musical ornaments.

Its beauty lies in its contribution to the flexibility, the tenderness, and the richness of one tone as opposed to the thinness, the rigidity, and the coldness of another tone.

It represents the periodic changes of pitch, intensity, and timbre in sonance.

Richness of tone results from successive fusion of changes of tone as distinguished from simultaneous fusion in timbre.

Flexibility of tone results from indefiniteness of outline.

Tenderness of tone results from evidence of organic trembling.

The genuine vibrato is automatic and expresses the truth—like the spontaneous smile or the frown.

In cultivating the vibrato, avoid cultivating a simulated feeling; try to cultivate the power to feel music genuinely.

IS THE VIBRATO DESIRABLE?

We find evidence for the desirability of the vibrato in many sources, among which we may mention the following:

The universality of vibrato in good singing. No singing can be good without the vibrato, except for an occasional contrasting effect. Objective measurements reveal its presence, often in the most desirable form, at times when the singer denies having used it and the musical listener has failed to hear it as such. If any recognized musician thinks he can find one exception to this rule, it is his duty to document it by making an objective recording and to publish the fact. The issue involved is a vital one for good music, but it is confused greatly in most current theory and practice.

The automatic nature of vibrato. The fact that the vibrato in voice occurs automatically whenever the person sings with genuine feeling indicates that it is an inherent mode of expression in the esthetic mood. Like the smile or the frown, it is an organic, natural, and true expression of feeling. It can, of course, be imitated and learned, just as a smile can be forced; and to that extent it is an imitation of feeling.

Vibrato in instrumental performance. The fact that the violinist cultivates the vibrato at the expense of great effort and the fact that its difficulty is vastly increased in performance attests to its desirability in the highest of instrumental arts.

Conflict of vibrato with precision. The fact that the vibrato is a clearly preferred alternative to precision and smoothness in tone in the face of the violence that it does to intonation, melody, and harmony testifies to its great worth.

Place of vibrato in tone quality. The fact that in the best musical hearing the vibrato is not thought of distinctly as pulsation but as flexibility, tenderness, and richness in tone quality, all of which are regarded as desirable, constitutes significant evidence of its place in the musical situation.

WHAT ARE THE MARKS OF A GOOD VIBRATO?

As guides in determining whether or not a particular vibrato is good or bad, we have formulated some rules, such as the following:

The most desirable average extent of pitch, intensity, and timbre, singly or in combination, is that which produces flexibility, tenderness, and richness of tone, without giving undue prominence to the pulsating quality. That is, the effect is good when it produces the desired tone quality, but does not make us clearly conscious of the fact that there are distinct pulsations.

An extent of the pulsation smaller than that defined in the above rule fails, in proportion to its smallness, to contribute to the improvement of tone quality.

Freedom from irregularity in extent is essential to a good vibrato. As in all motor skills, the inceptive stages are irregular. A distinct mark of an unfinished vibrato is that it continues to be erratic in the extent of the pulsation in one or all of the three media. The extent may be large or small; it may increase or decrease within a single tone or in a succession of tones, but the change must be gradual and smooth. This rule applies also to the part-time or intermittent use of the vibrato in a single tone, which is always an indication of inadequacy.

Artistic performance demands variation in extent and rate throughout a performance. A uniform vibrato, even in the most perfect form, becomes monotonous and fails to function in phrasing, interpretation, and expression of the individuality of the performer.

The most desirable average rate is that which causes the best fusion of tone quality in sonance without producing a chattering through excessive rate. The faster the rate the more completely the fusion takes place in sonance within a medium range.

Slow rate not only fails in producing fusion, but makes the wave movement more prominent. High rate introduces a new element, namely, chatter, which takes the place of pitch wave.

In vocal vibrato the pulsations in pitch should be primary and dominant. This is true in its relation to intensity, primarily on the ground of its near universality in current good singing, but also on the ground of its relative prominence perceptually in the most refined vibrato.

The combination of synchronous pulsations in the three media makes a larger contribution to tone quality than its occurrence in one or two.

In instrumental music, relatively pure intensity pulsation is permissible, as in organ stops and in the use of beats within a region of tolerance for rate.

In solo parts, both vocal and instrumental, the artist has more latitude for giving prominence to the vibrato than he has in ensemble. This rule holds particularly for instrumental performances and, more specifically, for all other than the string instruments.

The more nearly alike are the timbres of the instruments within an orchestral choir, the greater will be the demand for the vibrato in that choir.

A bad vibrato is one which is excessive or erratic in the extent of pulsation in pitch or intensity. There is, of course, more bad vibrato than good in music; the principle is the same as that of the comedian's joke: black horses eat more than white horses—because there are more of them. There is more bad vibrato because individual singers find relative difficulty in producing good vibrato. Naturally, we dislike a bad vibrato, and we should discourage it, but that is no excuse for rejecting or disliking a good vibrato.

INDIVIDUAL DIFFERENCES IN PERFORMING AND HEARING THE VIBRATO

Scarcely any two persons hear a given vibrato alike. The reason for this lies in certain facts of individual differences, among which the following are conspicuous:

The vibrato ear. As in pitch discrimination or hearing ability, one person may be a hundred times more keen than another person in the capacity for detecting the presence of the vibrato or vibrato differences. This presents an embarrassing problem to the performer, and it accounts for the great confusion as to what is good and what is bad in the reactions of individuals in the audience. These individual differences in what we may call *vibrato ear* or *vibrato talent* inhibit us from saying that a particular vibrato is ideal, good, or bad without specifying for whom it is so. Ordinarily we aim at a particular group type such as the fine musical ear, the average ear, or the crooner-saxophone ear.

Feeling-response. As important as the ear response is the natural and temperamental feeling-response or the emotionality of the listener. As far as the arousing of feeling is concerned, the majority of persons in an average audience shed the artist's outpouring of a beautiful tone as a duck sheds water. It has no meaning to them; it does not arouse the appropriate feeling, and therefore is largely lost. We have the technical word *empathy* to designate this trait of "feeling oneself into a situation." Musical empathy is one of the most essential elements of musical appreciation.

Attitude and training. The attitude of the musician has been demonstrated in a shocking manner by the history of the attitude toward the vibrato—the inadequate and ridiculous descriptions, the fanciful explanations, the mystical implications, the groundless musical criticisms, the ill-directed and wasteful musical pedagogy that have been given to it. These musical tragedies have their common root in the absence of correct knowledge of the nature of the vibrato.

The listener's mood. In addition to all the above variables, we have learned to take into account the point of view of the listener; we have distinguished between the critical mood and the musical mood. Both are legitimate and essential, but each yields quite different results. The former must prevail largely in training periods and in critical activities, whereas the latter should prevail in the normal musical situation, the object of which is the derivation of pleasure.

We are dealing with esthetics, and esthetics is analytical and critical throughout. Therefore, in speaking of norms of beauty, indifference, or ugliness, we must confine ourselves to that which can be observed or felt in the critical mood. In view of these facts, the following four points are clear: (1) what makes a good vibrato or a bad one can be answered in terms of the extent to which it serves the purpose of contributing to the three specifically named elements of feeling-value to the tone; (2) there can be no single standard of goodness or badness, because the perception-value and the feeling-value depend upon the "vibrato talent" of the listener; (3) norms for best current practice are available and applicable; and (4) there is much room for improvement beyond these norms in the direction of an ideal vibrato for the fine musical ear.

HOW CAN WE APPROACH AN IDEAL VIBRATO?

Three stages recommended in ear training for vibrato are: (1) the acquiring of factual information such as musical terminology and nomenclature, analysis of the problem, demonstration of specific aspects; (2) the taking of practical exercises in the recognition, description, and evaluation of elements involved in each skill; and (3) the taking of drill exercises for the development of speed and accuracy in each operation. The mastery, and appreciation of feeling is really the ultimate goal in ear training. Only after these three stages have been pursued thoroughly can we undertake to master the rendition of the vibrato in voice or instrument.

On the basis of laboratory experience with the vibrato, I shall try to make some practical suggestions to the teacher on each of the above-mentioned three points.

We see and hear what we expect to see and hear. The astronomer and the star-gazing lover see entirely different heavens on a starlit eve. The botanist and the little girl picking flowers see entirely different things in the flora. On the same principle, a musician or student in music will tend to hear and recognize in the vibrato what he knows factually about it. The psychologist says, "I perceive what I am." Therefore, the first exercises in ear training for the hearing of the vibrato should consist of a systematic study of the known facts about this musical ornament, in order that the student may hear and recognize them intelligently and effectively. To ignore this order is to waste time and energy and to fail of high achievement.

But the astronomer and the botanist acquired their skill by practice. We can now set practice exercises for the development of skill in the detection of the vibrato, its systematic analysis, and esthetic judgments about it. One could study profitably for at least a year in this field; for, in order to understand and to appreciate the vibrato thoroughly, one is forced to recognize and to know hundreds of facts which are being introduced to the science of music.

For the purpose of furnishing training material, Figure 2, the performance score for Lawrence Tibbett's *Drink to Me Only With Thine Eyes* (Victor Red Seal Record, No. V1238), is presented. It will be interesting to play the record for comparison to what this performance score reveals to the eye quantitatively. Incidentally, this score furnishes an opportunity for comparing two singers, Kraft and Tibbett, showing differences in interpretation of the same song, note for note.

The procedure in training for hearing and control of the vibrato is simple. I would suggest the following short series of exercises and integrate them into skills. First, play the phonograph record, listening critically to the vibrato for its extent and rate of pitch pulsation, and then decide for yourself whether or not you regard these qualities as good or faulty. Second, play the record and compare note for note, over and over again; this is to associate the *pitch* pulsation actually heard with the number showing its extent. Do this until you have acquired some skill in naming the magnitude of the pulsation by merely listening as in ordinary music. If well done, this training is transferred to other music. It will prove a valuable tool, and it will stimulate critical listening and evaluation of the vibrato of all singers heard. Third, proceed in the same manner to identify and to judge the *rate* of pulsation, and associate the

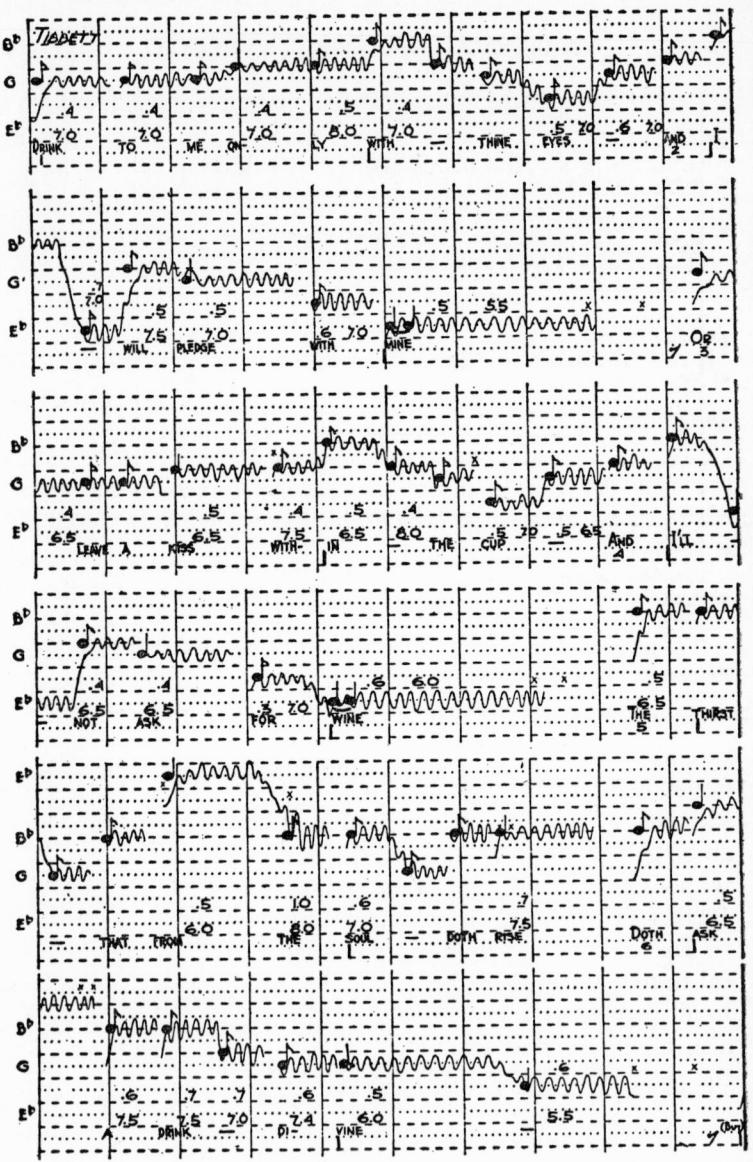

Figure 2a. Lawrence Tibbett's singing *Drink to Me Only With Thine Eyes*

The notation is the same as in Figure 1, except that the performance score for intensity is omitted. The differences are given in numbers on the upper line of the figure in terms of degree of loudness on a scale from 0 to 10, 0 being the softest, 10 the loudest. The rate of vibrato is indicated by numbers in the lower line, showing the number of vibrato cycles per second for each sustained note.

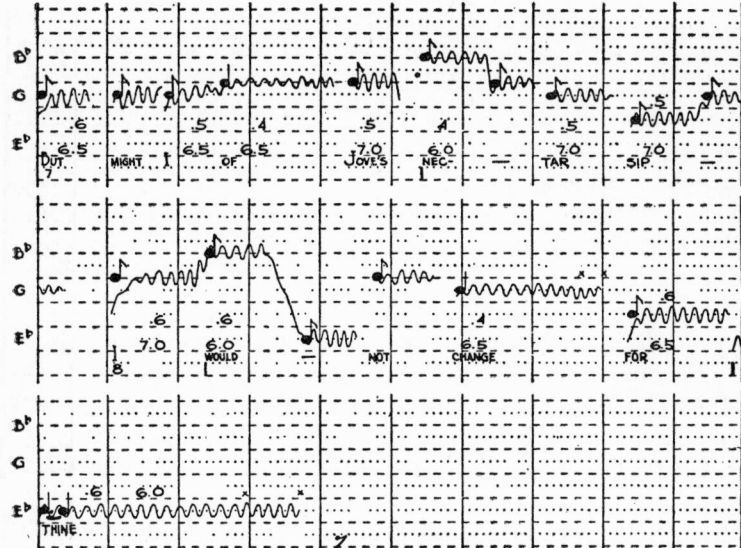

Figure 2b. Lawrence Tibbett's singing *Drink to Me Only With Thine Eyes* (cont'd)

rate as heard with the number shown to indicate the number of cycles per second. Continue this until you have developed a satisfactory tool for evaluating this aspect of the vibrato in all singing. Fourth, practice patiently the vibrato by singing, first without the record, and then in unison with the record. For further instructions, consult the reference given.

Exercises of this kind serve to sharpen the ear for the critical hearing of tone quality. The benefit will transfer not only to all forms of the hearing and performance of the vibrato but also to the hearing of numerous other factors that enter into the perception and control of tone quality.

HOW DO WE ADJUST THE VIBRATO PERFORMANCE?

Concerning a general theory for training in the vibrato, I would suggest the following considerations:

Whenever a student of voice has a natural capacity for singing with feeling, the vibrato comes in automatically. Then the problem with the musical student is not how to inject the vibrato, but how to modulate it.

This modulation should take place not through conscious innervation of particular muscles, but through the exercise of censorship of the ear, which has been refined for the hearing of the vibrato by exact knowledge of its nature and variables and by the acquisition of skills for the hearing, evaluation, and feeling of each variable in turn.

A part of this orientation for the vibrato is knowledge of the musculatures and the various physiological factors that determine rate and extent of vibrato. But the point here made is that the modulation of the vibrato will gradually take care of itself when the ear and the esthetic judgment have been trained.

On the basis of cumulative experimental evidence, I would predict that an approach to an ideal vibrato for a fine musical ear may be found in the enhancement of tone quality by a slight increase in the rate of the vibrato over the average rate now prevailing, and by a material reduction of the pitch and intensity extent. What would it mean to the musical world if our great singers were to reduce their vibrato to the extent now prevailing in the violin?

Chapter 6

PRINCIPLES OF DEVIATION FROM THE REGULAR

THE PURPOSE OF THIS CHAPTER is to indicate some of the approaches to the scientific investigation of an art principle in musical esthetics.

DESIGN

Esthetics in the past has dealt primarily with the composer's design, or the musical form which comes to us in the conventional score. But this score has a number of limitations. First, while it indicates pitch and time in definite notation, it has no significant dynamic notation for individual notes; and, while the quality of the tone is set in part by the harmony and the choice of instrument, the score has practically no note-to-note nomenclature for the quality of tone the composer desires from voice or instrument. In other words, the composer has only fragmentary means of indicating to the performer what he himself would do or would require. The score is certainly a very inadequate blueprint for the artist's performance. Yet the design which is cast in musical form is the basic contribution to the embodiment of beauty in music.

Second, true pitch and exact time or rhythm, as indicated with precision in the score, would make very poor music if it were followed mechanically. No good singer or instrumental soloist stays on the true pitch indicated by the score, even for a fraction of a second, and only in the sense of having a basic temporal reference does he perform in metronomic time. Regarding loudness, or volume, and timbre, or tonal quality, the performer has almost complete freedom, since the score says

---

Adapted from *Scientific Monthly,* 1942, *54,* 98–109.

little or nothing about them. The reason for this musical license is that beauty in the rendition of a composer's design lies most frequently in the artistic play with deviations from the regular —true pitch, even loudness, metronomic time or pure tone, or any of their combinations or derivatives. Here is a basic esthetic principle. This may sound like heresy, because one sanction of plain honesty in musical circles is to the effect that the performer must not garble the work of the composer; and, in training circles, we are rightly led to believe that true intonation in pitch and precision in temporal values as written are among the first skills to be acquired. We may accept these as good training principles, because the performer must be able to intone in true pitch and metronomic time with precision before he can master the skills of artistic deviation from them.

Third, it is due to the recognition of the principle of artistic deviation that artists find unlimited opportunities for variation and interpretation, for the expression of their creative power and artistic sensitivity, and for differentiating their individuality as artists. While we assign first place in esthetic value to the composer's score, we are led to see that the artist must himself become a creator, or at any rate a molder, of the beautiful forms which are crudely indicated in the score. Thus while there is a definite responsibility for the student of esthetics to evaluate the score as a contribution of the composer, it is the artist's rendition which the scientist records and analyzes. This rendition, in common language, is the music on which the listener bases esthetic judgment.[1]

THE PERFORMANCE SCORE

The experimenter in musical esthetics now parallels the conventional musical notation with performance scores which show exactly how the artist rendered the design set out by the com-

---

[1] In order to vitalize the illustrations here cited, the reader is referred to figures as they occur throughout the volume in order that the illustrations may be presented more fully and may be viewed in their true setting. Such reference also gives the reader a great advantage of preview and orientation in regard to what is coming and opportunity to integrate the general theme of this book. If time at this stage of reading does not permit such references, it would be well to postpone the reading of the remainder of this chapter.

poser. This differs from the conventional notation in that it shows exactly how the artist used his musical media in creating the art object—the physical music. Instead of indicating a single note, such as a quarter note, to specify pitch and time, it presents a graph showing the form of attack and release and the periodic and progressive changes in pitch—in short, all deviations from true pitch, whether artistic or erratic. It shows how the given quarter note was modified in duration for the purpose of rhythmic phrasing or as a result of lack of skill. It likewise represents quantitatively in fine detail how this one note fluctuated in intensity. The three factors, pitch, time and intensity, are usually indicated in a single score. (See Figure 1 in Chapter 5.)

In view of the fact that tonal quality is in a constant flux in a tone, performance scores are presented in the form of simple cross sections of a given note, or series of notes. In terms of a tonal spectrum, they are fair samples, showing the harmonic structure of the clang. Such a tonal spectrum is the basis for the hearing of timbre in a simultaneous fusion of the fundamental with its overtones. (See Chapters 7 and 32.)

By showing the sequence of tonal spectra throughout the duration of the tone, we get a performance score in terms of sonance. (See Figure 1, Chapter 9.) Thus we obtain a complete and objective description of the quality of tone as a whole.

Through such performance scores, we take the basic problems of esthetics from the ill-defined, intangible, and airy regions of speculation, doubt, and mysticism and reduce them to verifiable formulas on the basis of measurement. The invention of this simplified score is like the invention of a language; it enables us to transmit symbolically the result of countless observations and measurements in comparatively simple but scientifically indispensable graphs. These graphs may take a variety of forms, depending upon the instruments used, the data in hand, and the purposes to be served. The piano, for example, requires a special piano camera and a particular type of performance score. (See Figures 1, 2 and 3, Chapter 12.)

For each of the basic aspects of music, we now have units of measurement and zero points of reference. Tonal modulations are measured in terms of the number of vibrations of deviation from the pitch of the note as indicated in the score; dynamic modulations are measured in terms of decibel deviation from the threshold of audibility or a standard reference tone; temporal modulations are measured as deviations from metronomic time in hundredths of a second; and qualitative modulations are measured in terms of redistribution of energy in the partials, the zero point of reference being the pure tone.

The idea I wish to convey is that acoustical science with its cameras has now intercepted the sound wave, which is the universal medium of music, and enables us to measure, analyze, and present vast masses of facts in a simple and musically significant language. Thus, if we want to know what artistic devices Lily Pons employs in singing, Menuhin in violin playing, or Hofmann in his piano interpretations, we may now invite them into the laboratory studio, where they may perform under the same conditions as for radio; and complete and permanent phonographic and photographic records will be available after a single performance. For many purposes, the now available high-fidelity phonographic recordings may also be used as research material, provided adequate precautions are taken in regard to possible distortions. The phonophotographic record of the performance score will be the source material on which the future esthetician will work in discovering and in verifying the esthetic principles that operate in performed music.

THE PRINCIPLE OF DEVIATION AS A
MEDIUM OF MUSICAL ARTISTRY

The point of view here presented is of course not new to leaders in the musical profession, but there is frequently a tendency to underestimate or becloud the role that artistic deviation plays in music. Some critics claim that the types of detail shown in the performance score for actual musical artists are of little significance musically. Underlying this criticism we suspect there are survivals of mystic traditions in certain musical circles which indicate lack of scientific information.

One criticism is that the musical performance is more than

the physical sound. This "more" takes several forms, depending upon the culture level of the musician, sometimes making it difficult for him to realize that everything conveyed as music from the performer to the listener is conveyed on sound waves, in terms of which the performance score is built. He has some sort of mystic feeling that his own emotions, ideas of beauty, subjective interpretation or theories of musical values can be conveyed by some mysterious form of musical telepathy. When pressed for illustration he points vaguely to suggestion, gesture, association of ideas, smiles and frowns, environmental atmosphere, and the supersensory reality of music. These may profoundly modify the perception, appreciation, and interpretation of the physical tone, but they are not the music: the musical composition as it is actually rendered in physical tones is the only musical medium that can bridge the gap between the performer and the listener.

A more objective attitude is that of the musician who looks at the performance score and says that these minute deviations in pitch, loudness, duration, and tonal quality are smaller than the ordinary errors of musical observation; the listener does not hear them. To this the experimenter replies that, although they may not be heard individually, cumulatively they give character to the music we do hear and judge; just as in a painting, a figment of red or blue may not be noticed by the observer, but the total accumulation of color figments in pigments and their infinite variety, blending, and shading, gives beauty in color to the picture.

A third objection comes from those who say that most of these deviations are simply errors in performance. That is, of course, largely true for many incompetents who ply the art, and it is true also of even the best artists, because their capacity for achievement is relative, and because in many respects they assume a considerable region of tolerance for precision.

But in dealing with competent artists it is easy enough to find abundant material in the way of deviations that have esthetic value, even though they may not be heard individually as such. Frequently the performer himself is not aware of them, because they function as well-established habits. Furthermore, the objective study of the performance score reveals the operation of a great variety of esthetic principles which spring directly out of the emotional demands without the performer being aware of them as such. These are usually more numerous than the known or voluntarily followed principles.

This defense of the principle of artistic deviation from the beautiful is, of course, set up in contrast to the well-established esthetic principle assigning beauty to certain types of fidelity to the score. It is contended here that the basic esthetic sanctions, such as unity and balance, harmony and richness, contrast and symmetry, are obtained far more frequently by principles of deviation than by principles of fidelity and uniformity.

PHRASING

With these preliminaries, we may now turn for illustration to some well-recognized principles of esthetics which can be quantified and systematized by the experimental procedures here indicated. The most general term applying to principles of artistic deviation in practical music is that of phrasing. Phrasing is a comprehensive term and it covers a vast array of esthetic principles, subjective and objective, in musical artistry.

This is well illustrated by the record showing how a violinist indulges in deviation from regularity. (See Figures 3 and 4, Chapter 13.) If he had not so indulged, the lines for pitch, intensity, and time would have tended to be straight and would have indicated that the rendition was cold, unemotional, and devoid of artistic interpretation. The student of musical esthetics must ask hundreds of questions regarding a single passage. Assuming that the artist is competent so that the constellation of variations is significant, the student of esthetics must ask for every cross section of the score: Why did he augment or diminish the interval to this degree at this point? Why did he increase or decrease the loudness in this direction and to this degree at this point? Why did he take liberties with the metronomic time by lengthening or shortening, by anticipating or by overholding the note at this point? And if we had the timbre score in terms of the spectrum at each stage in the phrase, similar questions could be asked about that, and more of them.

The significance of the deviation is well illustrated when we attempt to compare two performers. (See Figure 2 in Chapter 12.) For example, if we ask two equally competent professional pianists to perform a given beautiful selection at their best before the camera, the performance scores will reveal a remarkable similarity in their interpretative treatments of note, measure, and phrase, although no mention may have been made of phrasing or of the purpose of the recording. This indicates that there is a common stock of principles which competent artists tend to observe; that the character of each measure or phrase tends to make the same emotional appeal to both; and that they unquestionably find similar outlets for the expression of their individuality in the esthetic interpretation. We should not, of course, assume that there is only one way of phrasing a given selection, but, even with such freedom, two artists will reveal many common principles of artistic deviation. Furthermore, insofar as there are consistent differences in their phrasing, these differences may reveal elements of musical individuality.

Then, again, if we ask one artist to play the same selection several times in succession with no other instructions than to play as beautifully as he can, he will tend to indulge in the same artistic deviations in successive playings, provided he does not definitely aim to give different interpretations. (See Figure 4, Chapter 12.)

The asynchronization of chords by advancing or delaying one hand against the other, or asynchronizing the leading note, is one of the common devices for artistic effect in phrasing. (See Figure 6, Chapter 12.) It has been shown that there are a variety of principles of asynchronization which co-operate to the same effect; that significant asynchronization may occur as frequently as in half of the chords; that each type of music makes the characteristic demand for this device; and that each player may reveal his individuality in the use of this device by both the frequency and the extent of the deviation. Some comparisons of artists in this respect are given in Figure 6.

One specific element in phrasing pertains to principles of diminishing or augmenting intervals in relation to accepted scales. Musical esthetics in the past has concerned itself with the interval, and today the fastidious violinist prides himself on his individuality and his skill in interval refinements, such as augmenting or diminishing an interval in various degrees for specific purposes. There are a number of rules which he recognizes, but ultimately his intonation is guided by a sort of moving feeling of the fitness of each individual intonation. When we make objective measurements of the performance of the best recognized violinists, we see that they all show certain common tendencies as to the direction, movement, and extent of deviations from standard intervals; that none plays consistently in either the tempered scale or the natural scale; but, on the other hand, that there is a marked tendency toward the Pythagorean scale. (See Figure 4 in Chapter 13.)

Let me mention but one more of the hundreds of varieties of esthetic principles that may be revealed systematically by a phrasing score, namely, the substitution of time for stress or stress for time, which in itself becomes a complicated structure of theory and practice. From the early classical times to the present, this has been a moot issue in poetry. But in music the issue becomes more evident and presents itself as a fascinating field for objective studies that may settle disputes that have existed for hundreds of years. In the best music we find abundant examples of the absence of stress in the accented note of the measure when the rhythm of the measure is very clear.

Some of these principles were known to the performer, and they served as a goal in his performance. The performance score can, of course, be used in verifying, elaborating, and systematizing these principles. Other principles, expressed with equal regularity, were not known to the performer but were the result of the unanalyzed feeling of satisfaction in a particular deviation. We must, of course, always assume that there is a certain range of mere errors, but these can often be teased out by utilizing comparative techniques in measurement.

Thus the phrasing score becomes a tool with which we can describe the artist's interpretation of a given measure, phrase or passage in terms of esthetic principles of deviation. In such terms we can set up esthetic goals for the acquisition of skills and emotional expressiveness. No one has yet made a complete analysis of a phrasing score or is likely to do so in the near future, because it represents such an endless variety of artistic outlets; nevertheless, at this stage we can take any esthetic principle recognized by a composer and trace it objectively in these scores, thus laying foundations for the classification of principles of artistic deviation. This is one of the elements in the beauty, or lack of beauty, of music. We do not now know how many esthetic principles are involved, how they co-operate, interfere, or integrate. But we do know that all of them are expressed in terms of the possible variants in the sound wave: frequency, amplitude, duration, and form. If we grant that the medium of music is physical sound, there is no escape from the principle that, in terms of four variables of a sound wave, there is room for an infinite variety in artistic deviation and that it can be expressed quantitatively in a performance score.

These physical performance scores can be converted, through the application of laws of acoustics, physiology, and psychology, into what we may call *hearing scores,* showing what the listener actually hears, which is quite different from the performance score of the artist showing what he actually played or sang. This difference will, of course, vary with an endless variety of factors in the ability and application of the listener.

MUSICAL ORNAMENTS

There is a great variety of musical ornaments: some are in general use and some are the trait of a school or period of musical artistry; others are spontaneous traits of primitive peoples, and still others are fanciful license of individual performers. They are all deviations from the regular, most of them of artistic intent.

MUSICAL LICENSE

Until recently music anthropologists described primitive music, such as that of the Indians or the South Sea Islanders, in terms of our conventional scales, simply mentioning that certain types of freedoms or "errors" were exhibited. But when phonophotography came in, the ridiculousness of that judgment was made manifest. (See all the figures in Chapter 24.)

NATURE OF THE ESTHETIC IN MUSIC

In the above I have shown how the scientist takes the actual music of the composer and performers and dissects it in the laboratory for the purpose of description, classification, and explanation of the phenomena involved. We have found reason to demand that a fundamental requirement of the artist is the ability to intone in true pitch and metronomic time. True pitch, metronomic time, pure tone, and even intensity represent fundamental esthetic values. But, while beautiful in themselves, they represent mainly points of reference for orientation from which artistic deviation constitutes the main groundwork of musical artistry.

At this stage we may well inquire what the phenomena here discussed have to do with esthetics. Many good musicians have never read a book on esthetics. Academically, this subject is usually treated as a branch of philosophy—just as psychology was treated half a century ago. But, just as psychology has now been taken into the laboratory, many problems of esthetics are now taken into the laboratory, and, wherever possible, scientific experiment is substituted for artistic speculation.

There is still room for a number of distinctive and legitimate approaches to the subject (as was pointed out in Chapter 2). The philosopher analyzes the concept of musical values, the theory of esthetic values, and the nature of beauty in relation to ultimate reality. Sometimes he is in danger of imposing a mystic or esoteric conception of the nature of the beautiful. The music historian and critic traces the evolution of musical concepts of beauty in terms of the progressive enrichment of musical composition and musical performance by the adoption of new media. The anthropologist traces, in a similar way, the evolution of the progressive development of music in races and nations. The artist formulates esthetic rules of performance and embodies them in artistic skills. The educator aims to increase the capacity for the appreciation of music and the development of musical skills in the light of available knowledge.

All these approaches nibble at the question: What is beautiful in music and how can we know it? One seeks universal principles, another seeks practical rules, another traces the evolution of this human power of exhibiting the beautiful, another aims to broaden our knowledge and to deepen our appreciation of it; and the latest comer to the field, the scientist, offers to describe, criticize, verify, and explain, wherever scientific procedure is possible.

Chapter 7

TONE QUALITY: TIMBRE

THE MOST IMPORTANT BASIC ATTRIBUTE of all music is tone quality. There is an infinite series of possible varieties, yet we have no adequate classification or suitable names. Tone quality, like harmony, volume, and rhythm, is a complex process in which there function the four elemental attributes of tone: pitch, intensity, duration, and timbre. In terms of these, we can measure and describe all kinds of tone.

Tone quality has two fundamental aspects: (1) *timbre*,[1] representing the simultaneous presence or fusion of the fundamental and its overtone at a given moment, and (2) *sonance*, representing the successive presence or fusion of changing timbre, pitch, and intensity in the tone as a whole.

THE NATURE OF TIMBRE

This and the next three chapters will deal with timbre. Physically, the timbre of a tone is a cross section of the harmonic structure for the moment represented by the duration of one vibration in the sound. It is spoken of as a tonal spectrum.

---

[1] The word *timbre* (pronounced *tim-ber*) is of French origin, meaning stamp or character. It is not used extensively in music, and the French spelling seems to add mystery to its connotation. It is proposed that we use the word as frequently and as naturally as we use *pitch* or *time* and with the same degree of clarity. We may retain the French spelling in the transition period for the sake of continuity; but let us take it out of the realm of mystery and confusion. The latest edition of Webster sanctions both the English pronunciation and the French spelling.

Adapted from "The Harmonic Structure of a Beautiful Tone," *Musical Quarterly,* 1939, *25,* 6–10; "In Search of Beauty in Music," *Musical Quarterly,* 1942, *28,* 302–308; "Objective Factors in Tone Quality," *American Journal of Psychology,* 1942, *55,* 123–127; "The Quality of Tone: Timbre," *Music Educators Journal,* September 1936.

Psychologically and musically, *timbre is that characteristic of tone which depends upon its harmonic structure, fundamental pitch, and total intensity.*

The harmonic structure [2] is expressed in terms of the number, the distribution, the relative intensity, and the phase relations of the harmonics in a tone. In a given instrument this harmonic structure usually varies with the pitch of the fundamental and the total intensity of the tone.

It is in terms of timbre that we differentiate the tonal character of musical instruments, of voices, of vowels, and other sounds in art and nature. Just as pitch, the psychological or musical aspect of tone, is defined in terms of its physical counterpart, frequency, so timbre, the psychological or musical aspect of a tone, is defined in terms of its physical counterpart, harmonic structure. For certain purposes, however, timbre may be defined in purely psychological terms which give recognition to purely mental accessory factors.

The harmonic structure of a tone in terms of harmonic analysis has long been known in mathematics and physics, but has not come into general use in music and psychology owing to the complicated nature of the measurement and therefore the general ignorance of its meaning. Now, however, we have instruments which give us measures of precision and which are great timesavers. Therefore, we can say that timbre is satisfactorily harnessed for experimental work in the laboratory, we can collect samples of sound waves in any form of music and we can submit them to exact measurement. In radio and in the recording of music, utilization of the knowledge of the harmonic structure of sound plays an important role.

There are three stages in the measurement of timbre. First, is the recording of sample sound waves of a musical selection on very high-speed motion picture film as described in Chapter 4 and illustrated in Figure 2. Second, is the enlarging of this and the running of it through the harmonic analyzer to

---

[2] It is unfortunate that the terms *harmonic structure* and *harmonic analysis* have two distinct meanings in music. For the present we must depend upon the context to know whether we refer to musical harmony or to timbre.

Figure 1. Henrici harmonic analyzer

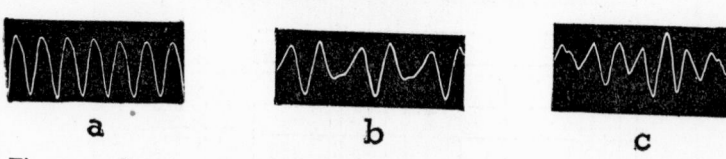

Figure 2.   Sample of oscillograms for three tones on the bassoon, each for one hundredth of a second

(a) the highest (523 dv) played *p*; (b) the middle register (194 dv) played *f*; (c) the lowest played (82 dv) played *f*. The space between two white dots in each figure marks off one wave; the lower the tone, the longer and more complex the wave.

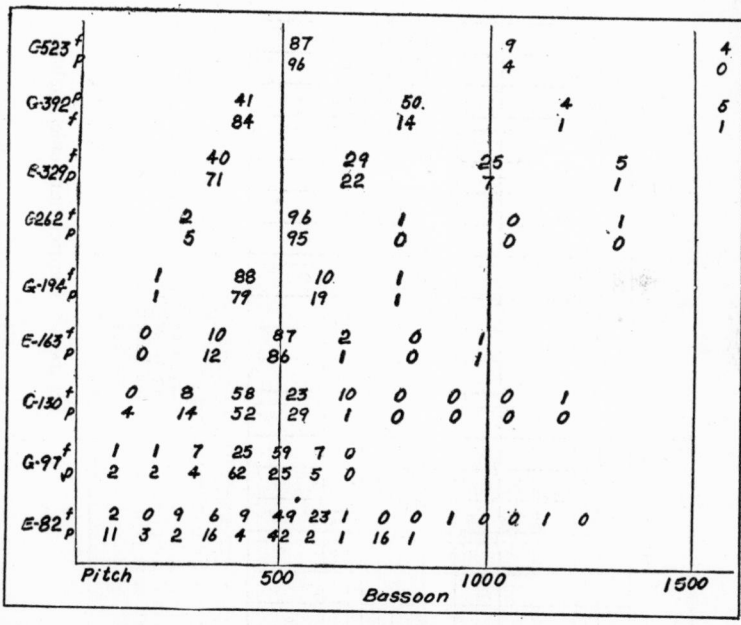

Figure 3.   Readings from the dials on the Henrici analyzer, which converts the wave form into its constituent partials and shows the relative strength of each partial

The numbers and letters at the left indicate the pitch level of each of the nine tones and whether the playing is *f* or *p*. The pitch of the partials is indicated at the bottom. The consecutive numbers represent consecutive partials, zero indicating the absence of a partial. For example, in the lowest tone played softly, 11 per cent of the energy lies in the first partial or fundamental, 3 per cent in the second partial, 2 per cent in the third, 16 per cent in the fourth, and so on.

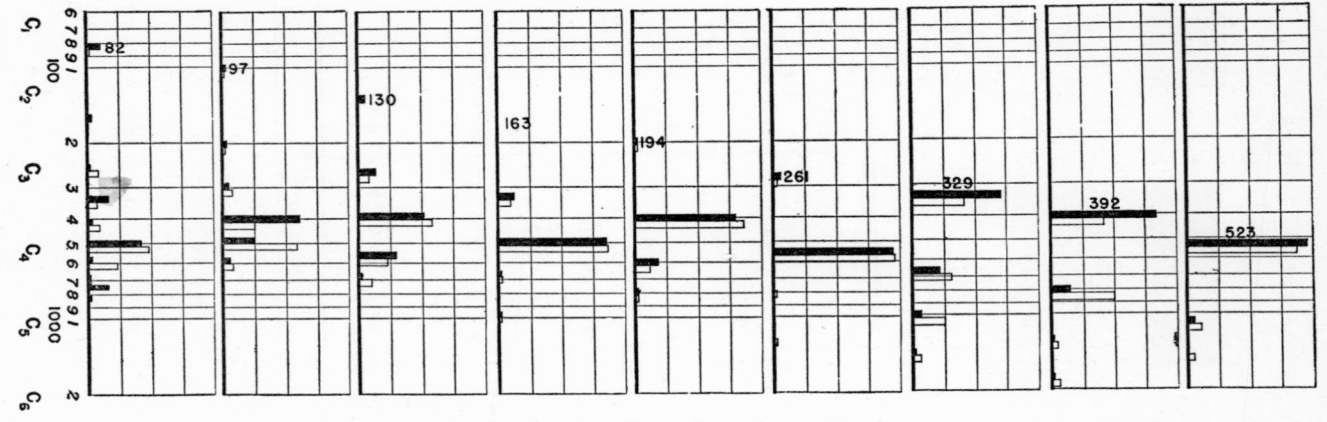

Figure 4. Tone spectra comparing loud and soft tones throughout the register of the bassoon

    The pitch of each note is indicated by the number over the first bar, which represents the fundamental. The black bar represents a soft tone, and the bar in outline represents a strong tone. The height of each bar shows the percentage of energy in each partial. The pitch (frequency) of each partial is indicated at the bottom by the letters and numbers above them.

obtain the data for the construction of a tone spectrum, as in Figure 3. Third, is the conversion of this table into tone spectra as in Figure 3.

The harmonic analyzer (Figure 1) is the instrument which converts the form of the sound wave into its constituent partials, showing which partials are present and showing the relative strength of each, as shown in Figure 3. It is capable of recording as many as forty partials which may be present in a complex tone. The instrument is too complicated for description here except to say that the enlarged motion picture film is drawn slowly under the pickup in the foreground and the result of the mechanical analysis is read from the graduated wheels at the top. Instead of describing the technical procedures here, I offer sample measurements on a single instrument, the bassoon.

THE TIMBRE OF THE BASSOON

A competent artist on the bassoon was asked to play an arpeggio from the lowest to the highest notes of the instrument in which he could produce a good tonal quality. Each note was played two times, first in moderately loud, f, and second, moderately soft, p, before the high-speed motion picture camera in the recording studio. Figure 2 shows sample waves from the highest, the middle, and the lowest register of the instrument, and Figure 4 shows spectra for the seven notes in the arpeggio, sampling the resources of the instrument as recorded in Figure 3. It can be observed in Figure 2 that the lower the tone, the longer and more complicated a single wave becomes.

To construct a spectrum for each of these sample tones in the arpeggio, we take one typical wave from each oscillogram and run it through the harmonic analyzer, which reduces the wave form to its constituent partials (fundamental and overtones) so that we can read off the results on the dials of the analyzer in terms of percentage of energy for each partial. From this we construct a table as in Figure 3. Here the record is shown for the nine notes of the arpeggio, and for each one the tone was played f and p in turn.

Thus the table shows what partials are present or absent and percentage of energy in each contribution to the characteristics of the tone as a whole. Comparison of the figures for f and p shows the specific aspect in which the soft and loud tones differ both in number of partials present, their distribution, and the relative percentage of energy in each. From this table we construct for each tone, a spectrum which reveals at a glance all the characteristics of the tone as a whole, as in Figure 4.

Here we have a profile which shows the nature of the bassoon tone as simply and as clearly as a profile of a human face or the picture of a tree or a landscape. A person who understands the principles involved can see at a glance the exact characteristics of each tone. He can give an exact definition in terms of the number of partials present, their distribution, and the relative amount of energy in each. Thus we acquire an exact and realistic language which is completely standardized, which is as universal as mathematics, and in terms of which we can express ourselves and can reason in musical esthetics.

We should hardly speak of the bassoon, but rather of *this* bassoon; other instruments would differ. The same is true for the picture for this player; other players would differ, and the same players cannot play the same note alike twice. Similarly, the picture holds only for the resonance characteristics of this musical recording studio. We obtained materially different pictures when we repeated the recording in the adjoining "dead room." All these variables are present in all musical hearing of music. But the significant fact is that, in these tone spectra, we can see quantitatively finer detail than the musician can hear with unaided ear. After all, any competent observer can see that Figure 4 pictures a bassoon, however closely it may resemble other instruments.

We see that the body of the lowest tone comes from the sixth and seventh partials. Reading numbers in the next to the bottom line of Figure 3, and looking at the bars in Figure 4, we find that 49 per cent of the energy for the strong tone, f, is in the sixth partial and 23 per cent in the seventh. There is only 2 per cent in the first partial or fundamental, none in the second, 9 per cent in the third, 6 per cent in the fourth, 9 per cent in the fifth, and so on up to 1 per cent in the fourteenth partial which is the highest in this low tone. Here, then, is a quantitative picture which determines the timbre or harmonic structure of this tone in the bassoon at a pitch of 82 double vibrations played *f*.

There is a surprising absence of energy in the fundamental and its first four overtones as indicated by these numbers. We do hear the fundamental distinctly, and it is so prominent that no one would name any other pitch as the fundamental by hearing. Yet it carries only 2 per cent of the total energy in the tone. This is due to the presence of subjective tones, particularly difference tones, which are supplied subjectively by the ear and which give us a much fuller sound than that represented by the actual physical tone.

The characteristic quality of the bassoon lies in the region just below 500 double vibrations, or about at B_3, which represents its resonance region. This is seen by following the staggering of the long bars in this region, making a vertical column regardless of the fundamental pitch in all the nine notes.

As the fundamental pitch rises, the tone becomes thinner and purer, so that for a pitch of 523 double vibrations played *p*, 96 per cent of the energy is in the first partial or fundamental which happens to coincide approximately with the resonance region of the instrument. This principle is shown by the degree of complexity in the three wave forms, the highest being almost a pure sine wave as from a tuning fork seen in Figure 2. Figures 3 and 4 show how this principle holds throughout all the stages examined in the rising scale.

There is no very marked change in timbre concurrently with change in degree of loudness, as is shown in Figures 3 and 4. Yet, there are a number of observable tendencies which are stated quantitatively in these figures.

These observations may suffice to demonstrate the possibility and significance of the measurement of timbre. Scores of similar facts might be demonstrated for any tone but perhaps the most vital thing to the musician is the fact that we have here, in terms of harmonic analysis, an exact language which has musical significance.

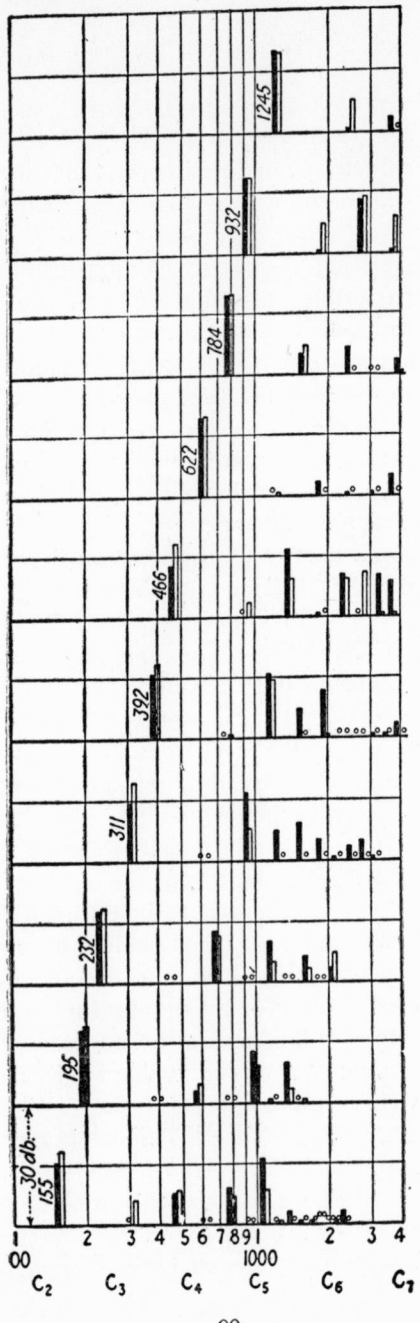

Figure 5. The clarinet

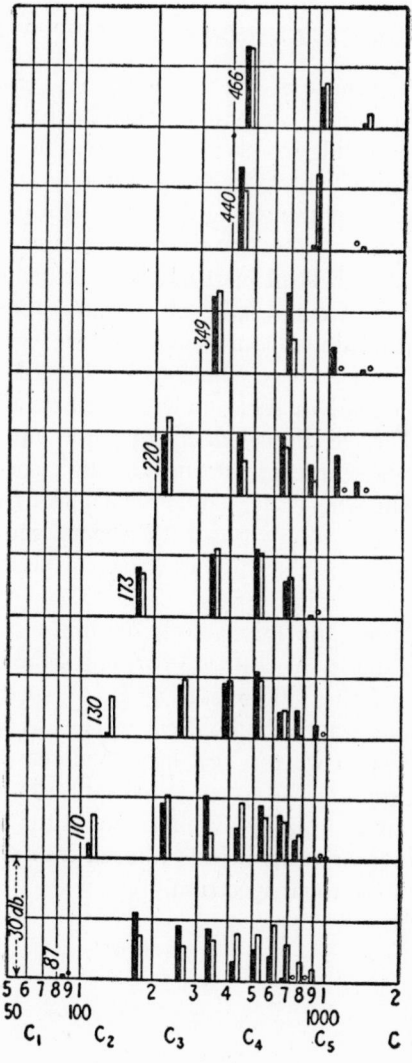

Figure 6. The French horn
Legend for Figures 5 and 6 same as for Figure 4.

16

Instead of thinking of the variety of tone quality as chaos and indescribable confusion, this line of reasoning shows how science dispels the confusion by analyzing the phenomenon into its component elements which can be verified by exact measurements and represented by defined and verifiable concepts.

TONE SPECTRA FOR THE CLARINET AND THE FRENCH HORN

Tone spectra like those of the bassoon are given in Figure 5 for the clarinet, in Figure 6 for the French horn. The baritone horn, the cornet, the slide trombone, the flute, the oboe, and the tuba may be seen in Chapter 17 of the author's *Psychology of Music*, and, for each of the strings of the violin in Chapter 18 of the same volume.

The student of orchestral instruments is urged to see what fundamental meaning for music he can find for himself in these figures. The great thing about scientific tone spectra is that they tell the story of an exceedingly complicated situation in profuse and exact mathematical and physical detail. It would take several chapters to discuss adequately the individual data, their organization and interpretation in a single spectrum. The competent musician who understands principles of acoustics in psychological interpretation of esthetic theory can pursue his own line of interest in checking evidence in support of new theories as well as in discovering specific facts not generally known. To illustrate, he might well set himself the task of asking a hundred questions or more for which the answers can be found in one of these figures. Try it. A spectrum is like a high-fidelity photograph of a landscape. Here is source material in terms of which we can see, hear, and reason about the nature of beauty in a musical tone. What interests one observer may not interest or be seen by another. As in the viewing of a landscape, the observer often injects himself into what he sees, hears, and feels in the tonal spectrum.

Chapter 8

A BEAUTIFUL TONE MADE TO ORDER

Two BASIC METHODS of science are applied to experiment and measurement in musical esthetics, namely, the method of the natural sciences and the method of the physical sciences. The biologist collects fair samples of plants and animals; he describes them, classifies them, and traces the natural history of their development and habitats. The physicist starts with an hypothesis, objectifies it and develops the laws of its operation by varying one factor at a time until he has an adequate array of facts for the explanation and control of it.

Every musical phenomenon has a natural history. The scientist can now trace, describe, and explain this natural history, its development, its functions, and means for its control. This procedure was illustrated in preceding chapters. Let me present here a specific illustration of experimental procedure in the analysis and evaluation of tonal beauty by the method of physical science. The illustration pertains to one specific aspect of tone, namely timbre.

A TONE GENERATOR

A graduate engineering student who had been discouraged because he had no money to finance himself came to see me about registering for graduate work. The electrical engineers did not encourage the project about which he had some ambitious convictions, namely, the building of an electrical organ. After careful analysis of his plans and an evaluation of his ability, it was agreed that he should take about three years to build a single note according to his specifications, the time to be

Adapted from *Pioneering in Psychology,* Chapter IV, 45–47; various parts of *Revision of the Seashore Measures of Musical Talents;* and the *Music Educators Journal,* September 1936.

spent on the construction of a tone generator representing one key of the organ and an experimental study of the possibilities for the control and enrichment of the tone produced by it. He was assured that, if he would build this generator for the psychological laboratory under the joint direction of engineers and psychologists and let it become the property of the laboratory, he could be guaranteed all the facilities of the workshops in psychology and engineering, supply of all needed material, and probably a graduate stipend for that period. This "contract" proved advantageous to psychology in that it not only gave us a new type of instrument capable of meeting new situations in psychology, but also represented a very great saving in the cost of construction.

This was far from building an organ, but it proved a notable undertaking, and it was completed with great distinction. The electrostatic tone generator consists of sixteen partials, the equivalent of sixteen pure tones, any number of which may be combined into a rich tone of harmonic structure. It has the possibility of varying the basic pitch, the number of partials, the amount of energy in each partial, and the phase relations of each partial. Mathematicians assure us that with sixteen units, each with so many variables, we can produce more than a million varieties of tonal timbre.

No such enormous number of tone qualities can have practical significance in music or in experimental work in acoustics and phonetics. To simplify the situation, we select as many types and degrees of qualitative difference in tone as may be significant for actual music or for an experimental situation. The setting for each pattern is wired to a keyboard like an organ console so that the different qualities of the same note can be played as on the organ by merely pressing the appropriate key. While a musician can hear a large number of differences in tonal timbre experimentally, in practical music he probably does not intentionally employ more than twenty or thirty varieties. These connections, for experimental purposes, are made with a stencil like the stencil on a player piano which, when run through at an even speed, will play selected patterns identically any number of times.

With this generator, it is possible to take the harmonic analysis of any desired tone and reproduce the tone synthetically insofar as it is covered by the first sixteen partials. To make sure that this reconstruction is accurate, we have only to make harmonic analysis of the artificial tone and compare that with the specifications from the original tone.

One can readily see what a wide range of opportunities for experiment the presence of such an instrument provides in the laboratory. There are many kinds of tone generators on the market, but I think it has been generally agreed that, at the time of its construction, this one combined the best features of all and had several new features.

One superior feature of this apparatus is that any representative series of tone qualities of harmonic structure can be set up for the purpose of experimentation. Thus we can make it speak any of the basic vowels or their variants insofar as they are composed of harmonic structure within the range here covered; we can take the harmonic analysis of the performance of an artist in voice or instrument and reconstruct it synthetically; we can set up scales for the measurement of a sense of timbre; we can set up hundreds of varieties of specific experimental controls for the detailed study of specific issues involved in tone quality; and, strange as it may seem, not only can we set up a tone according to quantitative and qualitative specifications, but we can define, verify, describe, and reproduce each and all of such tones with precision.

This sounds a little like magic, but it helps take the concepts of timbre and sonance out of the prevailing chaos. We can humbly say that, within reasonable limits, it makes us masters of this most complicated and important element in tone production, the quality of the tone. This principle is of course fundamental for the incoming avalanche of electronic musical instruments.

To accomplish this invention a mastery of principles of electrical engineering was essential. This was supervised by the head of the electrical engineering department. Of equally vital importance was a critical knowledge of the composition and function of elements of musical sounds from the point of music and acoustics. This was supervised by Dr. Don Lewis, who was specializing in studies of timbre in the department of psychology. The student-inventor himself had the necessary ingenuity and drive. Result: he obtained ideal training in research, and the laboratory was enriched by possession of a rare and exceedingly valuable instrument. The inventor has completed a second model of a one-manual organ.

VARIANTS FOR MEASUREMENT IN THE TONAL SPECTRA

In modern botany the scientist finds that there may be millions of kinds of a particular plant in existence. To describe that group of plants, he does not have to examine all of them but selects systematically a significant number of fair samples which he can describe with precision and classify into genera, species, and varieties to the nth degree. This study is then fractionated so as to cover what is worth knowing. One series will cover the structure, another the function of each part of the plant as a whole, another the practical uses to which it has been put, another the laws of physics and chemistry found in operation, another its origin and adaptation to climatic conditions.

In the same manner the scientist interested in the description, classification, and explanation of esthetic values in music may select for experiment fair samples of observable beauty or ugliness and reduce them, if we may use botany as an analogy, into genera, species, varieties, etc., in an adequate classification with a stabilized terminology and a pattern for the definition of each and every factor. Having selected fair samples, he may put them to experiment in search of esthetic values in many ways for many purposes in the experimental course of each judgment. He may thus reveal the principal factors in the tonal spectrum as to the kind and degree of esthetic value and may discover and explain the nature of these values.

In the preceding chapter we saw that the physical spectrum is an adequate quantitative definition, description and graphic representation of the timbre in the physical tone. We then proceeded by the natural history method of selecting samples and analyzing them into their component elements of structure.

We shall now proceed in the opposite direction by the methods employed in physics and acoustics; we shall build up specific types of beauty in tonal structure for the purpose of describing, defining, and evaluating them as esthetic types. The beauty or ugliness in the structure of a musical object can be varied under control by use of the tone generator, and can take an infinite variety of forms. This is the method of physical science in acoustics as employed in experimental esthetics. This mass of forms may, however, be reduced to a few fundamental types of variables, some of which we shall consider here.

We take the best obtainable tone from actual music and make desired changes in the timbre of it in order to produce its optimum form for a special esthetic purpose. Working on a panel of the tone generator (which works very much like the instruments in the control room of a good radio station), the experimenter operates dials and switches to control all the resources of the instrument, his object being to set up accurately defined spectra upon which we may base esthetic judgments. Here are some of the significant variables possible.

Number of partials present. Richness is one of the basic elements of beauty in the tone. The number of partials present is a principal factor in determining the degree of richness of a tone. The number of partials may vary from a single first partial, which is the fundamental, up to as many as 20, 30, or 40 or more. At one end of the richness series is the pure tone which has only one partial, the fundamental. This is commonly represented by the sound from the tuning fork or a note in the highest register in some instrument, such as the flute or clarinet, under limited conditions.

For many purposes in music, particularly in the coloratura field of a singer, the aim is to get a pure tone free from harmonics. At the other end of the series is noise which, for many esthetic purposes, plays an important role. In music, the drum is perhaps the best representative of noise.

To determine the effect of the number of partials in estimating the richness of a tone, we build up a tone of given pitch and vary the number of partials present; but all other factors are kept constant. Among these variables which must be kept constant are: the fundamental pitch, the total intensity of the tone, the amount of energy in each of the partials, and absences in the serial order of the partials. Starting with a pure tone consisting of the first partial only, one partial at a time is added, and the resulting increase in richness of the tone and the types of changes in its beauty are observed. The experiment is repeated with different fundamental pitches and different degrees of total intensity.

With the tone thus built according to specifications readily available, we proceed with psychological measurements, employing expert observers as judges of value. While each of the variables introduced will bring about a distinct change in tone quality, musically all the tones will be of relatively low esthetic value as long as all the partials present have the same degree of energy; that is, are equally strong.

The net result of such a series of experiments lies in both the qualitative and quantitative description of the various types of beauty which can be produced by varying this single element, the number of partials. While we have no names for these types, we have, at each stage, an exact acoustical description of the tone so that it can be repeated, verified and measured.

The distribution of partials. The largest variable in determining the beauty-ugliness quality or esthetic value of a tone is the distribution of the partials. The kind and degree of beauty depend upon the location of partials in the harmonic series and the degree of grouping for relative dominance. To investigate the esthetic value for different types of distribution of partials, the experimenter will vary this factor alone while all other factors are kept constant. He can then run different series of experiments to determine in turn the effect of gaps at different pitch levels of the spectrum, their relationships in the position of the gaps, and the bunching of the partials present.

Good tones may be produced with astonishing gaps in the harmonic series of partials. For example, the first partial and several of the lowest partials above it may be absent; and yet, due to the operation of the principle of difference tones, the tone will be heard as if these partials were present. This was observed in the lower tones of Figures 2 and 3 in the preceding chapter.

Formants. The formant is a group of adjacent partials, in any register of a tone, which stands out in relative prominence. The best example we have of this is our vowels, any one of which may possess the same number of overtones, but the vowel quality as a particular "a" or "e" depends primarily upon formant structure. The character and position of formants is well illustrated in Figure 4 in Chapter 9 for the spoken vowel. The same principle applies to the vowel in the word as it is sung and to the corresponding vowel quality of the tone. Within certain limitations for economy, we can make the tone generator speak any vowel as it occurs in phonetic character in language, the musical work or tone character, by simply manipulating the number, position, width, form, and relative dominance of the formants.

To isolate and measure types of beauty due to formants, we must vary each of these factors one at a time and keep all other factors affecting formants constant. "O" as in *tone* has a different formant spectrum from "o" as in *ton*. Both may be beautiful, but each possesses an entirely different kind of beauty, and each may serve a different purpose in music. The choice of vowels for music is dependent upon the choice of words or characteristics of a particular language, and it is therefore an important factor in determining the esthetic value of a tone.

The fundamental pitch. Spectra for a rising order of fundamental pitch of the same instrument vary radically, as demonstrated in Chapters 7 and 13. The quality of bass or soprano tones is not comparable unless one considers their natural favored register. This has profound musical significance; and many of these changes are predictable. This is illustrated in the various families of musical instruments, such as the brass and the woodwinds, as well as in voice. To make esthetic studies of tones which are dependent upon the fundamental pitch, the tone generator is set to produce good tones of various kinds at different pitches, varying insofar as possible the factor of fundamental pitch only.

Related to the register is the matter of pitch range for instruments and voices. This is of great value and can be readily submitted to experiment.

Total intensity. When a note is struck on the piano or a mass chord in the orchestra, the kind of tone varies, in a predictable way, with the total intensity of the tone as a whole. Therefore, when a musician varies the intensity of his tone, he also varies its quality, because the louder the tone, the more partials—both harmonic and inharmonic—will be present. This is illustrated in the modern interpretation of piano touch where the quality of tone is determined by the force of the impact of the hammer on the string; that is, the intensity of the tone.

The relative intensity of partials. Intensity is one of the largest and most significant variables in tone quality. As we have seen, it is the basis for the formation of formants. Aside from recognizable groups which we call formants, the spectra may take an endless variety of forms in the distribution of relative intensity of partials. The strong partials may be bunched in the lower region of the tone, the middle region, or the upper region with radically different results in tone quality. In these bunchings, a great variety of types and features can be recognized. Indeed, the spectrum picture of the tone is to the tone what a photograph is to a landscape or even a human form or face. The expert who knows what to look for can readily distinguish one from another, and he can express himself in likes or dislikes, approval or disapproval, of particular types of beauty in music. Thus, smoothness of tone is an element of beauty, and, in the spectrum, this is indicated mainly by regularity or irregularity in the distribution of differences in intensity of partials. Since the spectrum showing relative intensity of all its partials is a complete picture of the tone, such a picture is the most universally usable symbol for direct inspection of a tone or for adequate definition and description of any of its parts.

It is evident that there is an inexhaustible field for experiment with our tone generators. Sounds from nature in musical art can be taken, and the tone generators can reproduce spectra for refined variation under laboratory conditions of measurement.

Inharmonics. The typical spectrum is expressed in terms of the harmonic series of partials. In actual music, inharmonic elements are usually present both in instrument and voice, and they add to richness and variety of tone. Many instruments are designed and operated so as to bring out discordant elements in the form of inharmonics which, if carried far enough, lead to a noisy character of the tone. For the purpose of experiment in the synthetic production of tones with the tone generator, any kind of inharmonics or other forms of noise can be added by accessory instruments. These may be due to the generating source, such as the piano string, or they may be due to accessory noises, such as scratches, thuds, and rattles which ordinarily represent faulty limitations of the instrument or the performer. Often, they are considered to have good quality as, for example, in the muting of the trumpet. Inharmonic partials can be identified and measured on the same principle as harmonic partials.

In the above discussion, I have spoken of a single tone of voice or instrument, because the single tone lends itself more readily to measurement than does the chord or voice, and the esthetic principles established for the single tone apply in the esthetic analysis of the chord, discord or noise. Indeed, these fundamental principles which operate in a single isolated tone are basic for all studies of melody and harmony.

A MEASURE OF THE SENSE OF TONAL TIMBRE

One of the first examples of the use of this tone generator for practical purposes was in the construction of an instrument for the measurement of the sense of timbre.[1] The sense of timbre is one of the six measures in the revised edition of the *Seashore Measures of Musical Talents.* It is a basic measure for the determination of the ability to hear and to appreciate

---

[1] Joseph Saetveit, Don Lewis and Carl E. Seashore. *The Revision of the Seashore Measures of Musical Talents,* University of Iowa Press.

differences in tone quality. This measure consists of a phonograph record made to specifications of desired differences of tonal spectra, each of which was produced by this tone generator. The tone selected had a fundamental pitch of $F^1\#$ and was composed of the first six partials.

The first thing to be determined was what degree of energy there should be in each of these six partials in order that a fairly rich and pleasing tone would be produced. If all the partials had been equally strong, the resulting tone would have been disagreeable. This was done empirically in a controlled series of experiments in which fair samples of the distribution of energy in the partials were set up on the tone generator and judgments were made by trained observers. This experiment was continued until general agreement was reached concerning the pleasing quality in the structure of a tone of a given degree of richness.

To produce the desired differences in the pleasing tone, enough energy was taken from the third partial and added to the fourth to make a perceptible difference in the timbre of the tone as a whole. The change in timbre therefore consisted in making the third partial less prominent and the fourth correspondingly more prominent. The other partials and all other factors in the tone remained constant. These differences ranged, by a graded series of steps, from the smallest perceptible difference for very fine ears to the largest difference required for very poor ears.

In measuring the sense of timbre, these tones were sounded by pairs, and the subject was required to record whether the two tones in the pair were the same or different in timbre. Of course, the nature of the term timbre had to be demonstrated concretely and adequately in a preliminary practice so that the observer and subject knew what to listen for. By measurements of this kind, large and significant differences among individuals are revealed. The same measure may be used to determine the effect of training, maturation, and many other factors which determine the hearing and appreciation of music.

This procedure is different from the ordinary way of testing the ability to distinguish one instrument from another as actually played when we have no means of knowing wherein the difference lies or the amount of the difference. Thus, the setting up of this measure gave us, for the first time, a strictly scientific measuring instrument for determining that ability which enables us to distinguish one instrument from another. This record could not have been made without the tone generator described or its equivalent. It is evident that, when we are dealing with the ability to appreciate beauty in tone quality, we are also dealing with a factor which plays a large role in judgments in the personal evaluation of beauty or ugliness in the quality of tones.

Chapter 9

TONE QUALITY: SONANCE

IN THE PRECEDING CHAPTERS, we have seen that timbre is the quality of the tone at a given moment, the time being represented by one sound wave, the spectrum of which is determined by harmonic analysis.

But we do not hear the quality of a single wave. A succession of waves is required to give us the experience of tonality. What we do hear is a sort of average pitch, intensity, and timbre, the result of a succession of changes in the structure of a tone from wave to wave. This we call *sonance,* which may be defined as *that aspect of tone quality which results from fluctuations in pitch, intensity, and timbre within a tone as a whole.*[1] While timbre gives us a cross section of a tone, sonance represents the body of the tone as a whole for the period of its duration.

THE INSIDE OF A BEAUTIFUL TONE

Let me invite the reader to a detailed and critical view of the internal structure of a beautiful tone. Figure 1 shows the analysis of a tone sung by a very good baritone at a mean pitch of 108 vibrations and moderately loud.

With laboratory instruments we can produce a complex sound in which the harmonic structure of the sound waves remains constant for any length of time. In that case the timbre

---

[1] Possible forms: noun, *sonance*; adjective, *sonant*; verb, *sonate*.

Adapted from *The Musical Quarterly,* 1942, *25,* 6–10; *American Journal of Psychology,* 1942, *55,* 123–127; *Music Educators Journal,* October 1936; *Scientific Monthly,* 1939, *69,* 340–350; Metfessel in *Phonophotography in Folk Music,* University of North Carolina Press, 1928.

for one wave furnishes a complete description of all the waves and, therefore, of the tone as a whole, because it is uniform. But such uniformity rarely occurs in music. In practically all musical tones, both vocal and instrumental, there is a continuous flux in the structure of the tone; that is, the spectrum changes from wave to wave. The result is a fusion of all these changes, a sort of average timbre, pitch, and intensity, which may be represented as a tone band with fringes. As timbre represents simultaneous fusion in one spectrum, that is, for one wave, so sonance represents successive fusion of changing timbre spectra.

Figure 1 represents a complete dissection of a vocal tone into its component elements. It shows what happens within a tone for a fraction of a second. All the odd-numbered waves were analyzed, as described in Chapter 7, for about a third of a second, covering two complete cycles of pitch vibrato. The numbers at the bottom represent the serial numbers of the sound waves in this section of the tone. The large numbers at the left are measures of intensity in inverse ratio, that is, in terms of the number of decibels by which each of the respective partials is less loud than the tone as a whole, the total intensity of the tone being designated as a base. The small numbers at the left and top represent pitch levels of the fundamental. The central column of numbers designates the partials by number.

The top line is the pitch line; it shows two vibrato cycles of the average extent and rate found in the vocal tones of the best singers of today. The next line shows the total intensity of the tone. In this case the intensity is remarkably even and shows no intensity vibrato. A tone of even intensity was chosen for the purpose of simplifying the illustration.

The pitch of each overtone is, of course, determined by the pitch of the fundamental, so we may assume that a pitch graph for each partial would take the same shape as the curve for the fundamental pitch.

The graphs for each partial are in terms of intensity or percentage of energy, the average intensity being shown at the left in terms of the number of decibels below the total intensity and the change of intensity by the up-and-down wave of the

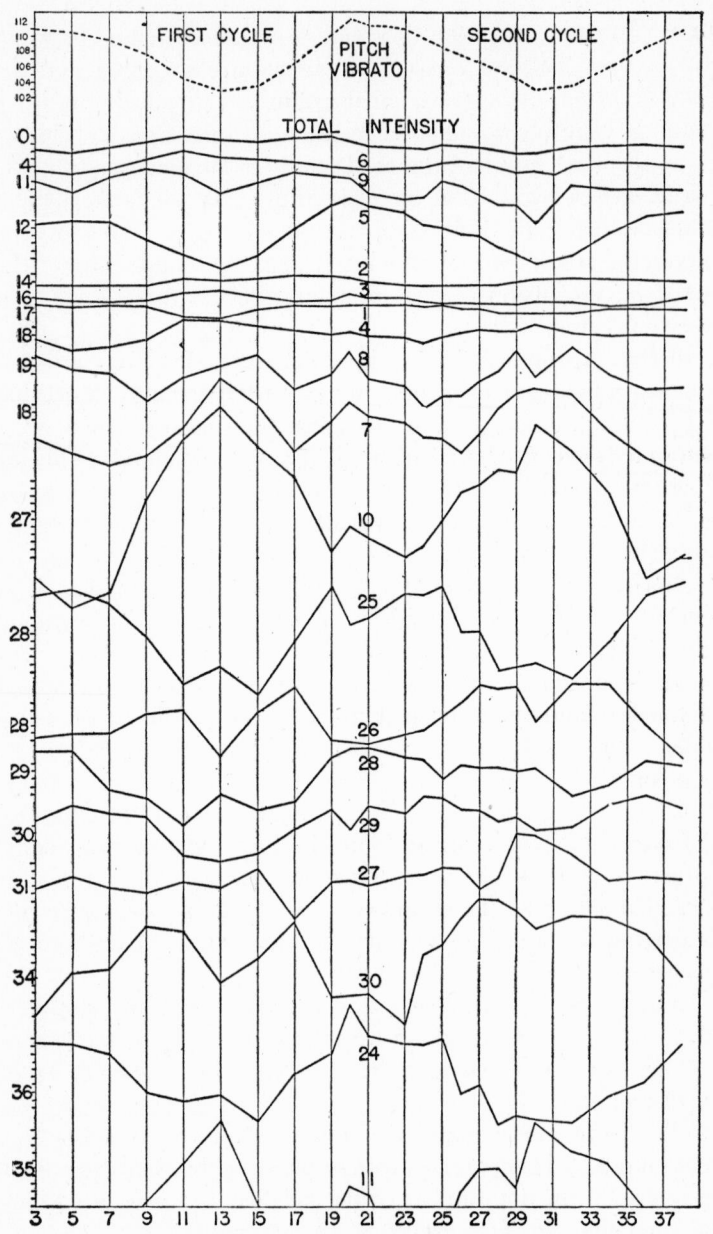

Figure 1. The harmonic structure of a beautiful tone

curve. In order to show the relative influence upon the loudness of the tone as a whole, the partials are arranged in a descending order as expressed in the number of decibels that each partial is of lower intensity than the total intensity of the tone. Thus, the sixth partial is the most influential because it is only 4 decibels below the total intensity; the ninth partial is next in influence, being 11 decibels below. The fifth is 12 below; the second, 14 below, etc. It is evident that the more intense the partial is, the more likely it is to influence the intensity of a tone as a whole.

In this picture we see clearly what the average relative intensity of each partial is and how this varies within the duration of the tone. With these details in mind, the reader is in a position to study the figure intensively and to answer for himself numerous questions which may naturally occur. Let us point out some of the most important facts and principles that are demonstrated:

(1) There is a pitch vibrato of the tone as a whole. The mean pitch of the tone is approximately 108 double vibrations, but the actual pitch pulsates above and below this by approximately a semitone and at the rate of approximately six pulsations per second. Since each partial is a definite multiple of the fundamental, it fluctuates in pitch in step with the fundamental. To complete the picture, the reader should interpolate a pitch graph for each partial, indicating a vibrato exactly like that of the fundamental. We can visualize here a pitch-pulsating body of tone in which eighteen components swing in perfect lock step and harmony. This accounts for the massiveness of the pitch pulsation which adds flexibility, tenderness, and richness to the tone.

(2) The intensity of this tone as a whole remains relatively even. But this evenness is the result of the component forces of all the interacting partials. Some of the partials remain relatively even; some fluctuate irregularly in various degrees; others show a distinct periodicity, either paralleling or opposing the pitch vibrato. The partials which carry the vibrato conspicuously are, in the approximate order of their influence upon the total intensity, the fifth, seventh, tenth, twenty-fifth, thirtieth,

twenty-fourth and eleventh. The exact degree of influence that they have on intensity, however, is somewhat more complicated than these diagrams would indicate. There are a number of factors, such as phase and degree of intensity change in relation to other factors, which are significant. The tenth and twenty-fifth counteract each other. So do the thirtieth and twenty-fourth. In other words, we have, within the structure of the tone for this short period of time, an internal commotion in which forces change in absolute strength, relative strength, opposition, and co-operation. Ordinarily we do not hear these changes in terms of each component partial. What we hear is a mixture or average intensity which, in this particular case, happens to be relatively even as a result of the balancing of conflicting forces.

(3) The intensity change of a partial may be effective in proportion to its nearness to the intensity of the total tone and to the amount of change. Compare, for example, partials five and ten; five is a strong partial and ten is a weak partial, but the latter has greater change. It is evident that some of these partials have so little energy that they have little or no effect upon the hearing. Nevertheless they are physically present in the tone.

(4) The structure of the tone in the periodic change corresponding to a vibrato cycle tends to repeat itself. Compare the internal structure of the first and the second vibrato cycles. This is a well-known phenomenon of the fundamental pitch, which, as we have seen, also repeats itself in all the partials for the two cycles.

Although there is no total intensity vibrato, we can regard each partial as a tone in itself, and, from this point of view, the intensity waves tend to repeat themselves in successive cycles. This is the basis for what we call the timbre vibrato, and it may play a very conspicuous role in our hearing and like or dislike of tone quality.

But the significant thing here is that in sonance we are dealing with two kinds of fusion: (1) the fusion from sound wave to sound wave and (2) the fusion of successive groups which we call vibrato cycles. These are two distinct forms of fusion, and the difference between the two is clearly perceptible in critical hearing. It has been proposed lately by Lewis that the timbre vibrato is due to the effects of relatively fixed vocal resonators upon overtones which vary continuously and systematically in frequency, in keeping with the pitch vibrato.

(5) The changes in timbre probably play only a minor role in sonance, because the changes in pitch and intensity, singly or together, are simpler and therefore more conspicuous perceptually. This is true whether these changes are periodic or irregular and erratic. The changes in timbre furnish a sort of background or atmosphere.

(6) We must bear in mind that the anatomy of the tone here presented is the anatomy of the physical tone in terms of its constituent components. We cannot possibly hear all this detail. What we do hear is a sort of economic and serviceable interpretation of what actually exists physically. What we have before us is an analysis of physical stimulus which gives us the experience of sonance in tone quality.

This is not all that our picture shows, but it is enough to indicate what sort of questions a musician may ask and answer in terms of this type of analysis. To repeat, our simplified scheme is this: In our experience of hearing and feeling of tone, the sonance depends upon the three factors of pitch, intensity, and timbre in the change from wave to wave and from vibrato cycle to vibrato cycle. In a secondary way we might add to these factors the rate of change. The psychological result of a complex situation of this kind we may call a tonal band, consisting of a certain range or massiveness of pitch, intensity, and timbre changes, with vanishing and irregular fringes of each. When, as in this case, eighteen variable tones impinge upon the physical ear, we do not hear the details, but we hear tone quality. This tone quality may be either musically agreeable or disagreeable. If the changes are strong and irregular, we get the quality of roughness. If they are smooth and moderate, we may get the qualities of flexibility, tenderness, and richness of tone.

SONANCE IN PITCH, TIME, AND INTENSITY OF THE TONE AS A WHOLE

In the above section we have seen how the inside of a tone is in a constant flux. If we think of the tone as composed of as many single pure tones as there are partials present, we get some conception of the resources available. Some of the resources for progressive change were illustrated in minute detail for one third of a second in Figure 1. Imagine this picture extended for the entire duration of the tone and you will have a realistic picture of this progressive change in timbre and the objectivity with which it can be measured and interpreted as a feature of sonance.

When, in the following, we discuss the sonance in pitch, intensity, and time of the tone as a whole, we should supplement that picture with this fourth central factor, timbre, and bear in mind that the progressive change in timbre as the integrated effect of the other three factors is likely to be more conspicuous and more significant than the change in the other three factors for the attainment of a good tone.

Let us now turn to four other factors of sonance, dealing in turn with the attack, the body of the tone, the release, and the portamento.

The attack. The attack in vocal intonation may vary in four respects: The pitch of the glide, the intensity of the glide, the rate of the glide, and the change of tone quality in the glide. Each of these may be studied experimentally in the laboratory.

Miller [2] studied the characteristics of the attack at the beginning of a phrase and after three forms of pause—the rest indicated in the score, the breath pause, and the transition pause. He produced performance scores from ten songs of professional singers (the music being taken from Red Seal phonograph records) and of six songs by amateurs in the music school performing before the cameras in the laboratory. The results of these measurements are given in Table I, which is self-explanatory. The condensed findings of these sixteen cases are also represented graphically in Figure 2.

---

[2] R. S. Miller, "The Pitch of the Attack in Singing," *University of Iowa Studies in the Psychology of Music*, Vol. IV, 1937, 127–171.

Granting that these songs and singers are fair examples, these facts are striking illustrations of the prevalence and significance of sonance in the glide at the beginning of a tone. It was recognized at once that the attack would vary with the style. However, these figures are convincing evidence of the prevalence and magnitude of the attacking glide, and they indicate that, in principle, the same phenomena appear in all forms of singing, even in the staccato movement, and can be accepted and tolerated in good singing. We are impressed by the marked agreement represented by the dash lines and dotted lines, showing how closely the average for a given singer conforms with the average for the group as a whole. On the other hand, these figures are averages which represent a large number of measurements. In the same song, certain individual characteristics become evident so that the technical expert would be aided to a considerable extent in identifying the singer by the character of his glides. The comparison of artists with amateurs shows that mean characteristics of the glide are present regardless of differences in degree of training and proficiency.

At this point let the reader stop and examine these figures systematically and critically in search of answers to questions which may have musical significance on such issues as: the average record for the entire group, a comparison between the artists and the amateurs, a comparison of individual artists, a comparison of different songs by the same singers, a comparison of the same song sung by different singers, a comparison of men's and women's voices, a comparison of different types of songs, the role of the vibrato, and the relation of the pitch extent of the sweep to the rate.

For this purpose it would be well to turn to actual performance scores which reveal the glide in its true setting, as in Figures 1 and 2, Chapter 5. It will be found that there is a mine of information about this one specific element which is a determinant of beauty in a tone. It is the experience of the great majority of musicians that, after seeing these facts about the glide represented graphically, they hear them; that is, after learning the facts, they hear the music differently than they did before. Under these circumstances, the clean attack is neither

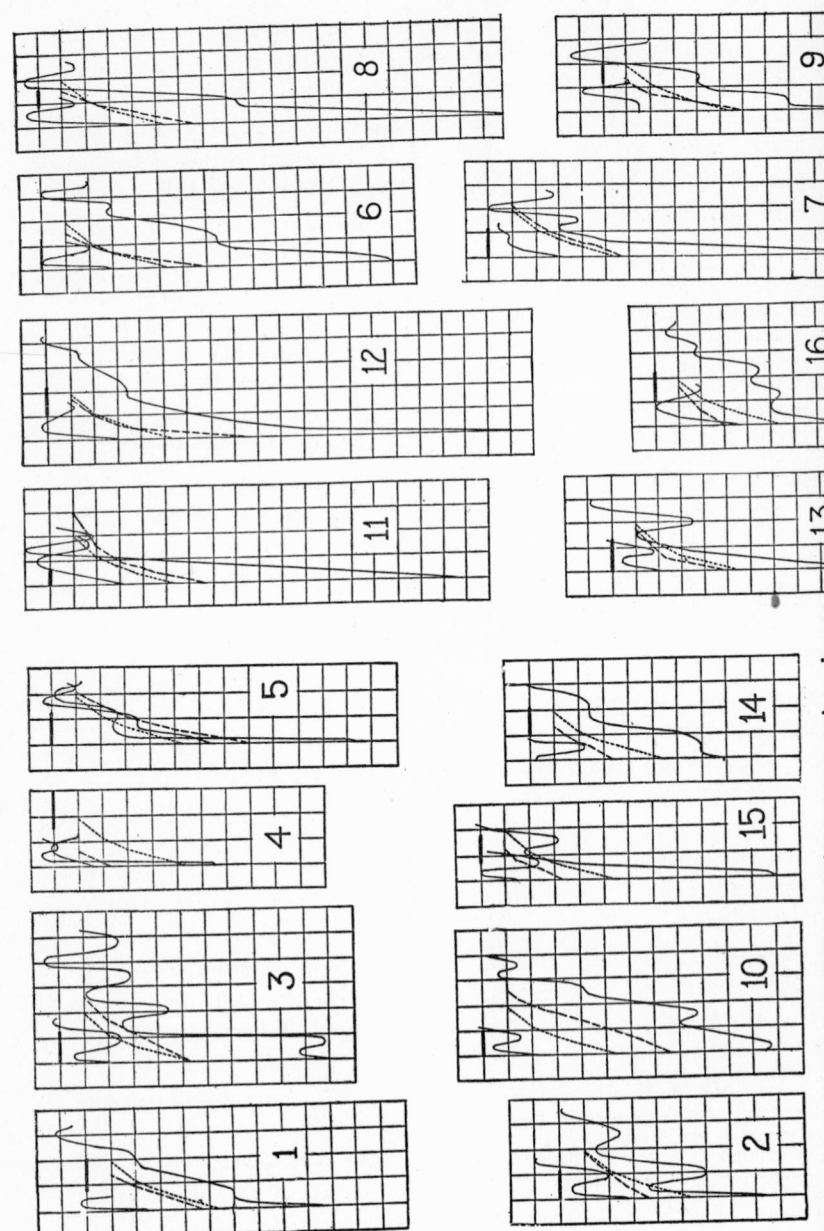

TABLE I

PER CENT OF GLIDES IN FREE ATTACKS

	N Tones	Port. Attacks	Free Attacks	Per Cent Glides
ARTISTS				
Gluck, Ave Maria...............	102	66	36	67
Alda, Last Rose of Summer.......	72	34	38	74
Ponselle, Ave Maria..............	89	58	31	61
Galli-Curci, Shadow Song.........	54	35	19	21
Galli-Curci, Last Rose of Summer..	51	29	22	18
Caruso, Celeste Aida..............	60	22	38	53
Caruso, Lost Chord...............	58	27	31	58
Caruso, Largo	53	23	30	73
Caruso, La donna.................	77	54	23	39
Martinelli, La Fatal Pietra........	60	34	26	58
AMATEURS				
Seashore, Ave Maria.............	103	49	54	84
Seashore, Waters of Minnetonka...	78	37	41	95
Seashore, Comin' thro' the Rye....	53	21	32	66
Vernon, Last Rose of Summer.....	69	27	42	33
Vernon, Comin' thro' the Rye......	52	19	33	42
DeLay, Caro Mio Ben............	114	33	81	48
All	1145	568	577	58

Explanation of Figure 2

The slanting dash line shows the average gliding attack for each song. The dotted line is average form for all these songs as to extent and duration. The upper curve in each figure represents the shortest attack for that song, and the lower figure, the longest attack. The horiozontal solid line at the top represents the true pitch of the main body of the tone. The horizontal spaces represent 0.1 second and the vertical spaces represent pitch in tenths of a whole-tone step. The different singers were identified by numbers: 1 to 10, artists; 11 to 16, amateurs. Most of these songs were in the legato style.

(From R. S. Miller, *op. cit.*)

desirable nor feasible. Let musicians check themselves on this point, and they will have a great surprise. Needless to say, it modifies their estimate of the value of the clean or level attack. They are led to reconsider their justification for teaching level attack.

What pedagogy gone awry, what unreasonable strain has been put upon the pupil, what money-saving in music education could have been realized by recognition of this fact!

After a similar study of the pitch intonation of eight artists, Harold Seashore [3] states his conclusions as follows:

> Artistic singers make their transitions from tone to tone with great flexibility of pitch. They use gliding attacks and releases, level attacks and releases, and portamento glides.
>
> About 40 per cent of all transitions are portamentos; about 35 per cent consist of a pause followed by a level attack; in about 25 per cent the pauses are followed by gliding attacks.
>
> Concerning gliding attacks the following facts appear: (a) Gliding attacks are almost universally rising in pitch inflection. (b) They occur in all kinds of musical relations, but are most frequent in the first tones of phrases, in long tones, and in tones where the melody trend is upward. (c) The average duration of such gliding attacks is 0.2 second. (d) The average extent of the pitch glide in attacks is about one whole musical step; duration and extent of glide are fairly well correlated. (e) Four types of gliding attacks are found, with one group most frequent. The form of each of these types is influenced by the pitch pattern of the vibrato in the attack.
>
> About 40 per cent of the tones end with a portamento glide, about 55 per cent with a level release, and only about 5 per cent with a gliding pitch pattern. Nearly all the gliding releases are falling.
>
> In tones attacked level, there is a tendency for the vibrato pattern to appear first in the upstroke of the cycle; in tones which end level, the final phase of the vibrato pattern usually is on the downstroke of the cycle.

The intensity changes in the gliding attack are in principle analogous to those of pitch both in magnitude and esthetic significance. They could be presented in minute and exact detail as we have seen for pitch. We can speak of a sonance pattern

[3] Harold G. Seashore, "An Objective Analysis of Artistic Singing," University of Iowa *Studies in the Psychology of Music,* Vol. IV, 1937, 12–157.

for intensity just as we speak of a sonance pattern for pitch in the attack. The two figures in Chapter 5 reveal their prevailing form and extent.

The third sonance pattern in the attack is that of rate of the glide. It is shown by the degree of slant in all performance scores. Here again we can say only that it is similar in magnitude and significance to the sonance in pitch and intensity and timbre, and is always an essential aspect of music.

On the basis of studies of this kind, we can generalize and say that, in good singing, the gliding form of attack in pitch, intensity, time, and timbre adds to the beauty of the tone, and that it is capable of exhibiting a vast variety of resources in vocal artistry. It lends flexibility and grace to the art and takes away the sharp edge of the tone. What has been demonstrated for voice holds for many instruments. It is of interest to note here that, in the later forms of a keyed instrument such as the electronic organs which, in the first models, exhibited clean attack, mechanisms have been introduced to soften up the attack of the tone to good effect.

By thus treating the gliding attack as esthetically good, we must not ignore the fact that in a gliding attack we find the commonest illustrations of slovenliness, absence of objective and lack of training, all of which lead to ugliness. But I think that we have made a forward step in esthetics when we say that, while slovenly attack is ordinarily bad and ugly, the gliding attack, in general, is a rich source of beauty in tonal intonation. It should be cultivated artistically as to extent, rate, form, and duration in pitch and intensity.

It would be interesting to determine why the gliding attack makes a tone beautiful. There are possibly two factors. One is that, in singing, the upward glide is a physiological necessity and therefore comes naturally. The other factor is that it is regarded as beautiful in certain media because we have become accustomed to hearing it. On the other hand, the glide is often not identified or heard as such in ordinary musical listening. It is, of course, often judged ugly because it is successive and exhibits slovenliness. One has to take into account the musical medium, as in different instruments, the result of different types of training, and the style of movement, as in the extreme cases of legato and staccato.

Body of tone. The body, that part of the tone which remains from the end of the attack to the beginning of the release, is also subject to changes in pitch, intensity, time, and timbre throughout the length of the tone. These changes may be eruptive, periodic, irregular, or progressive in each or all of these four factors. They may represent artistic principles, as in all forms of recognized ornaments and in the progressive modulation in one or more of these media, or they may represent erratic changes due to lack of skill. Both types are frequently present in a given tone. The relative absence of artistic modulation may, of course, be a mark of a lack of artistry.

Figure 3 contains an enlargement of the graphs for typical tones identified by their words in Figure 1, Chapter 5. This enlargement shows in detail what is revealed in the conventional score which is greatly reduced in scale in order to save space. The true pitch is indicated by the note from the score at the beginning of the horizontal line. That line tends to represent the *mean pitch* as heard, a mean between the crest and the trough of the vibrato waves. The slanting line, indicating the mean pitch as heard, tends to rise or fall with the tone as a whole. The graph for each tone shows clearly that the pitch in the body of the tone never remains constant at the physical pitch of the tone even for a fraction of a second. The discovery of this large and persistent role of the pitch vibrato led us to coin the term *sonance*.

The study of typical intensity curves in all performance scores reveals the same types of change in mean intensity where the vibrato occurs, and it confirms the rule that the intensity is rarely steady but changes in response to a great variety of causes.

Likewise, an examination of the time element in the performance scores reveals a great variety of temporal changes, many of which are essential to artistic value in phrasing while others are more or less erratic. In these changes we may find a mean rate analogy to mean pitch and intensity.

Under the eye of the cameras, we thus see an endless profusion of changes in the progress of tone. Many of these changes are not identified or heard in musical listening, but they contribute to the character of the mass impression of musical values in the sonance of the tone.

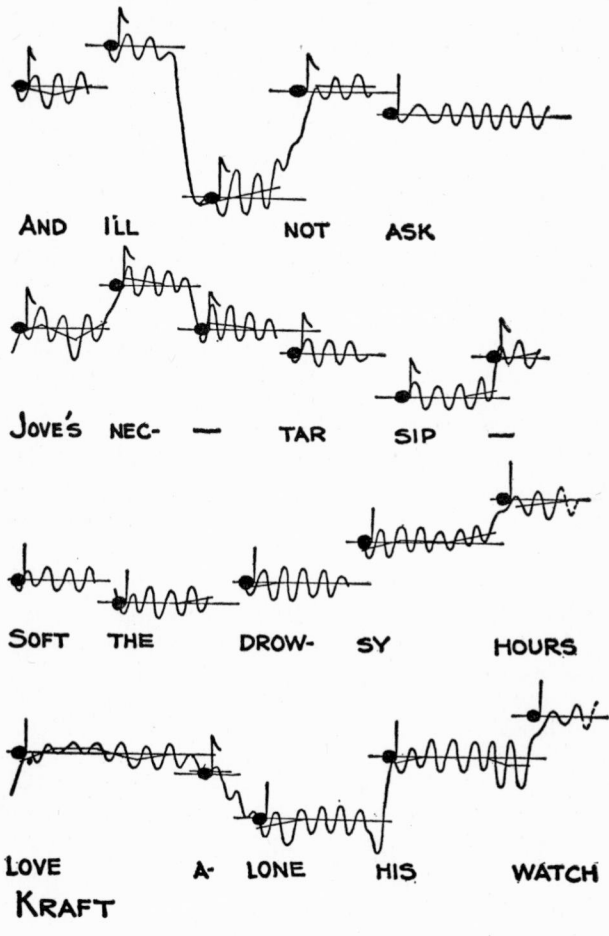

AND I'LL   NOT   ASK

JOVE'S NEC- — TAR   SIP —

SOFT THE   DROW- SY   HOURS

LOVE   A- LONE HIS   WATCH
KRAFT

Figure 3. Mean pitch
(From Harold Seashore, *op. cit.*)

The release. Regarding pitch, intensity, time, and timbre, the release may exhibit all of the characteristics of the attack in reverse. Yet the prevailing tendency of the release is to end a tone, when not running into a portamento, more abruptly than the glide in the attack. Indeed, experiments show that, if we record a good tone on a phonograph and then play it backward so that the attack becomes the release, the tone becomes intolerable.

Portamento. Portamento involves all types of change embodied in the attack of the body of the tone. Harold Seashore[4] summarizes his findings on the portamento of the eight artists whom he studied as follows:

> Portamento transitions are summarized thus: (*a*) They account for 40 per cent of all transitions. (*b*) Portamento glides appear about equally in the upward and downward melodic direction, although in the scores of the songs two thirds of the indicated portamentos are in the downward direction. (*c*) Portamentos appear in all sizes of intervals, with about 80 per cent of them confined to the small intervals. (*d*) About half of the portamentos are not indicated in the score, but are added by the singers. (*e*) The added portamentos involve syllables in which many of the nonvowel, voiced sounds (transitionals, semivowels, voiced stops and voiced fricatives), appear at the point of transition. Whether or not all of these nonvowel elements are sounded typically is a different matter; it may be that they are modified by being made more vowel-like. (*f*) The average duration of portamento is 0.13 second. The median, 0.08 second, shows that most portamentos are of shorter duration, with fewer portamentos of long duration. (*g*) The relation of duration of portamento to the interval traversed is quite close. (*h*) Seven types of pitch patterns are discerned, with nearly 80 per cent of the portamentos confined to three types. (*i*) Nearly all portamentos are carried on the syllable of the first tone to the second tone, but in a few cases the syllable of the second tone is articulated midway in the portamento, and in a few cases the whole portamento is on the syllable of the second tone in the transition.

---

[4] *Op. cit.*, p. 74.

SONANCE IN A VOWEL

Let us now view timbre and sonance together since this constitutes a complete description of the quality of a vowel. Figure 4 [5] represents the vowel *o* as in *top* spoken by two specialists in phonetics, *Ba* and *Ne* for comparison. Here are two profiles of a given vowel as spoken by two experts in the effort to sound the same vowel, phonetically agreed upon, alike. For each case we have a complete description of the harmonic structure of the vowel. Each sound wave is represented by a timbre spectrum in the form of vertical bars on the successive slanting lines. These show what partials are present and the relative intensity of each. For comparison of the relative dominance of each partial the "scale" at the left shows the length of a 10-decibel line. The sequence of sound waves is shown by the numbers at the bottom. This also shows the relative duration of the vowel sound. The *sonance pattern* is shown by the change in the spectra from wave to wave. The numbers at the side show the pitch levels. The progressive change in fundamental pitch is indicated by the shift in position of the bar for the front partial. The absolute intensity of the sound is not shown.

Let us notice some of the most striking characteristics of the quality of this sound. It will be observed that the two dominant groups of partials are in the region around 600 to 1,000 vibrations and are in close proximity. A third group is in the region of 2,700 vibrations. These regions are called formants. Vowels differ mainly in the relative position of formant regions. It is seen that these vowels are rich in overtones (there being as many as twenty at some stages) and that the overtones in the first formant region are much more prominent than the fundamental which represents the pitch that we hear. Also, if we follow any partial horizontally, we see that it changes, sometimes gradually and sometimes suddenly. In other words, we have identified this vowel by its formants, and there is an internal flux, which means that, from moment to moment, there

[5] From John W. Black, "The Quality of a Spoken Vowel," *Archives of Speech II*, 1937, 1–28.

is a changing quality of the tone that constitutes the vowel. It is evident, of course, that the two speakers sound the vowel quite differently, although we can see from the formant regions that it is the same vowel. We see exactly in what respects they differ.

For the purpose of illustration, I could just as well have selected this vowel in a song or an equivalent in tone from any instrument. The principle of description of tone quality would be exactly the same.

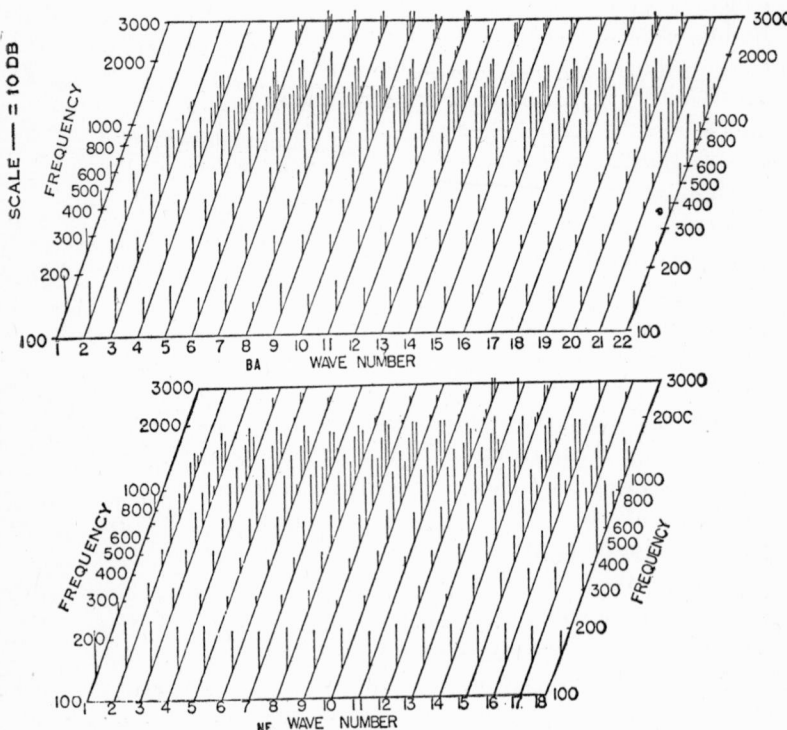

Figure 4. Acoustic spectra of the successive waves of two pronunciations of the vowel as spoken by *BA* and *NE*

(From John W. Black, "The Quality of a Spoken Vowel," *Archives of Speech II*, 1937, 1–28.)

Chapter 10

BEAUTY IN HARMONY: CONSONANCE

THE TERM *harmony* is used here in its broadest sense. It includes all variants, derivatives, and aspects of musical form which depend upon the agreeableness or disagreeableness of simultaneous or successive combinations of notes. Harmony has been a most fertile field for investigation by composers, mathematicians, physicists, and anthropologists. In this one field we find at present the main body of organized knowledge in the area of musical esthetics.

The problem has been approached from the point of view of musical evolution, of the historic development of musical invention and tolerance, and of musical theory and practice. All these approaches may be sound and satisfactory; the accumulated principles constitute the main body of legitimate esthetics today.

Psychology proper, in the current sense, has not operated extensively in this field. Yet there is a basic scientific approach to this broad and fundamental field of esthetics for the verification of theories, the discovery of new aspects of problems involved, and an integrating procedure in the setting up of verifiable knowledge about esthetic values in music. The present report deals primarily with individual tones taken away from actual musical harmonic situations for experiment. This is done on the principle of scientific procedure. It begins with exact descriptions, classifications, and measurements in the simplest and most basic situations and it makes this the groundwork for progressive reaching into more and more complicated musical situations.

Based on Malmberg, "The Perceptions of Consonance and Dissonance," University of Iowa *Studies in Psychology,* Vol. VIII, 1918, 93–132.

In view of these facts, I shall now give merely one illustration of how the psychology of music determines esthetic values in the field of consonance. This method is typical and adaptable for the hundreds of different aspects of harmony. For the purpose I will take a comparatively simple situation, namely, the determining of the rank-order of intervals within a middle octave of the musical scale. The procedure is called *paired comparison,* and the method of judgment is that of the *expert jury.*

THE METHOD OF PAIRED COMPARISON

To reduce the experiment to a basic setting in the simplest and best-controlled operation by the method of paired comparison, the following controls were observed. Pure tones were used as stimuli. The tuning was in just intonation. The chords were held to two tones, dichords. The resonance characteristics of the room were kept constant. Each of the eleven intervals in the octave above middle C was compared with every other, first in one order of the dichords and then in the reverse order. Each trial was repeated as often as desired. A purely cognitive judgment was required, namely, which of these two chords is the smoother? Vigorous warnings were given against being influenced by theory or feelings of like and dislike. The basic series took four forms; the judgment was based on (*a*) blending, (*b*) smoothness, (*c*) purity, and (*d*) fusion. Only trained observers were selected for the jury. The object in all cases was to determine the rank order of the intervals in a consonance-dissonance series apart from their musical setting.

THE JURY SYSTEM

The plan called for a jury of experts. We were able to assemble and hold together for the very long series of experiments a group of eight observers, all of whom were talented in music and had enjoyed a musical education. All of them but one, a professor of violin, were trained in psychological experimentation. The plan was to continue in one series of experiments until a unanimous verdict was reached by the jury, a tolerance of one negative vote being conceded in a few emergencies. All responses were in writing. In a given series all the trials for which the verdict was unanimous were regarded as final, and were therefore eliminated when the intervals for which there was disagreement were investigated more intensively. In the study of these disputed or difficult intervals, the jury engaged in extensive critical arguments, leading to a common ground on agreement. This agreement was then recorded as the rank order of the intervals under the stipulated conditions.

The procedure here employed is called operational, that is, the aspects measured and the conclusions drawn are limited to the specific conditions operating in the experiment. Therefore, our findings in this case are limited to dichords relatively free from their musical setting, and within the limitations set by the subjective and objective factors under control. It was realized fully that consonance-dissonance varies with the progression in the actual musical situation, and that with musicians the basis for the ranking of intervals is largely affective. It depends upon the purpose to be served and it is based upon knowledge of the mathematical ratios involved, the musical culture level, and other factors. The method followed here serves effectively to reveal the presence and the significance of such variants in musical situations.

VARIANTS IN THE EXPERIMENT

The rank order having been established for each of the four criteria of consonance-dissonance, under the basic operational conditions described above, experimentation was continued for the further solution of issues involved in the hearing of consonance-dissonance. (a) The order for pure tones from tuning forks with resonators was compared with the order for rich tones in the piano and the diapason stop in the pipe organ. (b) Just intonation was compared with a tempered scale, both in pure tones and rich tones. (c) The order established by a selected jury was compared with the order established by a large class of unselected sophomores, to determine to some extent the effect of musicianship or specialized training. (d) Similar comparison was made with a large group of fifth- and eighth-grade school children, to determine the effect of age and maturation. (e) The order for each of the four factors, when operating singly, was compared with the order when the jury was instructed to base the judgment on blending, smoothness, and purity all operating together.

SOME FACTS ESTABLISHED

(1) Stumpf's theory of fusion, to the effect that, musically, the rank order of intervals is inversely proportional to the reaction time in deciding whether one hears a single tone or a dichord, was rejected on the ground that the order yielded is in radical disagreement with the order found for the other three criteria, and has no general support in musical theory and practice. This does not deny the operation of fusion as a criterion in many judgments about consonance, but asserts that fusion cannot be regarded as a determinant of all consonance-dissonance, and cannot be established by the reaction-time method.

(2) While the other three criteria, namely, blending, smoothness, and purity, yielded slightly different rank order for certain closely equivalent intervals, they all function for some intervals, and may profitably be pooled in establishing a practical, basic rank order for consonance-dissonance in music.

(3) Each of these criteria is peculiarly favorable for certain intervals, namely, smoothness where the interval is rough, blending where the mathematical ratios are simplest, and purity as a last resort. The order in which each of these is favored by the consensus of opinion of the jury is shown in Table I.

(4) There are slight differences in the rank order for pure tones and rich tones.

(5) There are slight, but relatively negligible, differences in the rank order of just intonation and a tempered scale.

(6) College sophomores, as a class, yield the same rank order as a faculty jury, but show a larger individual variability in the judgment, due to lack of training and difficulty in the control of a large class experiment.

TABLE I

BASIS OF JUDGMENT FOR INDIVIDUAL PAIRS

	c′ g′♭	c′ d′♭	c′ f′	c′ d′	c′ e′	c′ e′♭	c′ g′	c′ c″	c′ a′♭	c′ b′	c′ a′
c′ d′♭	s										
c′ f′	b	s									
c′ d′	s	s	s								
c′ e′	b	s	p	s							
c′ e′♭	b	s	p	s	p						
c′ g′	b	s	b	s	s	s					
c′ c″	b	s	b	s	p	p	b				
c′ a′♭	s	s	b	s	b	s	b	b			
c′ b′	b	s	b	b	b	b	b	b	b		
c′ a′	s	s	s	s	s	s	b	b	s	b	
c′ b′♭	b	s	b	s	b	b	b	b	s	b	s

b—blending; p—purity; s—smoothness. The order of the intervals in this table is the order used in giving the test.

(7) Children in the fifth and the eighth grades of the public schools yield the same general rank order as adults do, but the range of variability is larger, due to lack of training and inability to follow complicated directions. It is, however, not uncommon to find pupils in the fifth grade who have better *sense of consonance* than their teachers or their parents, indicating the early operation of talent.

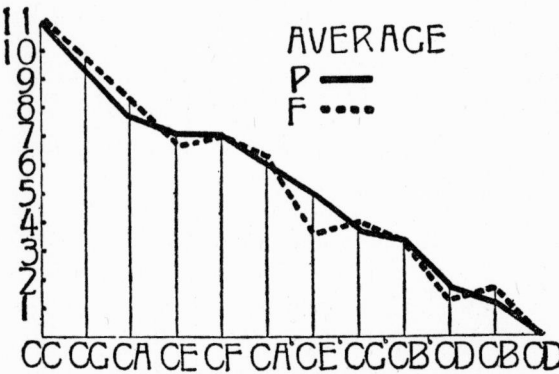

Figure 1. Rank order of consonance-dissonance for resonated tuning forks and piano

(8) The original report shows graphs illustrating all of the above cases. Of these, Figure 1, comparing the rank order for piano and tuning forks, that is, rich tones and pure tones, is representative.

(9) The measure of the *sense of consonance* in the *Seashore Measures of Musical Talent* is based upon the above considerations; but it has been left out of the revised edition, pending the development of more simplified instructions and objective elimination of affective judgments and the effect of sequence.

(10) The type of control here introduced throws much light on the reasons for disagreement among musical authorities on this subject; disputes are resolved when we identify and control the factors which operate in the judgment. Hence, when further musical theories are taken into the scientific laboratory, we may dispel confusion, explain divergence of opinion, and record verified facts about harmonic values in musical esthetics.

Chapter 11

WHAT RHYTHM DOES

THERE ARE TWO FUNDAMENTAL FACTORS in the perception of rhythm: an instinctive impulse or tendency to group impressions in hearing, and action and a capacity for doing this with precision in time and stress. The subjective tendency is so deeply ingrained, on account of its biological service, that we irresistibly group uniform successions of sound, such as the tick of the clock, into rhythmic measure. The supposed limping of a clock is often purely subjective. This is called subjective rhythm to distinguish it from objective rhythm in which the grouping is actually marked, as in music and poetry. If a long series of quarter-notes were played with absolute uniformity in time and stress, the listener would inevitably hear them divided into measures and would actually hear the appropriate notes accented. This is one of nature's beneficent illusions.

A crude but adequate illustration of this is found when one is lying in a Pullman sleeper and the successive beats from the crossing rail joints set up a time which carries tunes that come into one's head. The rails seem, as it were, to beat the time emphatically into measures. The writer recalls once being haunted by the plantation melody, "What kind o' a crown you gwine to wear? Golden crown?" As he allowed the imagery of the melody to flow, the accentuation of the click of the rails became very prominent and satisfying as rhythm. One who is trained in observing himself may observe this tendency toward rhythmic grouping in any or all of his activities. Take, for instance, the homely act of eating. One who has a highly developed sense of rhythm may feel, even in eating soup, the various movements divided into measures with their artistic grouping of long interval and short interval, some objectively and others only sub-

From *Musical Quarterly*, 1918, *4*, 507–515.

jectively marked with occasional cadences; yet a person watching the movement might not be able to see any rhythm in the actual movements.

The objective rhythm, as we find it ordinarily in prose and poetry, is marked by emphasis of time or intensity, or both. Occasionally it may be also through pitch, although that always involves intensity. It is also probable that it may come through senses other than hearing.

Subjective rhythm is more fundamental than objective rhythm and always plays a large role in the objective. This is why we find rhythm more essentially a matter of personality than a matter of objective grouping. All rhythm is primarily a projection of personality. The rhythm is what I am. For him who is not endowed with this talent the objective rhythms in nature and art are largely wasted.

While the perception of rhythm involves the whole organism, it requires primarily five fundamental capacities. The first two of these are the sense of time and the sense of intensity, which correspond respectively to the two attributes of sound, and which constitute the sensory media of rhythm. The third and fourth are auditory imagery and motor imagery, that is, the capacity for reviving vividly in representation the auditory experience and the motor attitudes respectively. The fifth is a motor impulse for rhythm, an instinctive tendency, chiefly unconscious and largely organic. These five factors may be said to be basic to the sense of rhythm. Other general factors, such as emotional type and temperament, logical span, or creative imagination, are intimately woven into the warp and woof of rhythm, but we shall probably find that these are secondary to the primary and basic forces named.

We may now define rhythm as an instinctive disposition to group recurrent sense impressions vividly and with precision, by time or intensity, or both, in such a way as to derive pleasure and efficiency through the grouping.

The sense of rhythm, or perception of rhythm, as thus defined, is to be distinguished from rhythmic action, an important aspect with which we are not here concerned; yet it is a complex process and involves literally the whole organism in the form of a perpetual attitude of responsiveness to measured intervals of time or tone.

To gain some insight into the actual nature of rhythm it may be well to point out some of the things that rhythm does on the side of perception as distinguished from action. This will be equivalent to pointing out the sources of pleasure and means to efficiency in rhythm.

Rhythm favors perception by grouping. It has been demonstrated that, under happy grouping, one can remember approximately as many small groups as one can remember individual objects without grouping, namely, in listening to a series of notes, one can grasp nearly as many measures if they are heard rhythmically as one could grasp individual sounds if they were not heard rhythmically. This is a principle which is involved in all auditory perception. Individual sounds are grouped in measures and phrases, phrases and periods, periods and movements. The ability to grasp, in terms of larger and larger units, is a condition for achievement. The development of this ability results in the power to handle vast numbers of sounds with ease, and this success is a source of pleasure. This is true not only in poetry and in music, but in our natural hearing, even under primitive conditions. Thus, rhythm has become a biological principle of efficiency, a condition for advance and achievement and a perpetual source of satisfaction. The rhythm need not be conspicuous to be effective. It need not be objective. It need not be conscious. At best it is a habit.

Rhythm adjusts the strain of attention. In poetry and music, for instance, the rhythm enables us to anticipate the magnitude of units which are to be grasped. This in turn makes it possible to adjust the effort in such a way as to grasp the unit at the strategic moment and to relax the strain for a moment between periods. Of this, again, we may not be immediately conscious, but it may be readily demonstrated by experiment, as for instance, if we should break up a measure as in going from 2/4 to 3/4 time without warning.

Genetically, the ordinary measure in poetry and music is determined by what is known as the attention wave. Our attention is periodic. All our mental life works rhythmically, that is, by periodic pulsation of effort or achievement with unnoticed intermittence of blanks. This is most easily observed in an elemental process such as hearing-ability. To demonstrate it in a simple way, proceed as follows: hold a watch a distance from the ear and then move it toward the ear until you can just hear it, then keep it in this position for two or three minutes. Observe that you hear it only intermittently. To check this, raise your finger when you hear the sound and lower your finger when you do not hear it. Do not be influenced by any theory, but act with the keenest decision for every second. You will find that the hearing and silence periods alternate with fair regularity, the periods varying from two to eight or ten seconds in the extreme. This periodicity is primarily a periodicity of attention, and it reaches out into all of our mental processes. It is one of nature's contrivances in the interest of the conservation of nervous energy.

This is a principle which is made use of in nature and in industry, as, for example, in our lighting current. The current which energizes our lamps is not, as a rule, a steady, direct current, but is alternating. That is, it comes in pulsations, usually about sixty a second which is frequent enough to give us the impression of continuous illumination. The rhythmic measure then, is simply taking advantage of nature's supply of pulsating efforts of attention. And when the measure fits the attention wave it gives a restful feeling of satisfaction and ease. This in turn results in what is known as secondary passive attention, which is a more economical and efficient form of attention than voluntary attention. Thus it comes about that we acquire a feeling of ease, power, and adjustment when we listen to rhythmic measures, because we get the largest returns for the least outlay. The tendency to seek this assumes biological importance because it tends to preserve and enhance life.

Rhythm gives us a feeling of balance. Rhythm is built on symmetry. When this symmetry involves within itself a certain element of flexibility which is well proportioned, we have grace. Thus, when we read an ordinary prose sentence, we pay no attention to the structural form; but, when we scan the dactylic hexameter, we fall into the artistic mood, distinctly conscious of a symmetry and beauty in form, and in this sense rhythm becomes a thing in itself. Poetry may contain ideas and music may represent sentiment, but the rhythmic structure is in itself an object of art, and the placid perception of this artistic structure takes the form of the feeling of balance under various degrees of delicate support. Children sense the rhythm of poetry before they sense the meaning.

Rhythm gives us a feeling of freedom, luxury, and expanse. Rhythm gives us a feeling of achievement in molding or creating. It gives us a feeling of rounding out a design. This sense of freedom is in one respect the commonplace awareness of the fact that one is free to miss the consciousness of periodicity in countless ways, yet chooses to be in the active and aggressive attitude of achievement. As, when the eye scans the delicate tracery in the repeated pattern near the base of the cathedral and then sweeps upward and delineates the harmonious design continued in measures gradually tapering off into the towering spire, all one unit of beauty, expressing the will and imagination of the architect, so, in music, when the ear grasps the intricate rhythms of beautiful music and follows it from the groundwork up through the delicate tracery into towering climaxes in clustered pinnacles of rhythmic tone figures, we feel as though we did this all because we wished to, because we craved it, because we were free to do it, because we were able to do it.

Rhythm gives us a feeling of power; it carries. Rhythm is like a dream of flying; it is so easy to soar. Once the pattern is grasped, there is an assurance of ability to cope with the future. This results in the disregard of the ear element, and results in a motor attitude, or a projection of the self in action, for rhythm is never rhythm unless the person feels that he himself is acting it, or, what may seem contradictory, that he is even carried by his own action.

Paradoxically, rhythm stimulates and also lulls. Pronounced rhythm brings on a feeling of elation which not infrequently results in a mild form of ecstasy or absentmindedness, a loss of consciousness of the environment. It excites and it makes us insensible to the excitation, giving the feeling of being lulled. This is well illustrated in the case of dancing. Seated in comfort and enjoyment in pleasant conversation, the striking up a waltz is a call which excites to action. It starts the organic, rhythmic movements of the body the moment it is heard and the person is drawn, as it were, enticingly into the conventional movements of the dance. But no sooner is this done, in the true enjoyment of the dance, than he becomes oblivious to intellectual pursuits, launches himself upon the carrying measures, feels the satisfaction of congenial partnership, graceful step, freedom of movement—action without any object other than the pleasure in the action itself. There comes a sort of auto-intoxication from the stimulating effect of the music and the successful self-expression in balanced movements sustained by that music and its associations.

The same is true of the march. When the march is struck up it stimulates the tension of every muscle of the body. The soldier straightens up, takes a firmer step, observes more keenly, and is all attention. But, as he gets into the march, all this passes into its opposite, a state of passivity, obliviousness to environment, and obliviousness to effort and action. The marked time and accent of the band music swings the movements of all parts of his body into happy adjustment. He can march farther in better form, and with less fatigue.

Rhythmic periodicity is instinctive. As we saw above, the grouping into natural periods of the flow of attention is a biological principle of preservative value. It is likewise true that the tendency to act in rhythmic movements is of biological value, and for a similar reason. If a person does not know where to put his hand or foot the next movement, he is ill at ease and will be inefficient in the movement. But, if movements may be foreseen and even forefelt, and an accompanying signal sets off the movement without conscious effort, a more effective action, a feeling of satisfaction prevail. Anything that accomplishes these ends in the life of a species will tend to become instinctive, to develop a natural tendency always to move in rhythmic measure. When our movements are not actually divided into objective periodicity, we tend to fall into a subjective rhythm. We cannot have adequate perception or rhythm without this motor setting. The bearing of this instinctive motor tendency on the perception of rhythm lies in the fact that with the motor instinct goes an instinct to be in a receptive attitude for the perception of such rhythms, both subjective and objective.

Rhythm finds resonance in the whole organism. Rhythm is not a matter of the ear or of the finger only; it is a matter of the two fundamental powers of life, namely, knowing and acting. Therefore, indirectly, it affects the circulation, respiration, and all the secretions of the body including the hormones in such a way as to arouse agreeable feeling. Herein we find the groundwork of emotion, for rhythm, whether in perception or action, is emotional when highly developed, and results in response of the whole organism to its pulsations. Such organic pulsations and secretions are the physical counterpart of emotion. Thus, when we listen to dashing billows or trickling rain drops, when we see the swaying of the trees in the winds, the waving of the wheat fields, we respond to these, we feel ourselves into them, and there is rhythm everywhere, not only in every plastic part of our body, but in the world as we know it at that moment. This response we call empathy.

Rhythm arouses sustained and enriching association. One need not tramp through the woods where the Wagnerian scenes are laid in order to experience the rich flow of visual association with a rhythmic flow of the music in *Lohengrin*. In most persons it comes irresistibly through free imagination. Our consciousness of pleasure in music is often a consciousness of seeing and doing things rather than a consciousness of hearing rhythm, the tendency being to project ourselves through the sensory cue of hearing into the more common fields of vision and action.

Rhythm reaches out in extraordinary detail and complexity with progressive mastery. Rhythm makes use of novelty. The simple rhythms soon become monotonous, but one can find endless opportunity for enrichment by the complications of which the measure, the phrase, or the more attenuated rhythmic unit are capable. This is true both for perception and for action. A rhythmic nature tends to live more and more in the exquisite refinements and far-reaching ramifications of rhythmic perceptions and rhythmic feelings of movements, real or imagined. This power to radiate and encompass may be vastly enhanced by training in the rhythmic arts.

The sense of rhythm is like the instinct of curiosity: it takes one into wonder after wonder. As has been said, curiosity asks one question of nature and nature asks her ten. One degree of rhythmic perception acquired becomes a vantage ground from which we may approach higher levels, and each of these, in turn traversed, leads to higher vantage grounds, level after level, vista after vista. They need not be objective, nor need we be conscious of them as such. It is a state of organization into rich meaning.

The instinctive craving for the experience of rhythm results in play which is the free self-expression for the pleasure of expression. As Ruskin puts it, rhythm is "an exertion of body and mind, made to please ourselves, and with no determined end." It makes us play, young and old. It determines the form of play, in large part. Through play it leads to self-realization by serving as an ever-present incentive for practice. In music and poetry we play with rhythm, and thereby develop it into expansive and artistic forms.

This inventory of the sources of pleasure in rhythm is fragmentary and inadequate, but it should accomplish at least two ends. It should dispel the notion that the perception of rhythm is a simple mental process or action, and it should make us realize that to the person who is endowed with this gift in a high degree, it is one of the great sources of pleasure, not only in music and art, but in the commonplace of everyday achievement and pleasure

Although the sense of rhythm responds to training, there are great individual differences in capacity for achievement. From the point of view of quantitative analysis, two factors must be borne in mind : first, that the relative presence or absence of one or more of the basic capacities for rhythm determines the permanent traits of the developed musical mind in rhythm, and, second, that the relative presence or absence of such capacities in childhood may be regarded as a fair index to achievement, or the ability to profit by rhythmic training.

Chapter 12

SOME ASPECTS OF BEAUTY IN PIANO PERFORMANCE

MANY MUSICIANS are deeply impressed with the enormous possibilities for characterizing musical artistry and expression of musical feeling in terms of the art of touch on the piano key. Where there is ignorance of the issue, there will always be debate and contending theorists.

THEORY OF PIANO TOUCH

The prevailing theory is that the pianist determines the quality of a tone directly through artistic touch. This theory has been completely refuted by scientific experiments, the findings of which are being accepted by many well-informed leaders in the profession. The best available book on the subject for musicians is by Professor Ortmann[1] whose findings may best be summarized as follows:

> The pianist has at his control only two of the four factors in music, namely, intensity and time. Pitch and timbre are determined primarily by the composer and the instrument.
>
> The pianist can control the intensity only in terms of the velocity of the hammer, at the moment at which it leaves the escapement mechanism, and by the action of the pedals.

---

[1] Otto Ortmann, *Physical Basis of Piano Touch and Tone*, Dutton, New York, 1925.

Based on "Piano Touch," *Science Monthly*, 1937, *45*, 360–365; "The Iowa Piano Camera and Its Use," University of Iowa *Studies in the Psychology of Music*, Vol. IV, 1937, 252–262 (with Mack T. Henderson and Joseph Tiffin); "A Musical Pattern Score of the First Movement of the Beethoven *Sonata, Opus 27, No. 2*" (with Laila Skinner). In the same volume pp. 263–280.

There are only two significant strokes on the key: the percussion and the nonpercussion. The difference between these is that the former contributes more noise to the piano tone, and the latter gives the player better control of the desired intensity.

Aside from the addition of noise, the player cannot modify the quality of the tone by the manner of depressing the key or by manipulations after the key has struck its bed except, perhaps, by a momentary partial key release and immediate key depression, damping the tone somewhat but not entirely.

He can control the time factors which influence quality only by the action of the dampers either through the keys or the pedals.

In general these facts have been known for a long time by instrument makers and occasional musicians, but most musicians have failed to recognize their significance or admit the facts. Let us examine these facts a little further.

The piano action for any key consists of a compound lever system, the purpose of which is to facilitate and control the force of the blow on the string. Insofar as it depends upon the striking of the key, either intensity, the physical fact, or loudness, the mental fact, is a function of the velocity of the hammer at the moment that it impinges upon the string. After that instantaneous moment, the tone can be modified only by the dampers.

On this fact we may base several observations. It makes no difference whether the key is struck by an accelerating, retarding, even, or any form of irregular movement; the only significant thing the player controls is the velocity of the key at the exact moment the key action throws off the hammer. This energizing of the hammer is as instantaneous as the flight of the ball when it leaves the bat. This easily observed physical fact has profound significance in the theory and critical judgments about music. Nor can the economic aspect be ignored when it is considered how much money is spent on trying to teach pupils something that cannot be done, that is, to vary the quality of the tone by later manipulation of the key after it has once released the hammer

This limitation of the function of touch would detract in no way from the resourcefulness of the instrument and the opportunity for individual expression or the indirect effects of intensity which are legion. On the other hand, it clarifies, glorifies, and reveals the extraordinary refinement that is necessary in this artistic touch. The elaborate care taken in the development of form, weight, pressure, and rate of arm, wrist, and finger movements is fully justified insofar as it results in a refined control of the intensity of the tone, but not for any independent change in tone quality.

The hammer is released just a trifle before the key reaches its bed. Like the bat and the ball, it has only one form of contact with the string, namely, an instantaneous impact followed by an immediate rebound. Therefore, no amount of waggling, vibrating, rocking, or caressing of the key after it has once released the hammer can modify the action upon the string. The only way in which the key can further affect the string is by a new stroke of the hammer. This can easily be verified by manipulating a key near its bed and looking at the action of the hammer.

The pianist can produce a great variety of tone qualities indirectly, but only by controlling the intensity of the tone. The piano is so constructed that it can produce a large series of tone qualities, each of which is a function of the intensity of the tone. By controlling the intensity through touch on a given piano, the pianist draws out the particular characteristic tone quality for that intensity on that piano. The pianist has trained himself to recognize this release and may therefore think either of intensity or tone quality in tempering his touch.

The quality of the piano tone is the result of three major factors: the physical response of the piano, the resonance characteristics of the room, and the force of the stroke by the performer. The specialist in acoustics can now chart the quality or response of the piano and set up a scale showing how these characteristics vary with the intensity of the tone. However, it is not visionary to say that the future musical artist can look at these charts and see that for a given force of his stroke, a given tone spectrum will result for this piano in this room.

Likewise, the technician can measure and chart the resonance characteristics of the room for varying intensities of sound.

Many of the qualitative changes which come with changing intensity are the result of resonance, reverberation, or damping effects of the sounding board and the rest of the piano, the thuds and rattlings on the keys, as well as the acoustical characteristics of the room. At the present time artists regard inharmonic and percussion accessories to piano response as legitimate and essential contributions to tone quality. Is it possible that this attitude may change? We are facing an era of radical change in the nature of music. It is difficult to predict what will happen to concepts of piano playing.

This problem of piano touch is of profound significance in the prediction of success or failure in music. The two considerations for mastery on the whole are the sense of time and the sense of intensity as far as capacity for tone production is concerned. Therefore, in assigning a student to an instrument we should lay primary emphasis on those two qualifications. The fact that the player cannot control the tone quality directly, however, does not absolve him from many obligations to cultivate tone quality, and there is no objection to his thinking largely in terms of quality rather than intensity.

THE PIANO CAMERA

We have just seen that, of the four factors in musical performance (pitch, intensity, timbre, and time) two, pitch and timbre, are determined by the piano. Therefore, only intensity and time need be recorded to obtain an adequate statement of piano playing. The Iowa piano camera was designed to record these two factors. It has been proved remarkably simple to operate, reliable, and adequate in the musical situation. It gives a photographic record of the beginning, the duration, the moment of ending, and the relative intensity of each note in an entire selection played under normal conditions.

Figure 1 is a sample of the photographic record, actual size, covering 0.68 second. The vertical lines show time in 0.04 second and can be estimated to within 0.01 second. The horizontal white tracks represent the keys of the entire keyboard. The dark, horizontal bands are due to the inner framework of the piano, but they aid in the identification of the keys. For each note, the length of the white space B is proportional to the time necessary for the hammer to move through the last 12 millimeters before striking the string. The length of the bar A gives a similar measure of the time necessary for the hammer to travel the preceding 12 millimeters. Thus, $A + B$, the velocity of the hammer and, in turn, the force of the impact and intensity of the resultant tone near the beginning of the tone may be determined. The dark bar following this shows the time of retreat of the hammer from the string, and this, together with the white bar following, gives the length of time that the key was held. For the duration of the white bar the hammer was free from the strings, but at the end of that time the strings were damped by the return of the key. The end of the last black bar indicates the complete return of the key, and shows the time necessary for it. The pedal action is represented by the white line at the base, showing that the pedal was free preceding the chord, that it was put into action in time to sustain this chord, and that it was held in so as to cover the next note.

The camera is surprisingly simple and inexpensive. It imposes no restrictions upon the player and does not interfere with routine use of the piano in the studio.

Thus it is seen that all time factors, the moment of incidence, the duration, and the moment of cessation of each tone, are measured directly in 0.01-second units on the tracing for each key and the damper pedal.

The intensity of the tone is measured in terms of the rate of impact of the hammer as expressed in millimeter units of the section AB in the photogram. These units are converted into decibel readings of 17 steps. Each step represents approximately 2 dicibels, thus giving a range of 34 decibels.

THE PIANO PERFORMANCE SCORE

The photogram of the type in Figure 1 is a complete chart in itself; but, for detailed analysis and publication, this photo

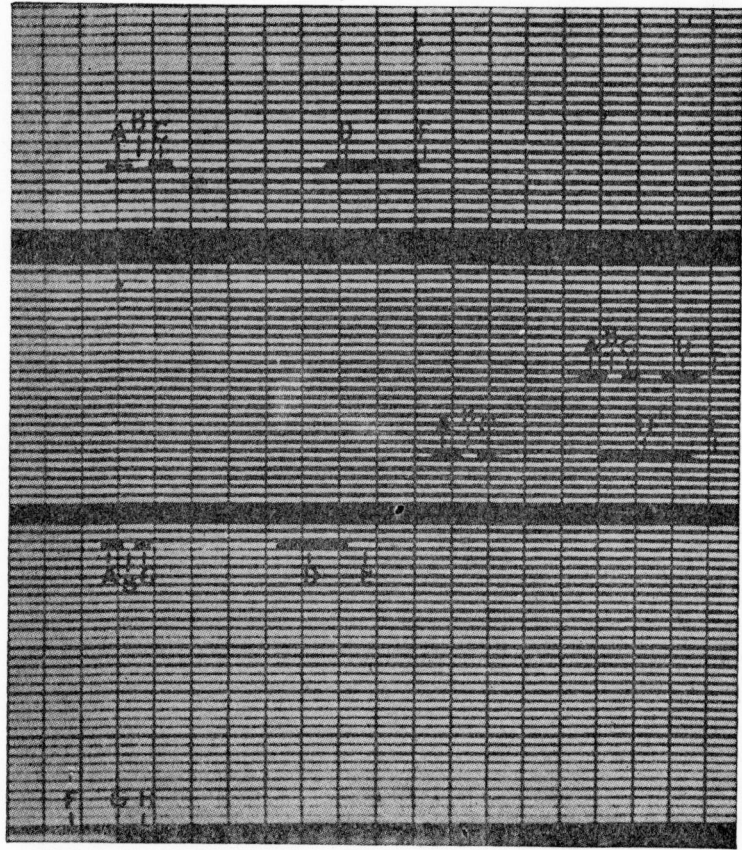

Figure 1. Sample of actual film taken on the Iowa piano camera

record is transcribed into a musical performance score as in
Figure 2.

To represent the facts in musical notation, we utilize the
conventional staff and substitute bar graphs for the conventional musical notes (Figure 2). The position in the staff indicates the pitch of the note. The dotted slanting line is interpolated to show the degree of asynchronization in the first chord.

The relative loudness of each note is indicated by the number above each note. These are arranged in a scale of 17, in

which 1 denotes approximately the softest note that can be played with musical significance, and 17 the loudest.

The quality of the piano tone is the result of three major factors: the physical response of the piano, the resonance characteristics of the room, and the force of the stroke by the performer. The specialist in acoustics can now chart the quality of response of the piano once and for all and then set up a scale

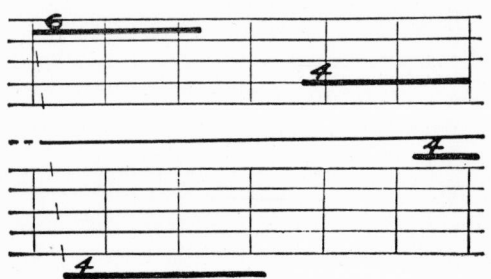

Figure 2. The photogram of Figure 1 transcribed into the
musical pattern score

showing how these characteristics vary with the intensity and time. However, it is not visionary to say that the future musical artist can look at this chart and see that for a given force of his stroke, a given spectrum will result for this piano in this room. Likewise, the technician can measure and chart the resonance characteristics of the room for varying intensities of sound.

Any musician can read this score at sight and note the actual time and intensity values insofar as they are musically significant. The pitch and timbre factors are fixed by the structure of the instrument and the composition, except as modified by the damper pedal. This pattern score is so constructed that, when advantageously reduced, it can be printed as a musical notation and does not require much more space than is required for the conventional score. A sustained example of the form and use of the piano performance score is given in Figure 3.

Professor Philip Greeley Clapp played under the piano camera the last movement of Beethoven's *Sonata, Opus 27,*

No. 2. The record covers more than a hundred feet of film on the type of Figure 1. This was transcribed as in Figure 2. Figure 3 shows the first of twelve pages of the performance score. This page contains a wealth of information, showing note for note how the artist interpreted this movement of the sonata by his performance.

Let the musical reader at this point take the printed music score for comparison and investigation, and evaluate the detailed characteristics in the performance of each note.[2]

In terms of the performance score, he may identify specific marks of artistry, verify art principles, discover data for new principles, and characterize the performance of the artist in great variety of detail in accordance with his interests. Artists may be compared; the results of specific piano techniques may be seen; criticism, both theoretical and practical, may have an objective basis. If the reader should think of any moot question concerning the art of piano playing, such as some specific problem in phrasing, he might turn to this type of score for material which will clarify his terminology, quantify many of his facts, and place in his hands techniques for dealing with such artistic problems in a clear and scientific manner. His problem can be defined; it can be isolated for study; the phenomenon in question may be reproduced; and the logic of science may operate in formulating the relevant facts for esthetic theory and practice.

THE ASYNCHRONIZATION OF CHORDS

Before we had perfected the piano camera just described, Vernon[3] employed the Duo-art piano recordings in his studies of the principles of asynchronization in the incidence of piano chords. He employed recordings of selections from Beethoven and Chopin as played by recognized artists and "editors" and certified by these players as satisfactory.

---

[2] For full aid in reading the score see author's *Psychology of Music,* Chapter 19, or Vol. IV in the University of Iowa *Studies in the Psychology of Music,* 252–279.

[3] "Synchronization of Chords in Artistic Piano Music," by L. N. Vernon, *Objective Analysis of Musical Performance,* University of Iowa *Studies in the Psychology of Music,* Vol. IV, pp. 306–346.

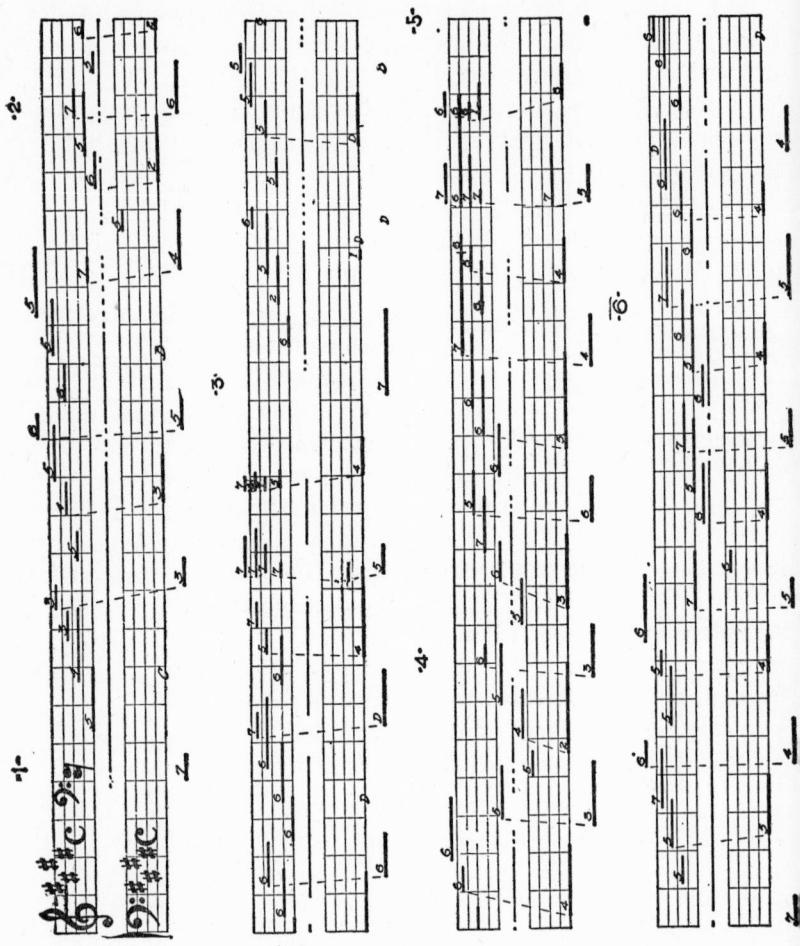

For every chord in these selections he drew a vertical line through the beginning of all the notes that did not synchronize within an error of plus or minus 0.01 second.

Then he observed whether the deviating note or notes represented a delay or an advance and measured the extent of that deviation.

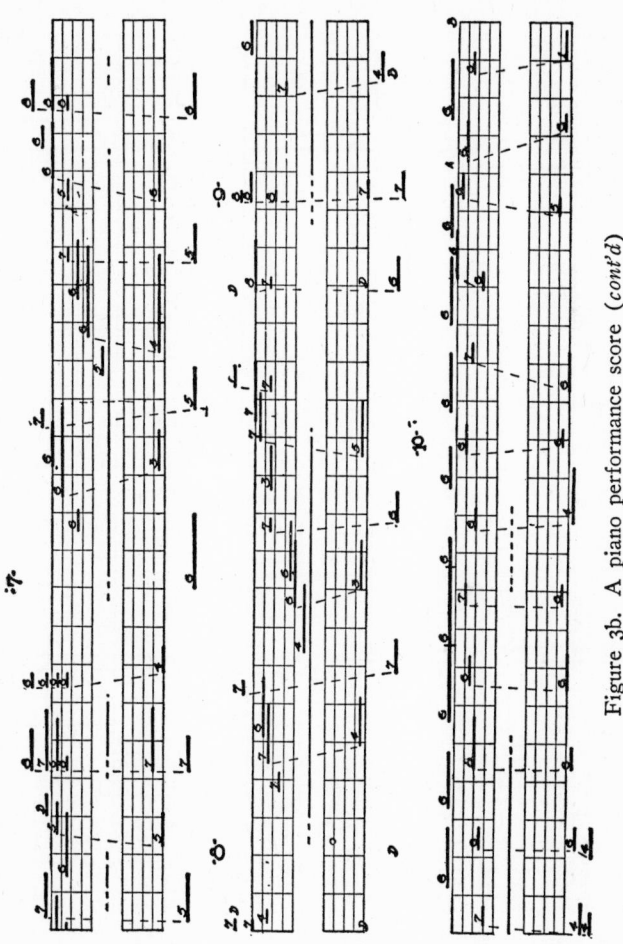

Figure 3b. A piano performance score (*cont'd*)

The data in Figure 4 represent the quantitative findings and are self-explanatory. They are the objective record of the musical behavior of the artists, and they are of statistical significance. But the main goal of the investigation was to discover, to verify, and to explain principles by the natural history method of procedure in identifying and classifying the col-

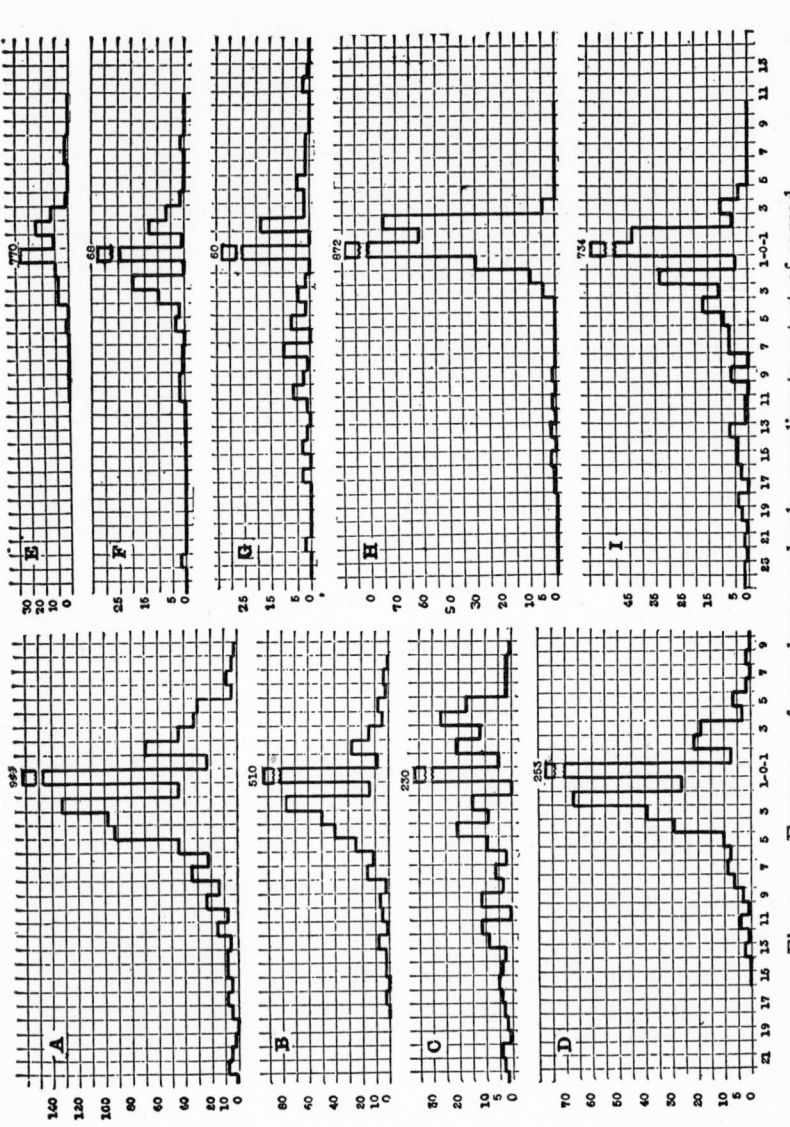

Figure 4. Frequency of asynchronous chords according to extent of spread

The players are identified by the letters *A* to *I*, the extent of deviation is indicated at the bottom in terms of 0.01 second. At the bottom of each figure the frequency of a given extent of deviation is indicated by the numbers at the left and the relative height of each column in the graph. Figures to the left of o indicate delay; to the right, advance of tone.

The professors were: A. Bauer, entire *Sonata Pathetique;* 1831 chords. B. Bauer, first movement; 845 chords. C. Bauer, second movement; 451 chords. D. Bauer, third movement; 536 chords. E. Bachaus, first movement; 849 chords. F. Hofmann, *Moonlight;* 135 chords. G. Paderewski, *Moonlight;* 136 chords. H. Hofmann, *Polonaise;* 1043 chords. I. Paderewski, *Polonaise,* 923 chords.

lected specimens for description and explanation in terms of significant musical terminology.

The experimenter states the general conclusions as follows:

(1) Pianists may play as many as half their chords asynchronously.

(2) The frequency of deviation within a selection varies directly with average extent of deviation. Thus, great frequency is not caused by many small accidental deviations. Rather, it is probable that most of the deviations are intentional. It was shown experimentally that even the smallest deviations studied here can be perceived easily by musicians, which makes it even more possible that the deviations are intentional.

(3) The frequency and extent of deviation vary greatly from pianist to pianist and from selection to selection. However, a player tends to be consistent in extent of deviations within a given selection.

(4) When tempo is slow or changing, more asynchronous chords occur.

(5) Melody notes may be emphasized by being played early or late in a chord. A spread may be used to give stress or emphasis to the whole chord.

(6) Contrary to expectations, asynchronization is not closely related to beginnings or endings of phrases, or to changes in tonality.

To implement his findings the experimenter prepared a tentative check list of interpretations which seemed to him to represent the "best fit," bearing in mind that, in spite of his training as an experimental psychologist, his acquaintance with musical literature and the current practices of piano teachers, as well as his own experience as a pianist, he must allow a considerable margin of error for personal interpretation. His tentative check list of principles runs as follows:

EXPLANATORY PRINCIPLES INDUCED BY STUDY OF ASYNCHRONOUS CHORDS IN THEIR MUSICAL SETTING

I. Accidental.
1. Unsystematic and irregular; no apparent purpose.
2. Others like it done differently; no apparent purpose.

3. Small (2 units or less) ; no apparent purpose.
4. Difficulty of moving a continuously rolled octave from one note to another, or stopping it on time.
5. When the two hands have different rhythms, synchronization is difficult.
6. Intervals of more than one octave rolled for mechanical reasons.
7. Chords with many notes are more liable to deviation than chords with few notes.

II. Chords may be spread due to deviations in tempo or parts, or to create an illusion of deviation of tempo.

1. At places where the tempo is broadened, there is a tendency to roll chords.
2. On the last chord of a phrase the melody may be late to create the illusion of a ritard.
3. In accelerations, the melody may run ahead of the accompaniment.
4. One hand may use a tempo rubato while the other holds steady.
5. Chords are spread more frequently in slow than in rapid passages.
6. Chords may be played asynchronously in atempos.

III. Notes may be brought in singly to facilitate perception.

1. When the bass is heavy and thick the top notes may come in singly to give them clarity.
2. In close chords the melody must come first or be louder to have any clarity. Making it louder may make it earlier.
3. When it is desired for contrapuntal reasons to mark certain parts they may be brought in one at a time.
4. Melody notes may be marked off by being asynchronous.

IV. When the completion of a predetermined chord is detained, it emphasizes the chord.

1. Accented chords are given an illusion of stress by having their completion detained.
2. In building a climax, progressive stress may be gained by making the melody progressively later and later. The peak chord of a climax may be heightened by a roll.

V. Chords are played asynchronously to soften the outlines of the piece when otherwise they would be angular and abrupt, or when there would be too much detail in nonfocal material.

1. When a phrase has an abrupt ending, the last chords may be irregular to soften the abruptness.

2. Irregular or rolled chords help to smooth out dynamic changes in which there are too few steps to allow an even growth.
3. There is a tendency to spread chords at the beginning of phrases.
4. When a melody is played with greater legato than the accompaniment, the melody notes may be displaced for the sake of the legato.
5. When a body of tone is needed without greater percussion, the chord may be rolled.
6. When there is a large jump in any melodic line, the abruptness may be softened by having the melody arrive late.
7. When the tonality changes there is a tendency to make chords asynchronous.

In this list the trained musician will recognize some of the well-known principles and possibly will discover a number of tendencies hitherto unknown. The experimenter measured perception of capacity for hearing temporal deviations and found that this may vary over a considerable range even among trained musicians. He was able to establish the fact that while ordinarily errors of plus or minus 0.02 second may be looked upon as chance errors in performance, musicians with a fine sense of time can hear deviations as small as 0.01 second.

Chapter 13

ASPECTS OF BEAUTY IN VIOLIN PERFORMANCE

IN OTHER CHAPTERS of this volume, many of the problems pertaining to violin technique and performance are considered. Thus we saw in Chapters 7 and 8 the treatment of the concept of timbre and sonance, respectively, as two factors in tone quality. The present chapter is largely in the nature of a reminder which will implement realistically some of the principles discussed directly or indirectly in other chapters. The present exhibits may be regarded as fair samples of technique for the blazing of scientific trails in the field of violin performance.

TIMBRE: TONE SPECTRA FOR THE D AND THE G STRINGS OF THE VIOLIN

Figures 1 and 2 show the conventional way of depicting the timbre of a tone graphically in acoustics. The terminology in these figures is the same as that for the bassoon, as shown in Figure 3, Chapter 7, except that in that instance spectra for loud and soft tones were compared, while here only the spectrum for a tone of medium loudness is given. It may be well for the reader to refresh his memory of the principles involved in the building of tone spectra by rereading that chapter at this point, with the specific object of clarifying the concept of spectrum and acquiring skill and insight into the nature of differences in orchestral instruments.

PHRASING SCORE

As we have seen, every element in the interpretation of musical tone can be expressed in four terms: pitch, time, intensity, and timbre as represented physically in phonophotographic records of the sound waves. For practical purposes the first three factors are transcribed into the same type of performance score as illustrated in the case of voice in Chapter 5. On account of the necessity of showing an entire spectrum for each note to represent the timbre, that element is usually represented on a separate score in terms of selected samples of tone spectra, as illustrated in Chapter 7, and in Figures 1 and 2 in the present chapter.

On the basis of such photographic records, a variety of types of performance scores may be constructed to meet specific purposes. Figures 3 and 4 represent highly detailed phrasing scores for violin performance. These were both recorded in the "dead" room and therefore represent the actual performance of the instrument apart from reverberations or outside sounds.

To aid in the reading of these phrasing scores, let us look in some detail at the Menuhin score, Figure 3. The first note is played 0.05 of a tone sharp and the tie which follows is played in true pitch. There is a fairly even pitch vibrato in the sustained tone of the tied notes, about 0.2 of a whole-tone step in extent and at the rate of a little over 6 pulsations per second. The first short note was comparatively strong, being 10 decibels above the average intensity of the selection as a whole. The intensity dropped immediately in the tie to 4 decibels above average in a gradual *decrescendo*. There are traces of the intensity vibrato in about half of the sustained tone. The first note was overheld 0.2 second. The tied notes were overheld about 0.06 second. Then follows the pause for which we record only the duration. The phrasing score shows that this pause was overheld 0.2 second.

Treating the next five notes as a unit, we find a characteristic pitch performance for rapid movement in that there is never any even pitch on any one of the notes, but there is a rapid glide on a vibrato which passes through the true pitch at some point. This is rather strange in view of the fact that we hear the intervals played with considerable precision of intonation. We can make only an approximate location of the pitch for each note as is done in the phrasing score, where the first note is regarded as 0.2 sharp, the second as 0.15 sharp, the third as in true pitch,

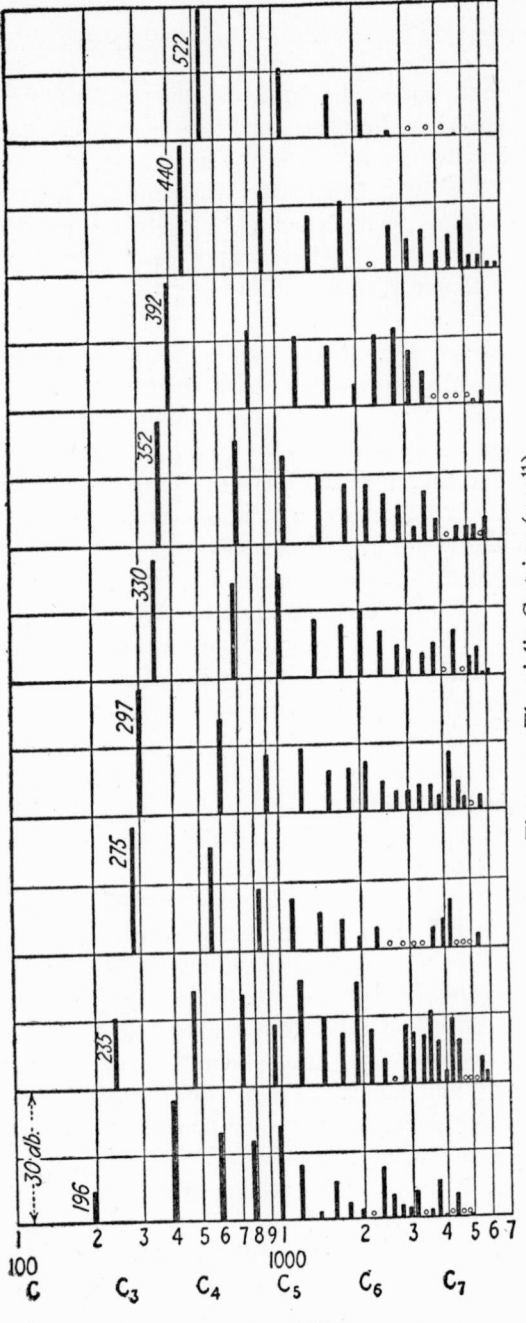

Figure I. The violin G string (small)

Legend for Figures 1 and 2 same as in preceding figures in Chapter 7 except that each of those gave separate spectra for a loud and soft tone, whereas these violin spectra represent only a tone of medium loudness.

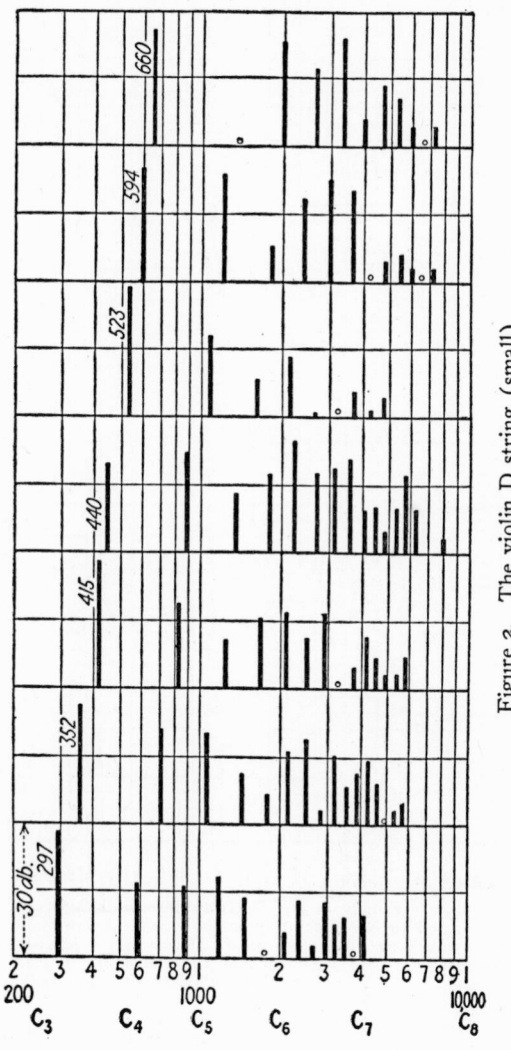

Figure 2.   The violin D string (small)

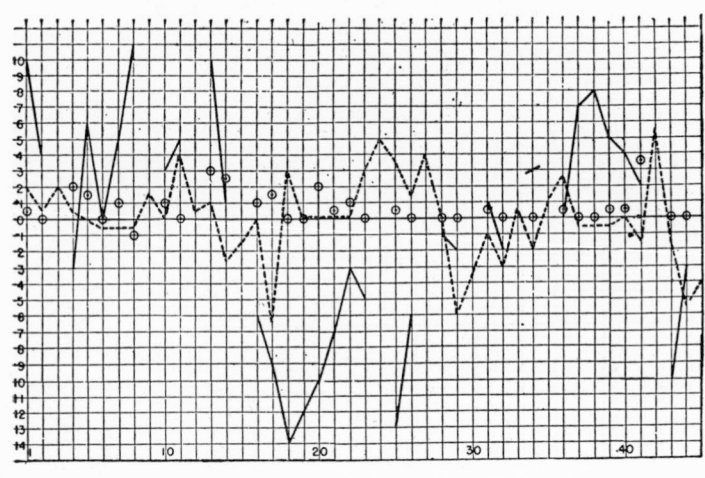

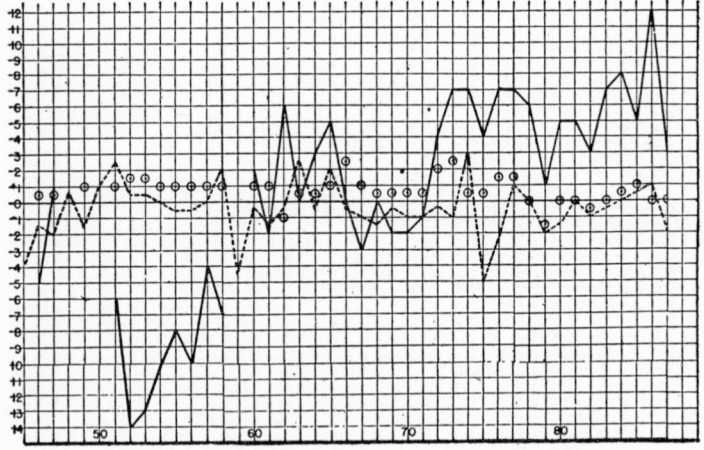

Figure 3. *Tzigane* (Ravel) as played by Menuhin

Successive notes are shown on the abscissa. For pitch, units on the ordinate represent 0.1 tone, and the zero point indicates exact intonation in the tempered scale. The circles mark the mean-pitch level of successive notes. For intensity, units on the ordinate represent 1 decibel, and the zero point indicates the average of the mean intensities of the notes. The solid line indicates the mean intensity for successive notes. For duration, units on the ordinate represent 0.1 second and the zero point indicates exact distribution of time throughout a measure in accordance with the score. The dotted line indicates temporal overholding (+), or underholding (—) of successive notes.

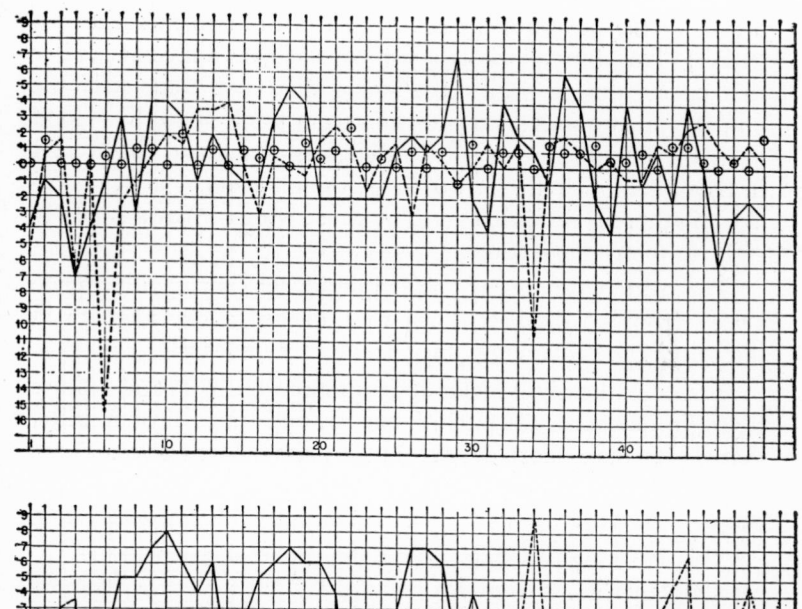

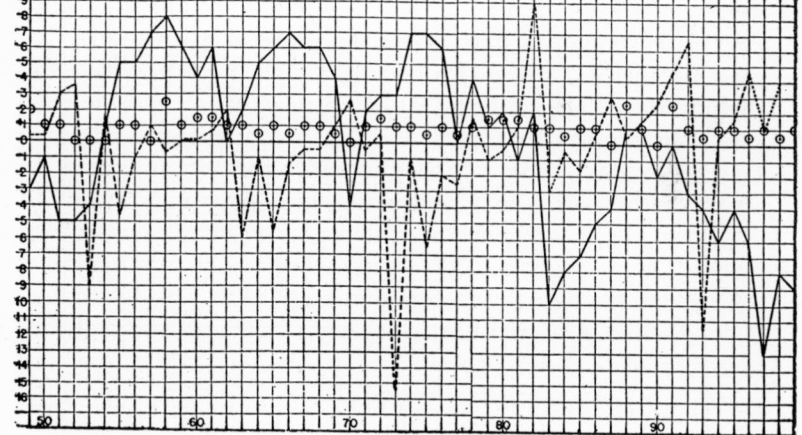

Figure 4.   Phrasing score of *Ave Maria* (Schubert-Wilhelmj) as played
by Slatkin

Legend same as Figure 3.

the fourth as 0.1 of a tone sharp, and the fifth as 0.1 of a tone
flat.

The intensity pattern for the same group shows an element
of vivacity in its zigzag, starting 3 decibels below average with
a dip in the middle. This gives a peculiar effect of a primary

accent in the beautiful figure which ties the two measures together. The short pause is again overheld 0.15 second. After this pause, during which the sound does not completely die out, the pitch glides with precision from the first to the second note, the first being regarded as slightly sharp and the second in true pitch. For these two notes, the intensity is above average and there is little change. The pause which follows is nearly right in metronomic time.

The next two notes are played decidedly sharp, with a wide sweep from 10 decibels down to 1 decibel above average in intensity. The following pause is slightly underheld.

Treating the eight notes as a group we observe a definite figure in deviations of pitch, intensity, and time. Dynamically, that represents a sharp drop from the previous two notes. Some degree of similarity between the pattern for time and intensity can be observed.

This is enough to show how these observable scores may be read together so as to give a detailed insight into the nature of the phrasing. The musician will read much more into the picture than is given here in words. The essential fact is that we have an exact record of the way in which this artist phrased in terms of three or four media with which the violinist works. The graph is in the tempered scale based on metronomic time, and, while no claim is made for measure of absolute loudness because the photograph of Menuhin's record was made from a phonograph record, the relative changes in the intensity of the tone represented are reliable.

What the student of music will get out of this depends upon what he wants to know, for example, in Figure 4. The reader may ask, e.g., how would the player augment or diminish an interval so as to approach more closely to the natural scale or the Pythagorean scale? What other types of tendency tones in the lowering or raising of pitch does he exhibit? Which deviations are errors? When he plays with the vibrato, what is the mean pitch? What degree of precision in pitch intonation does he reach? What are his characteristic forms of portamento? How are intervals reached in the most rapid passages?

On the dynamic and the temporal side, we may ask how loud did he play? How well did he control his intensity? What is the intensity pattern for the primary accent, the secondary accent, and the unaccented note in the measure? What is the dynamic pattern of each phrase as a whole? How does the dynamic pattern co-operate with or oppose the pitch pattern or the time pattern? How is rhythm established through accent? What is the temporal rhythm pattern? What are the phrasing patterns of tempo? In what respect are pitch, time, and intensity repeated in two phrases?

In answering these questions we are bringing the study of phrasing into a form where we can make exact analyses. The same line of observation and reasoning may now be applied through the reading of the Slatkin score and by comparing the characteristics in phrasing. It is from studies of this kind that principles of phrasing so universally practiced, but so little known and understood, may be organized and explained. This has a bearing on the moot question of whether science can contribute to artistry in music. We are just at the opening of a brand-new field and it will be a good while before the musician and the scientist can build up an atmosphere favorable to the functioning of acoustic science in the artistic field. The student of the psychology of music in the future will understand how principles of phrasing may be studied scientifically. There will gradually be at his command a system of principles of phrasing which can be verified and greatly enriched and illustrative of how musical feeling is expressed through the four factors in phrasing. It will make him a critical listener so that he will hear and appreciate elements in phrasing which have passed unrecognized heretofore. He will have a conception of norms of precision, principles of artistic license, and the comfortable feeling that skill in phrasing need not be a mysterious art.

The student of the psychology of music in the future will understand how principles of phrasing may be studied scientifically. There will gradually be at his command a system of principles of phrasing which he can understand because he is familiar with the factors involved. It will make him a critical listener so that he will hear elements of phrasing which have passed unrecognized before. He will have a conception of norms of precision, principles of artistic license, and the comfortable feeling that skill in phrasing need not remain a mysterious art.

AUGMENTING OR DIMINISHING OF INTERVALS: SCALES [*]

There is a standing controversy among artists who play stringed instruments as to whether they are performing in the natural, the tempered, or some other musical scale. This concerns both individual notes and intervals. Some violinists aim to play in the natural scale whenever they are not playing with accompaniment or in ensemble. Others tend to surrender grudgingly to performance in the tempered scale. But the majority compromise by deliberately sharping or flatting certain tendency tones, regardless of any particular scale. Most violinists would say that the recognition of these tendency tones depends upon the musical context. Indeed, certain violinists can be recognized by their characteristic use of certain tendency tones.

Greene had six recognized violinists perform without accompaniment in the so-called "dead" room, which eliminates all reverberation from the walls and shuts out all outside sounds.[1] Each one played a portion of a familiar selection. In these records, Greene selected the major and minor second and the major and minor third as intervals to be measured as fair samples, because these intervals are the most frequently used. Most of these intervals fell in the octave above middle C.

Figures 5 and 6 are samples of his findings. These figures may be interpreted in terms of the first composite graph in Figure 5. Pitch is designated at the bottom in hundredths of a

---

[1] The performers were Scipione Guidi, assistant director and concertmaster of the St. Louis Symphony Orchestra; Frank Estes Kendrie, professor of violin at the State University of Iowa and conductor of the University of Iowa Symphony Orchestra; Arnold M. Small, concertmaster of the University of Iowa Symphony Orchestra; and Ellis Levy, Jacob Levine, and Felix Slatkin, members of the first violin section of the St. Louis Symphony Orchestra.

---

[*] From the *Music Educators Journal,* October-November 1937, and based upon Paul Greene's "Intonation in Violin Performance," University of Iowa *Studies in the Psychology of Music,* Vol. IV, 1937, 232–250.

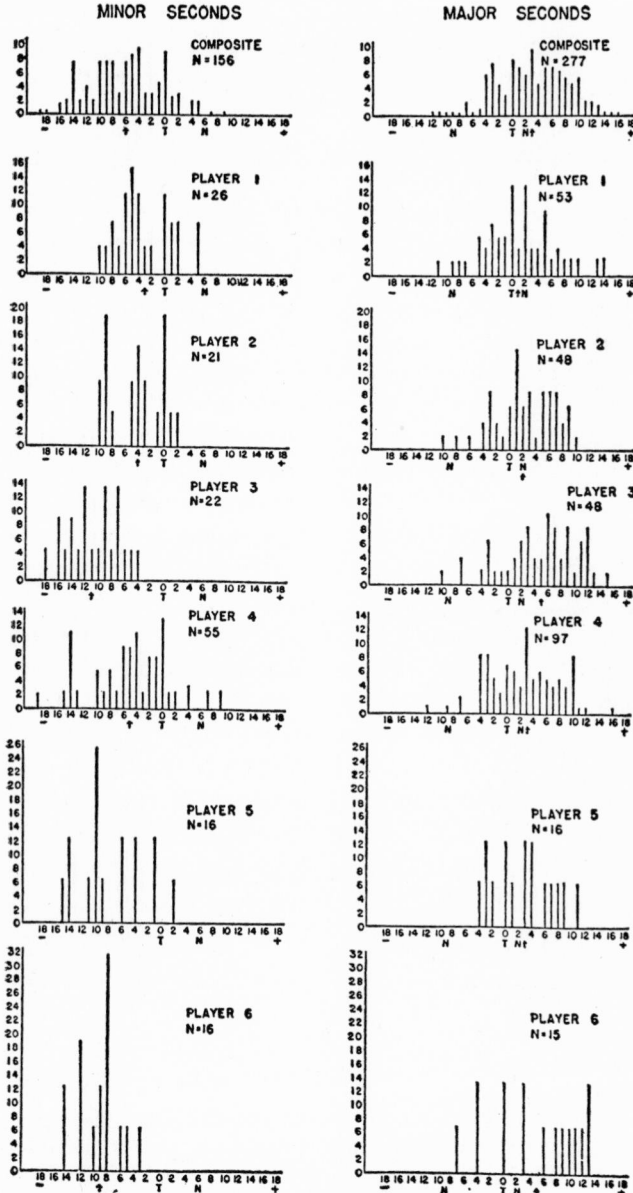

Figure 5. Minor and major seconds

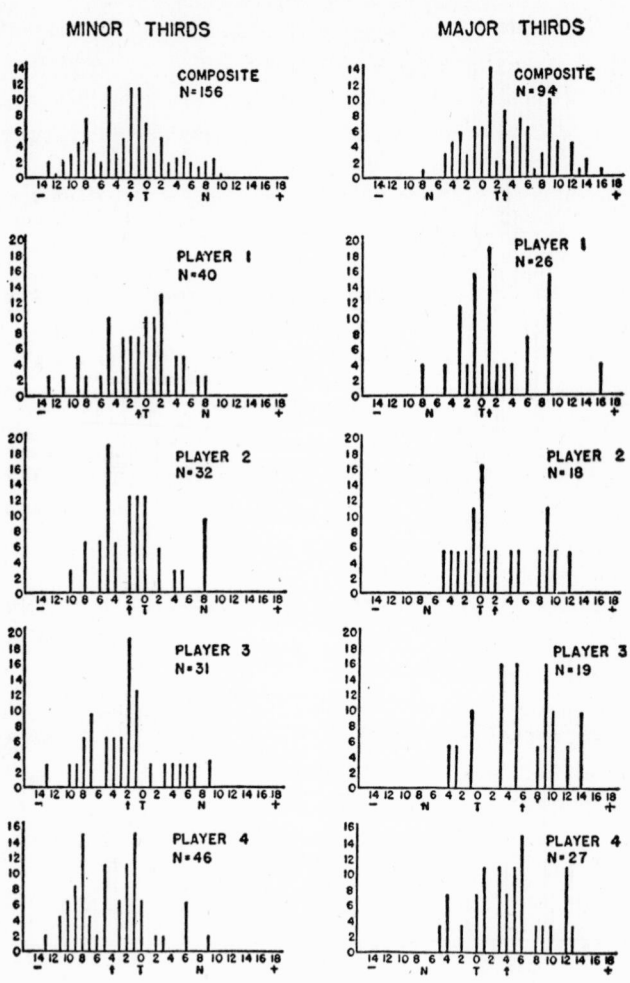

Figure 6. Minor and major thirds

tone. T denotes the true location in terms of the tempered scale and is designated as zero. N denotes the location on the natural scale or just intonation, namely, 0.06 tone above the tempered standard. The arrow indicates the average of all performances, namely, 0.06 tone below the tempered scale value or zero. The vertical bars indicate the percentage of the total number of cases in which a given deviation from a tempered scale occurred. Thus it is shown that the general tendency is to diminish this interval 0.06 tone below the tempered standard and 0.12 tone below the natural scale standard.

This composite graph gives us the general tendency for the group, but it is significant that each player reveals a characteristic tendency of his own. Similar interpretations may be made with the other three intervals.

Here we have in black and white a fair sample of facts in regard to this moot question. They not only show the general tendency for this group of violinists, but they give us a concrete picture of the degree of variability both for the group as a whole and for individuals. Indeed, each individual is characterized to some extent by the figure at hand. The broad general conclusion is that these violinists do not play these intervals characteristically in the tempered scale or in the natural scale, but deviate rather consistently from both.

The question then arose whether there is any recognized scale that fits the performance better, and it was found that the Pythagorean scale comes to the front. Figure 7 sets forth this fact in a very striking way. P indicates the Pythagorean scale value, and T and N, the tempered and natural scale values, respectively. The arrow indicates the average performance for the groups in all records obtained on the intervals under consideration.

Thus we see that the minor second is diminished from the tempered scale and is played within 0.01 tone of the Pythagorean scale value, but 0.12 tone from the natural scale value.

There are two recognized major seconds in the natural scale value. The average performance is 0.03 tone above the tempered scale value, which is only 0.01 tone from the larger natural interval and the Pythagorean, but is 0.12 tone above the smaller natural interval.

In the same manner the minor third is diminished 0.02 tone from the tempered scale value, which places it within 0.01 tone of the Pythagorean scale value and 0.10 tone below the natural scale value; whereas, in the major third, the interval is augmented to 0.03 tone above the tempered scale value, which again places it within 0.01 tone of the Pythagorean and 0.10 tone from the natural scale value.

Thus we see that, on the average, minor seconds and minor thirds are diminished from the tempered scale and tend to coincide with the requirements of the Pythagorean scale, whereas

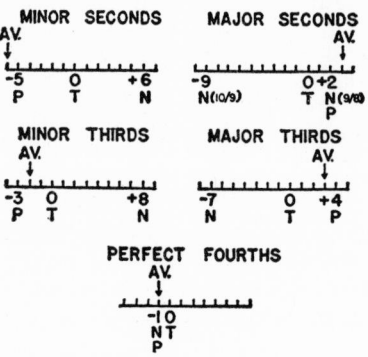

Figure 7.   Comparison of scales

major thirds and major seconds are augmented and again tend to conform with the Pythagorean scale. The measurements on the perfect fourths were made as a control to discover the tendency where there is close agreement theoretically in all the scales.

Greene's researches lay a cornerstone in the structure for the discussion of the theory and the practice of intonation in relation to scales, and they reveal the methods by which any controversy on the subject in the future may be settled by objective measurement. The problem is not simple; it involves countless issues regarding the hearing of intervals, skill in performance, and the whole problem of artistic deviation from the regular in musical esthetics.

The findings of this investigation are as follows: (1) The six violinists typically performed in neither the natural nor the equally tempered scale. (2) As compared with natural and equally tempered intonation, major seconds and major thirds were enlarged, minor seconds and minor thirds were contracted, and perfect fourths on the average tended to approximate the theoretical scale values for that interval. (3) The two theoretical varieties of major seconds, in the natural scale, were not significantly differentiated by the group of performers. (4) The observed interval tendencies held for performances of each of the three played selections. (5) Upward and downward progression of the intervals had no measurable effect upon either the direction or the extent of their typical deviation from the theoretical scale values. (6) The individual performers agreed very closely as to the direction and extent of tendencies to modify intervals, only slight variations in the extent of deviation being found. (7) Duration of tones had no measurable effect upon either the direction or the extent of variation of the played intervals from their theoretical scale values. (8) Individual players showed slightly different patterns of intonation, but as a group they tended to approximate the interval extents of the Pythagorean scale.

THE EFFECT OF THE MUTE ON THE VIOLIN TONE

Modern laboratory equipment for the measurement of all conceivable kinds of tone quality is opening up a new and vast field for investigation of the exact performance of any instrument in any feature. Let me give here a single illustration: the effect of the mute upon the violin tone.

Horne studied the effect upon a violin tone of mutes differing in material, shape, size, and weight, with two differing violins, and found significant differences in the effect of different mutes. I will report here only the characteristic effect of a mute commonly used, a commercial 7-gram 5-prong metal mute, cork separated. The findings are for a Venetian *Zanoli* violin dated about 1750.

The four open strings were studied. They were played by a mechanical bower which assured good quality and constancy of tone. The exact overtone structure for each tone was determined by harmonic analysis. Horne's procedure was to play the open string under the most favorable conditions for good tone quality and then repeat the note exactly in the same way except for the application of the mute. The experiment was set so as to answer two questions. First, how does the mute affect the total intensity or loudness of the tone? Second, how does it change the overtone structure, that is, the timbre, of the tone as a whole?

The results are shown in Figure 8, which contains tone spectra of the muted and the unmuted tones for each of the four open strings which will be regarded as fair samples. The solid bar represents the relative strength of each overtone of the unmuted string, and the open bar for the muted. The bars are in terms of decibel values, and therefore represent the relative musical significance. The reader need not bother about the technical aspects of these spectra but should remember simply that the relative significance of an overtone is indicated by the height of the bar which represents it. Each spectrum shows what overtones are present, their distribution, and their relative prominence. The pitch from 200 up to 10,000 vibrations together with the location of the C's is shown at the bottom and is the same for all four figures.

By comparing these diagrams of the muted and the unmuted tones, we can see exactly what the mute accomplishes. A violinist familiar with his instrument will be interested to observe in these graphs exactly what the mute does to the fundamental and to each of the overtones. The situation is complex, but we have here a large mass of exact information on which we may make, among others, the following generalizations:

(1) The mute reduces the total intensity of the tone. To our surprise it is shown that there is in general no lowering of the intensity of the fundamental. The decrease in intensity comes largely through the middle range of overtones.

(2) The effect is quite radically different upon the four strings. For the G string, there is a general tendency to weaken to a marked extent all the overtones above the first. For the D string, there is a general tendency to weaken the first seven overtones and there is an irregular tendency to strengthen the highest overtones. For the A string, there is a general tendency to weaken the first four overtones and strengthen the next

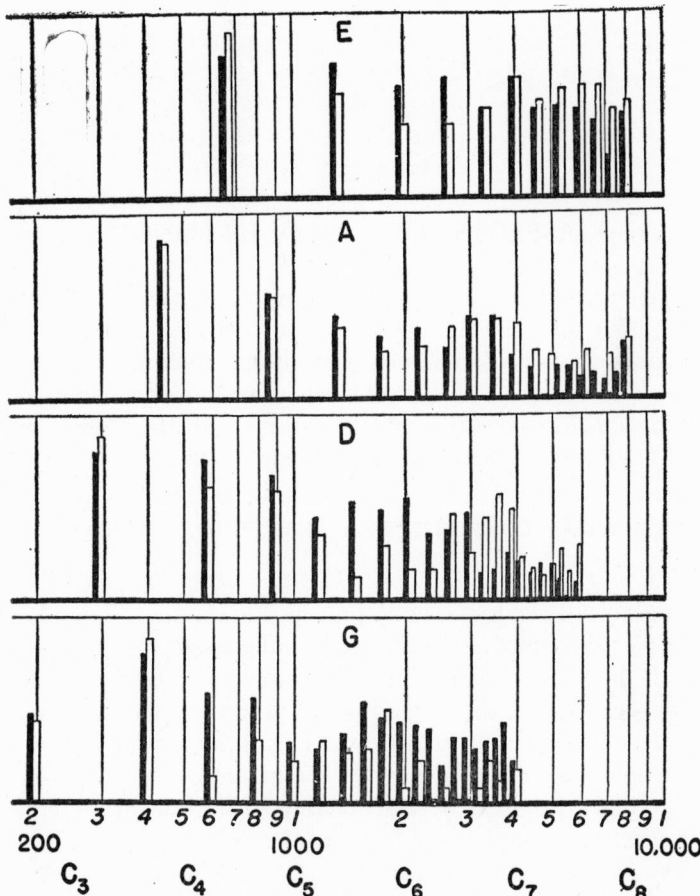

Figure 8. Tone spectra showing the effect of the mute upon the loudness and the quality of the tone. Solid bars, unmuted; open bars, muted tones.

ten. For the E string, there is a tendency to weaken the first three overtones and strengthen the highest six.

(3) The effect of the mute upon the overtone structure in good playing varies with the pitch level, the loudness level, the natural timbre of the string, the character of the instrument, and the character of the mute.

Chapter 14

ASPECTS OF BEAUTY IN SONG

THE TOPIC OF THIS CHAPTER has been treated in specific aspects throughout many of the preceding chapters. I will here merely give some further examples of types of approach to the problem of good singing. The list of such possible issues that have bearing on musical esthetics will expand, and the field is wide open for experimentation of a scientific order.

WHAT CONSTITUTES A BEAUTIFUL VOICE?

The practical musician and critic may be disappointed in not finding an answer to that question in this chapter. The reason is simple: the function of science in esthetics is first to observe, record, describe, classify, and explain every tangible aspect of the musical object, the song; then to proceed in the same manner in the analysis of the singer, and again, in the same manner, in the analysis of the listener. It is a gigantic and endless task, but we make progress by fractionating it into discreet steps so that a verifiable system of facts can be built.

The goal of science in music, however, is the same as the goal of philosophy in music, namely, insight into the nature of musical values. But philosophical esthetics works in the opposite direction by beginning with the formulation of a general theory or theories and applying this to the actual musical situation in uncontrolled observation. The books on esthetics are full of theories which are supposed to be all-comprehensive, but they often fail in the modern attitude of critical science.

However, many points of agreement may be reached tentatively from both directions. For example, it may be agreed that a wide and unbroken register of voice is an esthetic value, that feelingful and artistically cultivated phrasing by the voice is an esthetic value. On many issues of that kind the scientist, the artist, and the philosopher agree. But this agreement reminds one of the instructions given by a judge to a young lawyer: "Always render your decisions with clarity, but never give the reasons, because the chances are that your decision is right but the reason is wrong." The scientist would admit this and say, "We do not have enough verified facts." The philosopher would say, "After all, the conclusion is more a matter of common sense than a deduction from a general theory." And the practical musician might say, "That's what I like, and what I like is good to me."

THE FORMATIVE PERIOD FOR BEAUTY IN VOICE *

In presenting a plea for the cultivation of a beautiful voice, permit me, as a psychologist, to emphasize the following points: (1) The significance and the possibility of a beautiful voice has been overlooked to an astonishing degree by educators and society in general—psychologists not excepted. (2) The approach to a beautiful singing voice should be made through the early cultivation of a beautiful speaking voice. (3) A lovely and effective speaking voice is not only an index to character and personality but is one of the most potent means for the cultivation of these. (4) Musicians should recognize that their most effective ally in the cultivation of a beautiful singing voice lies in the early promotion of the development of an understanding of the meaning and the possibilities of a good speaking voice. (5) This development takes place most naturally through the spontaneous activities of self-expression in the schoolroom, playground, and the home, when wisely nurtured.

In our modern tendency to force early development of children in an unnatural way by encouraging too early the beginning of formal lessons on instruments, musicians have much to account for. They have thwarted the effective operation of natural motivation, they have started the child toward a lopsided personality by diverting his energies and interests from

---

* Based on articles in *Parents Magazine* and National *Parent-Teacher Magazine*.

normal development of other equally important resources, and they have often injured mental and physical health by fostering precocity. Fortunately, this tendency is being counteracted to a large extent by the effective and natural development of music in the kindergarten and elementary grades.

We seldom hear a musician giving serious attention to the development of the voice in early childhood. Indeed, we are told that, because the voice is in for such a radical change through maturation, it is not important to begin early training.

Let me enter a plea for early attention to the development of the voice in boys and girls. I do not mean the early formal training for musicianship or speech exhibition, but rather training for the appreciation and understanding of the significance and the possibilities of a beautiful voice in music and speech. And let us put speech first, because the natural quality of a child's voice is set very largely for life in the first six years, in spite of the great changes which take place with maturation. This setting is acquired vastly more in speech than in song, and the development of the speaking voice normally comes before the development of the singing voice.

It is an extraordinary thing that an ugly speaking tone is tolerated not only in the voice of the ordinary cultivated person but in musicians, even great singers, without any great feeling of incongruity. Likewise, it is a deplorable fact that teachers who are to serve as models for the development of personality in the elementary schoolroom have seldom if ever given any attention to the character of their own speaking voices. Bad voice quality seems to be taken for granted in the educational world just as distortion of facial features, bowleggedness, or a miniature stature are taken for granted as fixtures. It is to be hoped that with a new speech consciousness "a little child shall lead them."

The present world seems to be eye-minded as far as education is concerned, paying little or no attention to the voice which is by far the most effective medium for social intercourse and is more expressive of character than any other means of communication that we have.

With the coming in of corrective speech, dealing with the disabilities, educators are being awakened to the fact that they have neglected a most important positive factor, namely, the possibility of making the child's normal speech more beautiful. All the world loves a beautiful child, and all the world should know that this love attaches very largely to beauty in speech.

I have sponsored a movement to offset the treatment of children's voices in the movies by encouraging the development of playlets which would exhibit lovely children in conversation, giving evidence of the marvels of beauty of speech from the very beginning of vocalization through the formative years. If artistic material of this sort were available, the movie world would immediately respond with enthusiasm, as it always does to child attractiveness. Shirley Temple's voice, both on the stage and in social conversation, is resourceful and effective; but it can hardly be said to be beautiful. This is due, in large part, to the heroic bravado parts she had to play with adults. Beauty is generally attributed to her voice as a halo effect from resourcefulness and effectiveness which, of course, are elements of beauty.

One educator has placed a little endowment upon each of his grandchildren with the stipulation that they shall have the income for a birthday present each year together with the annual reminder of a note pointing out the value of a beautiful speaking voice.

There are several steps that must be taken in organizing this training in the schools and in the home. The first is to teach parents and teachers the significance of a beautiful voice. That idea must be promulgated until everybody begins to take notice of it. This accomplished, more than half of the work is done, because the next step is not so much formal training as it is continuous and vital attention to the difference between the beautiful speaking voice and an ugly one throughout life.

Second, in teaching children in the kindergarten, in the grades, in the home, or on the playground, there is not so much need of formal lessons in voice culture as there is of constant *expression of appreciation* of beautiful tone quality and disparagement of the bad. The significant thing is that this is immediately tied up with character and personality. Shouting, screaming, snorting, rasping, and all sorts of disagreeable speech are nearly always expressions of a disagreeable personality trait. Likewise, the deliberate cultivation of sweetness of speech inevitably reacts back, hinging upon the easily observable fact that, while you can imitate a beautiful voice, you do not get far with that; it does not become a part of you until it is a part of the natural personality.

Third, let me therefore carry to music educators of America the earnest plea for their sponsorship of beautiful speech in the school, in the home, and on the playground, especially during the first six years of childhood. Let the educators give the support of their prestige to the recognition that a beautiful singing voice is in large part based upon habits of appreciation of beauty on voice quality during the early years of childhood. We have the comfort that proper attention given to the careful training of the voice in speech and in song in the early years has none of the drawbacks that prematurely forced formal lessons on musical instruments are in danger of having. It is also gratifying to know that, while not all children can become singers, nearly all children have latent capacities for good speech. Let musicians show leadership in bringing this issue to the front through teacher-training institutions, parent-teacher associations, and musical activities.

Fourth, from the point of view of motivation there is an advantage for the singing teacher to have the child come into later lessons in singing with a deep-rooted appreciation of good voice quality. The possession of this readily transfers to singing. Let us make our children voice-conscious!

HOW DO WE EXPRESS SPECIFIC EMOTIONS IN SONG? *

It is difficult to obtain a rigid concept of a given emotion, knowledge of all the means of expressing it, or command of all

---

* From *Music Educators Journal,* September 1940, based on Grant Fairbanks, "Recent Experimental Investigations of Vocal Pitch in Speech," *Journal of the Acoustical Society of America,* II, No. 4, April 1940, 457–466.

the personal resources for the singing interpretation of the score.

First, the *words* of the poet convey the theme and the meaning of the whole message. The right words, with any moderately generic melody, will convey at least the idea of the emotion. Second, the composer chooses what he feels to be an appropriate *musical form* to fit the emotion to be expressed. In this, he follows certain general principles of composition, but he depends far more upon his immediate feeling of the satisfyingness of a particular musical mode and mood, than he does upon theory. Third, the singer projects himself into the emotional attitude expressed by the words, and he takes great freedom with the score; usually, he supplements the song with dramatic accessories in his *interpretation*. This is, in skeletal form, the musical artist's answer to the question in our title. The problem seems baffling and intangible.

Is there any possibility of a scientific approach? I think there is decidedly, and will illustrate my faith by an example from an analogous situation in speech which has been recently reported from our Iowa laboratory. Fairbanks took this passage:

> *There is no other answer. You've asked me that question a thousand times, and my reply has always been the same. It always will be the same.*

He selected six well-trained dramatic readers, and asked them to read this passage in five different ways, expressing in turn their best conception of *contempt, anger, fear, grief,* and *indifference*. Each item was repeated six times, and phonographic and photographic recordings of the rendition were made.

These thirty samples of simulations were played in random order before a class of sixty-four advanced students of speech. The observers were provided with a list of twelve emotional states, namely, *amusement, anger, astonishment, contempt, doubt, elation, embarrassment, fear, grief, indifference, jealousy, love*. Their task was to select from this list of twelve, the appropriate name for each of the emotions expressed without knowing what the five intended emotions were. Their success is shown in Figure 1, which indicates a rather remarkable success in the identification of the intended emotions.

Remember that the words were exactly the same in all five situations. The judgment was therefore based primarily upon the representation conveyed by the sound from the phonograph record, without dramatic or other accessories.

The next stage was to analyze the performance score as photographed to determine on what elements of voice the identification was made. In accordance with the Iowa laboratory technique, it could lie only in one or more of the four elements of sound: pitch, loudness, time and timbre. Recognition of this fact simplified the problem enormously. For the purpose of this experiment, Fairbanks considered only pitch, the result of which is shown in the performance scores in Figure 2.

> For each emotion, the graph (Figure 1) presented is that of the simulation which was identified correctly by the largest percentage of observers. In Figure 2 time in 1-second intervals is indicated by vertical lines; the ordinate is the equal-tempered musical scale with horizontal lines marking the major triads. Notable in this figure are the few extremely wide downward inflections in the simulation of contempt, the generally wide, rapid inflections of anger, the irregularity of the pitch changes in fear, the . . . vibrato in grief, and the lack of distinguishing features in indifference. Typical variations of pitch level are revealed in Figure 3, which shows frequency distributions of the measured pitches for the two subjects who were generally most successful (left group) and least successful (right group) in producing identifiable simulations. . . .[1]

A close inspection of Figure 3 reveals that each assumed emotion calls for a fairly definite pitch level and pitch range. With this as a starting point, he could have analyzed the pitch characteristics into any or all of the numerous forms of pitch modulation. He could have proceeded then in the same manner with each of the other three factors. From these three figures,

[1] Fairbanks, *op. cit. supra.*

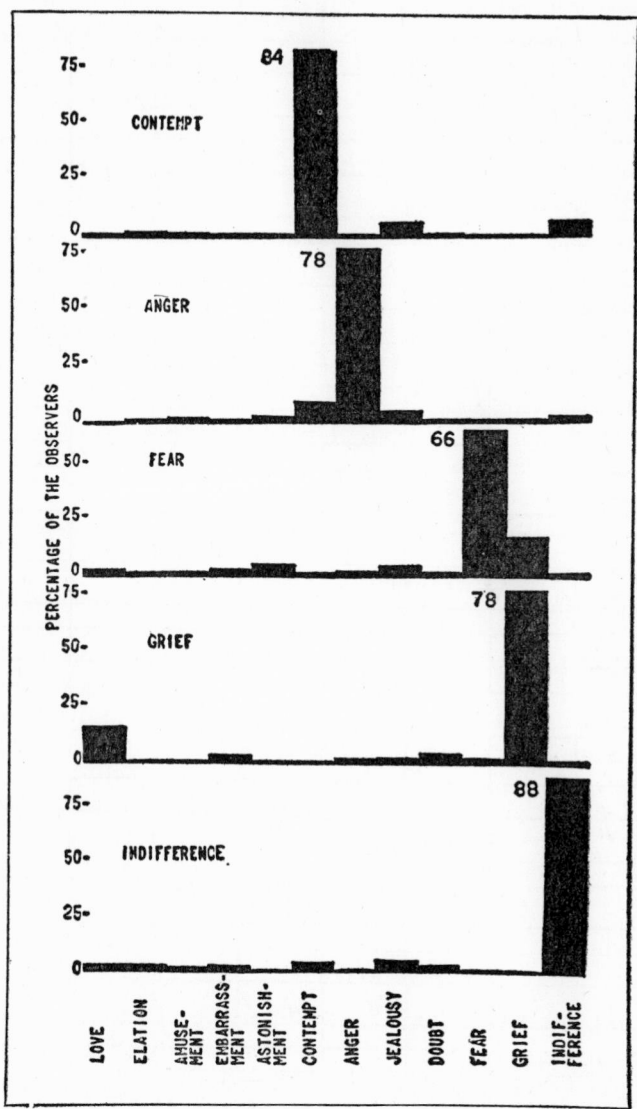

Figure 1. Distributions of identifications of simulated emotions by thirty-six observers

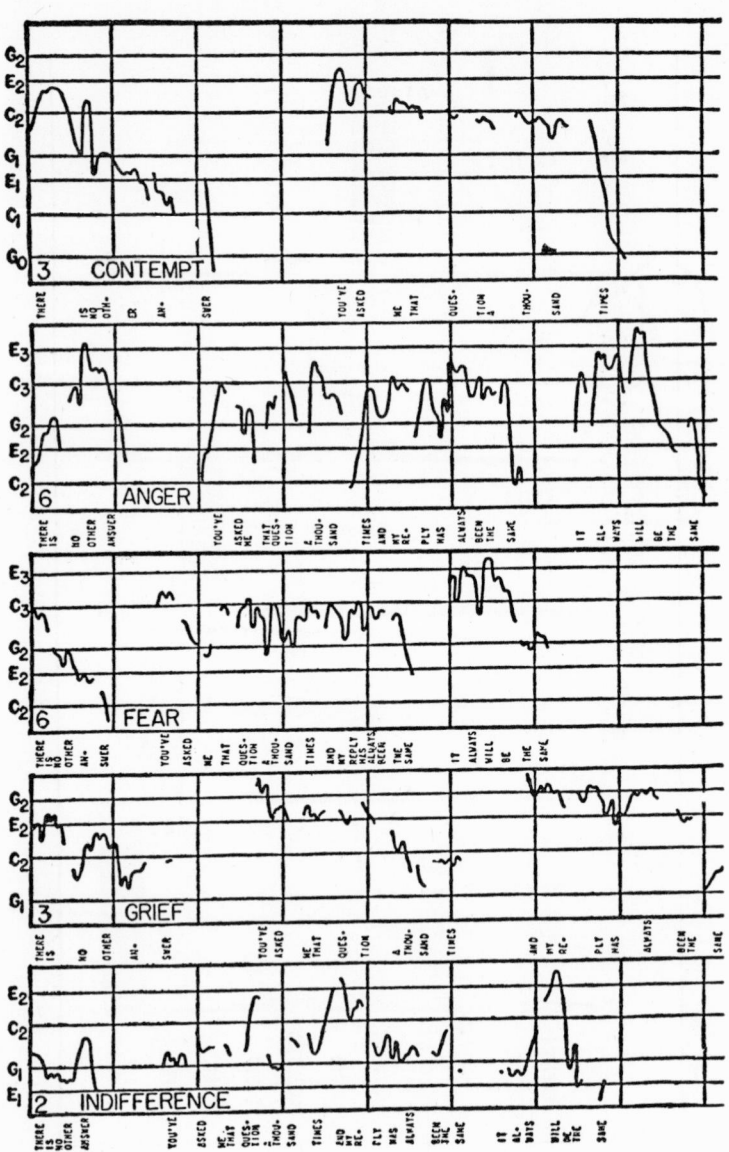

Figure 2. Pitch curves of typical emotional stimulations. For each emotion is shown the curve of the simulation that was identified correctly by the largest percentage of observers.

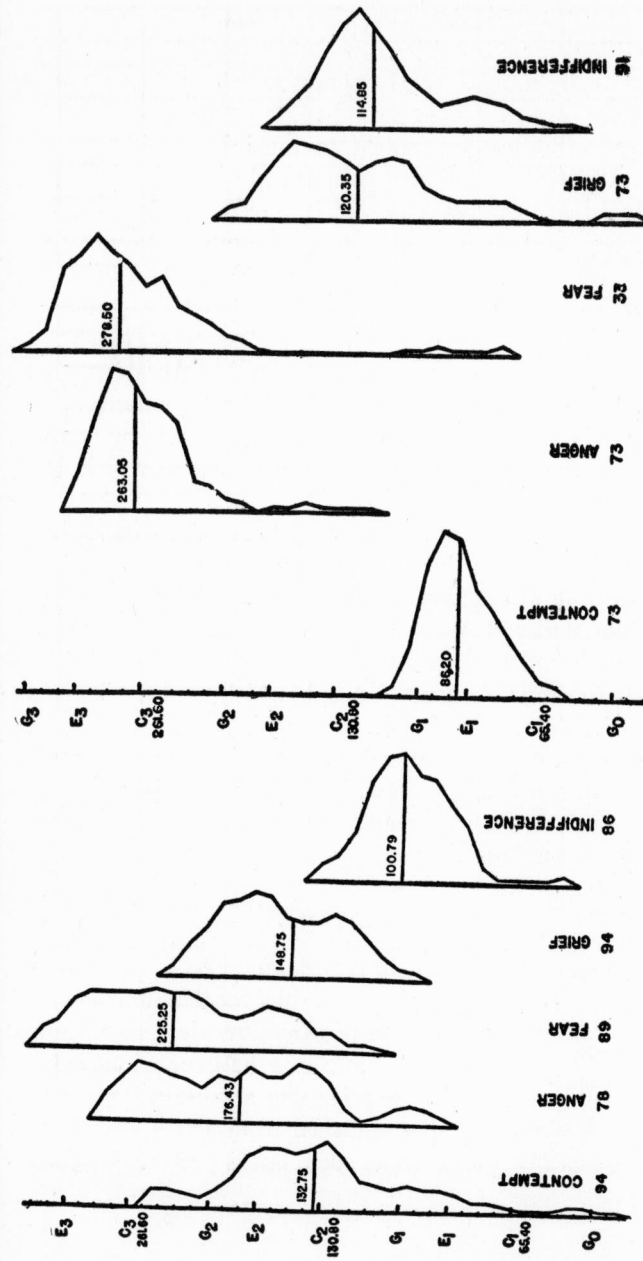

Figure 3. Frequency distributions of pitches used in simulating the five emotions by the two subjects who were most successful (left group) and least successful (right group) in producing identifiable simulations

anyone can see that the experiment has a clean-cut objective and verifiable scientific approach to speech; this approach is successful in spite of the comparative looseness in definition of the emotions studied.

Can this technique be applied to music? I think we can exactly parallel this experiment in the field of music. First, we must control the meaning conveyed by the words by using the *same* words. Second, we must select a number of the most recognized musical forms designed to differentiate emotions. Third, we must have these selections rendered by competent singers and recorded by phonograph and camera. Fourth, we must tabulate the degree of success in the identification, as in Figure 1. Fifth, we must have represented one or more of the basic elements of sounds, as in Figure 2. And sixth, by detailed analysis, we must identify specific tonal factors which have discriminative value, as in Figure 3.

Suffice it to say that by this type of approach, so well illustrated in speech, we can begin to lay foundations for *a science of the expression of specific emotions in song.* This experiment is now being undertaken in the Iowa laboratory, and, if it is validated, it should lead to a comprehensive series of analyses for each of the four elements through which the emotions can be expressed. To serve a double purpose, it is proposed that we take the same words which were used by Fairbanks and that we have half a dozen composers write melodies, limiting the expression for this first experiment to pitch in notes of even loudness, time, and timbre.

THE VOCAL TRILL [*]

The purpose of this item is to reveal, on the basis of measurement, some of the characteristics of the vocal trill which, although generally unknown, have profound musical significance. The vocal trill when actually sung as a half-tone interval, as frequently indicated, sounds exactly like a vibrato, and it has the effect of a vibrato as distinguished from a trill effect. The interval is generally not heard as such, but is perceived as flexi-

---

[*] From *Music Educators Journal,* January 1942.

bility, tenderness, and richness of tone, which is in large part the opposite of a trill effect. The same is frequently true for a whole-tone vocal trill, but this varies with the sensitiveness of the listener. It is only when larger intervals are employed that it is clearly recognized as a trill.

I recently selected five singers from an advanced class in the psychology of music, and, without warning, asked each one to trill on a half-tone step. Their performances were photographed and fair samples are shown in Figures 4 and 5. Inspection of these performance records suggests, among other things, the following facts, direct or related.

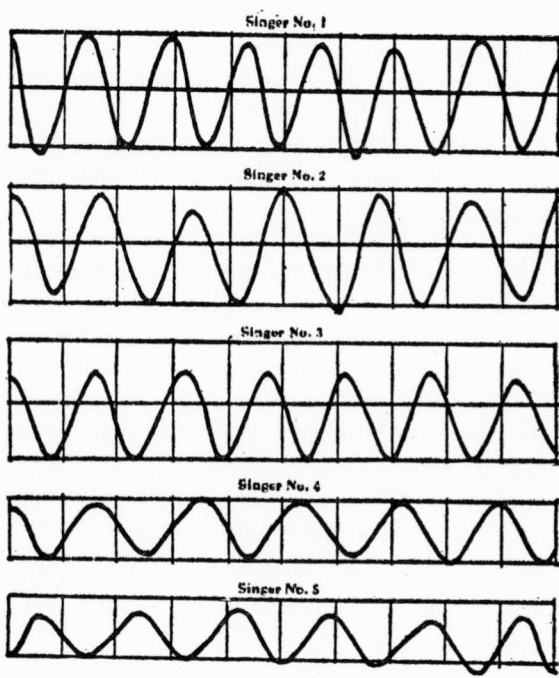

Figure 4. Voice trill

The form of the curve shows the exact form of the pitch inflection. The space between the horizontal lines represents two semitones, or a whole tone, and the length of each complete curve (or series of pulsations) represents one second. Singer No. 1 is a coloratura soprano; No. 2, a mezzo-soprano concert singer; Nos. 3, 4, and 5 are advanced students and teachers of voice; No. 5 is the only male in the group.

(1) The *form* of the physical pitch inflection in singing is exactly the same as for the vocal vibrato; that is, instead of representing two distinct pitches, there is a modulated inflection in the shape of a smooth sine curve. There is no sustaining of even pitch, either on the top or the bottom components: those levels are merely "flirted with." In this respect, the vocal trill differs from a trill on keyed instruments, which appears as two clean-cut intermittent tones, thus:

Figure 5. Piano trill

On stringed instruments and other instruments on which the performer can change the interval gradually, the form of the trill approaches that of the voice rather than that of the piano.

(2) In the vocal trill, the *extent* or magnitude of the interval is always overreached. The singers were asked to sing the trill on a semitone. All grossly overreached this, but were wholly unaware of that fact until confronted with the photographs of their performance. Singers 1 and 2, who approximated an interval of four semitones, reported that perhaps they did not make a vigorous effort to make it exactly a semitone, but rather had tried to make it a beautiful trill. Yet they were completely surprised when they saw their performance records.

(3) In *hearing* the trill, the extent of the interval is grossly underestimated. This is, of course, the reason for the augmentation of the interval to make it sound right. To many good listeners, an interval of a minor third may sound as a satisfactory half-tone or whole-tone interval when sung in the form of a trill.

(4) In other words, when the trill is heard as a trill and not as a vibrato, there is a marked tendency to hear it as a semitone or a multiple thereof.

(5) Where the composer has indicated the interval in the score, the singer almost always follows the principle of gross overreaching in the size of the interval in order to make it heard as indicated in the score.

(6) The *rate* of the vocal trill is about the same as the rate of the vibrato with a mode between five and six pulsations per second. This rate of the trill is determined by two factors, namely, the maximum speed that can be reached with reasonable ease and precision, and the limits of the region of tolerance, outside of which both slow and fast trills in voice and stringed instruments are unpleasant. The general tendency is to roll the trill as fast as possible. For the piano, the faster the trill, the more satisfactory it is; this is because of the increased continuity in the two interrupted tones and the ease of production.

(7) There are, therefore, two distinct types of trill: that of the keyed instruments, which is always rendered as intended or indicated by the score, and that of the voice and nonkeyed instruments, which is subject to all the distortions of production and hearing characteristic of the vibrato. In one, we produce and hear two distinct tones not connected by a glide; in the other, the entire trill is a continuous glide and is subject to all the principal illusions of the vibrato as described in my volume *The Vibrato in Voice and Instrument*.[2]

Random samplings of the phonograph recordings made by opera singers and observation by trained listeners tend to verify the principles exhibited in our graphs, a fact which suggests a rich and tangible field for scientific investigation in the analytical and experimental study of the recorded voices of great singers.

---

[2] University of Iowa *Studies in the Psychology of Music,* Vol. I, 1932.

PART THREE

EXAMPLES OF SOME SUBJECTIVE VARIABLES

Chapter 15

THE ESTHETIC JUDGMENT
ON MUSICAL VALUES

WITHIN THE LAST FEW YEARS experimental psychology has done more to reveal the endless variety of esthetic values in music than has any other technical source. It is a saying in the laboratory that, when you ask one question of nature, by means of controlled experiment, nature will ask you ten. And the asking of one of those ten will, in turn, unearth ten unforeseen but verifiable facts. Knowledge increases by a kind of magic chain.

SUBJECTIVE FACTORS OF LIKES AND DISLIKES IN MUSIC

The experimental method has enabled us to isolate and describe concrete esthetic values in the musical object, and to understand the ways in which they are rendered, heard, and appreciated. The experimenter in the psycholgy of music has little immediate interest in beauty as a whole; he turns by cautious steps to the examination of one specific type of beauty after another. This is well illustrated in the preceding chapters on the tonal spectrum.

In addition to the objective variables, the experimenter finds an exceedingly large and complicated series of subjective factors which play a leading role in the perception, feeling, and understanding of the listener to the variables in the tonal structure. While this book is devoted primarily to the description and interpretation of the music itself, it will be worth while to list and recognize some of the psychological factors determining likes and dislikes, which affect the composer, the performer, the listener and the critic. These are, of course, factors which must be controlled in the objective measurements.

Maturation. To the normal young child, all kinds of sounds, from the purest tone to the noisiest rattling, banging, sizzling, and drumming, tend to have musical value, both in hearing them and in performing them. In the process of maturation he progressively loses interest in many sound effects which he comes to assume are not musical, and at the same time, his growth from infancy up through the teens results in an increasing variety of interests, activities, and reflective evaluations of music. Music therefore has radically different esthetic appeals at successive stages from infancy through childhood and youth into maturity, purely as a result of intuitional maturation.

Training. The process of mental growth is facilitated, hastened, intensified, and organized by training. The beauty perceived in a tone quality, a melodic movement, a rhythmic pattern or the resolution of a sequence, varies from stage to stage more rapidly when training is added to natural maturation. The musician not only hears infinitely more than the untutored person, but, with his growth in musicianship, he hears in organized detail an increasing variety of variables in the musical form. Discriminative hearing and performance as well as insight into and understanding of music largely are learned through training.

Talent. Musicality is a gift, a hereditary endowment, one of nature's prolific investments. Recognition of this fact has only recently begun to function in the type of musical education where the attempt is made to educate the musical and the unmusical alike. It is the groundwork for specialization of interests in various types of music, such as the tonal, the rhythmic, the qualitative, and the dynamic. What is beautiful to one person may not be beautiful to another, and that statement may be fractionated into various aspects of beauty, to an extraordinary degree, in terms of natural talent. Individual differences in the largely inherited sense of timbre, of course, are among the largest determining factors in the ability to judge agreeableness or disagreeableness. If the patrons of a symphony orchestra compared their reactions, differences in musical feelings, ranging from no feeling at all to ecstasy, would be revealed.

Taste. Taste is the attitude of the connoisseur in music. It rests largely upon his natural talent, although it is often thought of as an acquired ability due to educational and environmental refinements. All musical values roll in confusion under the ban or approval of musical taste. It is true that the refinement of discriminating taste is one of the highest achievements, but, unfortunately, most of this taste is ill-founded imitation, inadequate and ruinous; yet it plays an important role in the assignment of beauty or ugliness to music.

Meaning. One of the marks of great music is its purely affective appeal and freedom from discreet forms of meaning. In practice, however, the human mind tends irresistibly to give meaning to every experience. This meaning takes two general forms. First, the music may be light or heavy, frivolous or serious. Experiments have shown that musical chords may be matched against the principal types of human moods. Second, in hearing music, there is the irresistible tendency to visualize and dramatize it in concrete situations which acquire meaning through each and all of the senses. The famous psychological illustration of this is the sight of a beautiful apple. The apple is not only seen; it comes through associated imagery in all the other senses. This is the outstanding characteristic of descriptive music, but the principle operates in various degrees in all forms of music.

The esthetic significance of this lies in the fact that the imagery through which the listener lives in hearing music is the associated imagery aroused by it. In the love song, for example, he may not be aware of the harmonic and melodic movements which constitute the physical music, but he envisages and for the moment lives with his beloved. This principle is illustrated in all types of intensive emotional situations, such as love, hate, fear, tranquility, war, and peace. The value lies not only in the music itself, but in its effectiveness in arousing associated imagery which may, of course, occur in infinite variety and may furnish the dominant content of the feeling.

The music on the radio at the present time is playing a tremendous role in that it takes us to witness scenes of the battlefield, the calamity at sea and the thrilling aspects of aerial warfare involving sacrifice, triumph and elation in achievement at the war fronts. These scenes are enacted at the fireside by sweethearts and wives and all the folks at home. The music is but a signal, a cue which touches off a strong emotion of events in associated imagery.

Here we must remember that as in the drama, tragedy, although depressing, is one of the highest forms of dramatic art. The same is true in music. Some of the most beautiful forms of music are those which make us weep.

Empathy. Empathy is the phenomenon of feeling oneself into a situation. In more or less primitive music we see this in the associated action of the listener, such as the clapping of hands, stomping of feet, swaying or dancing. We say this indicates that the music is "taking hold" of the listener. It has meaning which calls for action, and the action occurs because of associated imagery.

One aspect of culture is repression of such tendencies. The more cultured we become, the less we laugh at new situations. The laughter becomes a smile, and the smile becomes a highly attenuated reflex. Nevertheless, the smile and the frown are expressions of approval and disapproval and by them we feel ourselves into a situation; the more nearly unconscious they are, the truer they are.

Empathy in overt actions is relatively unconscious; it is an automatic response of the organism and it indicates a favorable or unfavorable attitude. Yet, to the cultivated musician, this habit takes the form of associated imagery through which the musician projects himself into an organic sharing in the production of the musical effect. Conversely, there is the example of the tendency, while listening, to imitate the action of a singer in the production of high and low tones.

Scientific insight. A home-loving peasant woman is entertaining a botanist in her beautiful flower garden. She is proud of and elated by its possession. Although she does not know a stamen from a pistil, the flowers and plants are thrillingly beautiful to her. They are beautiful also to the botanist, who sees thousands of things that, for want of knowledge, the layman cannot see. The botanist knows the distinctive functions of stamens and pistils and is thrilled by recalling the marvelous adaptation of nature in the evolution of the flowering plant. In the same discriminating way, he marvels at nature's adaptation of roots, stems, and leaves, not as wholes but in each of the countless elements which contribute to control and function in the making of the root, the stem, the leaf and the flower. If we could measure emotion, the two observers of the flower might show the same degree of feeling or emotional response to beauty, but it would be radically different in esthetic value.

And so it is in music. The primitive singer may sing in true pitch, but he may not know what pitch is. He may show artistic deviation from true pitch, but he has no name for it, and he may not know of its existence. The fundamental contribution of science to music is the laying of foundations for exact, permanent, and verifiable terminology which is the basis for analysis and discriminative evaluation of beauty or ugliness in music.

The esthetic mood. One of the problems in the therapeutic use of music is the fact that to enjoy music the listener must be in a sympathetic mood. He must be receptive to music and feel the need for it. It makes a great deal of difference whether a patient is temperamentally in a joyous mood or a depressed mood. In each of these, he may recognize numerous varieties, such as frivolous, playful, satisfying, or aggressive in the positive mood, or depressive, defiant, militant, or surrendering in the negative mood.

We have found that if music is to be used at all as a therapeutic agent in psychopathic hospitals, it has to be "tailor-made" for the patient. The same principle operates in normal mental life. We not only have different training, education, tastes, and experience which influence our response to music, but these and many other factors vary from day to day, from morning to night, from waking life to dream life. They are therefore strong determinants in the esthetic acceptance or rejection of the music for the moment.

Ordinarily we do not go into a particular mood voluntarily; our impulsive response to the total present situation *is* the mood. It constitutes the matrix or setting for the acceptance or rejection of new or present experiences. When moods become habitual, they are an aspect of temperament, and temperaments can be very censorious in esthetic reactions to music.

Critical attitude. Like all other artists, the musician may put himself into either of two radically different attitudes: the unanalytical attitude of appreciation or the analytical and critical attitude. In the former, he appraises the total impression or general atmosphere created by the music; in the latter, he turns to meticulous and critical examination of details in theory, construction, or performance. Each attitude serves its purpose, although the results are very different in the perception and appreciation of musical values.

Differential hearing. It is a well-established fact that, in an average audience of intelligent people, some may be particularly sensitive to any one of the four attributes (pitch, intensity, time, and timbre), and at the same time be relatively insensitive to any one or more of these four basic capacities. The result is that each person hears music according to the peculiarities of his own ear. This is analogous to color blindness. A most interesting phenomenon musically in this respect is *presbycousis*, which may be translated as "old age hearing" (See Chapter 22).

Kinds of value. The above subjective factors are elements in the listening situation which largely determine the goodness or badness that will be attributed to the music. These factors are emphasized to show what an infinite variety of forms may determine the esthetic acceptance or rejection of music by the listener. But we add greatly to the complication when we realize that all these subjective variables may react individually to each musical element in the physical structure: the likes and dislikes of melody as distinguished from rhythm, the dance as distinguished from the symphonic form, the drum as distinguished from the flute, and so on in endless variety down to the finest details of technique or musical structure.

Music, like all art, deals with values. In our daily routine, in the philosophy, performance and teaching of music, we are constantly aware of something that we like about the music. The more intelligent, the better trained, the more critical one is, the more minutely these judgments will be analyzed. The more the subject is approached from the experimental laboratory point of view, the more verifiable, the more describable, the more repeatable these judgments will be. Fundamentally, the judgment is "I like this" or "I like that"; it is largely a personal affair.

Three general conclusions should be drawn from this recital of facts. The first is that beauty in music may be of endless variety, depending upon the fixed complexity and possible orderliness in the physical music on the one hand, and upon the variety of factors in the listener which modify the agreeableness or disagreeableness of the music on the other hand. The second is that the feeling of beauty, the assignment of esthetic value, is a fickle mental process in a musical situation. It is ordinarily emotional and sentimental, flighty and alternating. Third, when we take music into the laboratory for scientific analysis, the first consideration is the possibility of setting the situation in such form that the reasons for the judgment can be given. To this we shall give further attention.

SCIENTIFIC ASPECT OF THE ESTHETIC JUDGMENT

In the preceding chapters we have seen examples of the structure of beauty in actual musical tones. In studying these, the reader must have asked himself: What ground has the scientist for saying that this or that or any one of scores of specific aspects of a tonal spectrum has esthetic value, or is good or bad?

A general answer to that question is that the right of the scientist to do so is restricted, because he must deal with one factor at a time and slowly build general principles which in themselves may become elements in the appraisal as a whole. His chief function is to identify and exhibit features in the actual musical situation which may or may not have esthetic value, which contribute either to beauty or to ugliness in various degrees under specified conditions. It is not his business to say authoritatively that this song or this sonata is, as a whole, beautiful. His function is rather to isolate, describe, and explain those elements in the structure (represented in the performance score) of the song or sonata which have the makings of beauty.

At this point he must square himself with those psychologists, philosophers, and musicians who are the apostles of wholeness, who believe that one cannot build up a whole from an examination of its parts. He must subscribe to the Gestalt position that a factor must be judged in the light of the total personality in reaction to the total situation. He will insist upon the artistic attitude in which the esthetic value of a symphony is considered largely a matter of the fitness of the creation as a whole in terms of balance, symmetry, repetition, and so on, as aspects of musical form. But he will be limited by the knowledge that his judgment is personal and may not have general validity.

This is, of course, true of the performer, the composer, and the listener in music. But none of those who have a critical attitude will deny the usefulness of analysis and specific evaluation of details which serve the total purpose. That is exactly the position of the scientist in music, except that he proceeds in the opposite order from the composer and the painter. They start with the total atmosphere and work down into details, whereas he starts with details in the artistic creation and reconstructs them into larger parts.

Let us describe as briefly as possible the procedure in the measurement of beauty in the laboratory. For this we may take again as an example that aspect of beauty in the cross section of a tone which we speak of as spectrum, or, musically, the timbre of the tone. These methods will apply in principle to all other types of measurement of esthetic value.

BASIC REQUIREMENTS FOR EXPERIMENTATION IN THE PSYCHOLOGY OF MUSICAL ESTHETICS

The first and foremost qualification is that the experiment should be set so that it conforms with the universally recognized basic principles of all applied science described in Chapter 4. These are implemented by observation of the *duodekalog* of principles set forth in the same chapter. All these conditions are complied with in the foregoing measurements of the tonal spectrum as a factor in tone quality. Failure on any of these fundamental requirements would immediately be recognized as a source of error in the basis for judgment.

Expert observers or judges. When the tone is exhibited as a performance score in the form of a spectrum or when the tone is heard under controlled and defined conditions as from the tone generator, it may be experimented with intensively by securing the systematic judgments of judges whose competence is the highest obtainable. This will limit our conclusions to persons of this type of maturity, personality, and training. But such judges are likely to give the most stable opinions.

The judgments will, of course, pertain to emotional values (for example, "I like this better than that" in two comparable situations), but the judgments must be made with an attitude of logical appraisal and with a feeling, "I can give my reasons." This is facilitated by fractionating the experiment so that the judgment is restricted to one isolated specific factor at a time— for example, is this p pure tone more agreeable than this f tone, other things being equal? Ordinarily it is well to have a variety of competent judges in order to make the decisions as generally applicable as possible. The same type of procedure may be followed for any homogeneous group representing a specific age, stage of training, or culture level.

The principal mark of a competent judge of esthetic value is that, in a situation which is experimentally controlled, he can give the reason for his judgment. Witness the judgment about a soft and a loud pure tone, or a specific consonance and dissonance. This ability to discuss the reason for the judgment facilitates the attainment of unanimity of judgments under the same conditions.

It is evident, of course, that in placing confidence in esthetic judgments, the first consideration is, "How competent is the judge? The experimenter? The artist?" In the second place, we must take into account the fact that what is beautiful to one person may not be beautiful to another, for a number of ascertainable reasons. What is beautiful to a person in one mood may not be beautiful in another. What is beautiful in one situation may become ugly in another.

Statistical reliability. The judgments must be countable, and they must be so taken that statistical reliability may be established for repeated judgments and judgments of individuals and a group. Particular care must be taken to avoid "halo" judgments, that is, the coloring of a judgment by overlapping general feelings.

The systematic arrangement of situations. If, for example, the value of the location of formants is the object of experiment, a sufficient number of situations must be created so that as many varieties in location as are likely to prove musically significant are represented.

Beyond these fundamental requirements, the experimenter must be alert to the elements of disturbing factors, both subjective and objective. He must repeat the experiment as often as necessary to secure reasonable reliability, and he must establish validity for the experiment by showing that it is a factor which operates in actual music.

Theory. The esthetic experiment proceeds on some hypothesis. It may be a well-recognized historical theory, or it may be a mere hunch or feeling for which there seems to be reasonable validity. To experiment without hypotheses would be a sheer waste of time. With a given spectrum before him, the trained scientist or musician proceeds on certain assumptions, for example, that there is beauty in certain kinds of richness of tone, that there are different kinds of beauty in a high tone and in a low tone, in a soft tone and in a loud tone, in a smooth tone and in a rough tone, in certain vowel qualities, etc. Glancing at the spectrum, the trained eye sees instantly which of these qualities are present or absent, and the esthetic values can be named offhand. In the same manner the specialist in acoustics is now familiar with a large number of physical principles, of combinations of partials, mutual enhancement of partials, inhibition of one partial by another, methods and limits of audibility, and methods and limits of tone production. He looks at a specimen spectrum in the light of his knowledge of all such variables, thereby facilitating his judgment and giving it more permanent value.

But one of the experimenter's first interests is to submit each of his assumptions to experiment and limit its application in terms of the many variables involved in each. For example, take a pure tone. The beauty of a pure tone depends upon the role it plays in relation to the theme, the performer, the instrument, and the frequency with which it occurs. In the flute, the pure tone is desirable, but in most of the orchestral instruments it is not. In the voice of the coloratura singer the pure tone has a charm, but in the contralto or the bass it does not. Granting that the experimenter or musician has a score or more of such clearly defined and familiar principles, when he comes to apply each of them he learns to take into account many clearly demonstrable conditions limiting the esthetic value of a pure tone. This is a process of classification which underlies economy and coherence in all observation and thinking. When a general principle is once established, it may be carried forward as a unit, making it unnecessary to verify it in terms of parts each time it is to be used. This is the way esthetic values have been determined historically in the musical profession, and the orchestra conductor is perhaps the peer of artists in making critical judgments about such musical values.

The laboratory experimenter, under favorable conditions, starts with knowledge of such ratings of musical values, but he carries them one step further by varying the elements in the situation one at a time while all other factors are kept constant.

Just as a scientific fact once reliably established does not need to be re-investigated, so an esthetic fact adequately defined and rated does not need to be rerated on operational principles. The competent judge of beauty in music has a large and ever-increasing kit of such established facts which vastly shorten his process of dealing with new hypotheses or possibilities.

Experimental control. For the reason stated in the foregoing paragraph, the experimenter tries to set up a situation in which as many of these variables as possible are either eliminated or kept constant. For example, in judging the relative types of value of beauty in the spectrum, he selects two spectra for comparison. These either may be selected from actual music and reproduced in their full setting, or they may be produced experimentally. The experimenter then selects the best psychologically and musically trained observers available and lets them vote their preferences independently, repeating the trials as long as necessary until the unanimous verdict, or at least a majority verdict, is reached. The larger the number of judges and the greater their competence, the greater will be the stability in their joint decision.

Take, as an example, two vowel tones in the spectrum, the *oo* and the *ee*. The first question which may arise is, "Which of these vowels has the greater musical resourcefulness?" By repeating the trial, taking into account conditions which determine the relative esthetic value, foundations are laid for a statement of when, why, and to what extent the *oo* quality is superior to the *ee* quality. Having mastered the technique and having determined the principal factors which condition desirability, we may take a dozen or more vowel qualities and compare each one in turn with every other one. By this method, known as paired comparison, we can determine the order of rank for vowel quality in timbre under known specific conditions.

In making such judgments we may use actual vowels as sung by recognized artists in musical situations. This, as we have seen, is the natural history method; that is, we take actual samples from musical art or musical nature and submit them to analysis in their actual musical setting. Another procedure is to produce the tones experimentally according to specifications as in Chapter 8, and to verify and amplify the judgments produced by the natural history method. This is the method of the physical sciences as illustrated in Chapter 8. It was shown that any desired spectrum or series of spectra can be set up on the tone generator, kept constant, and repeated at will.

The outstanding thing demonstrated by experimentation of this kind is that beauty in music cannot be defined adequately in terms of any single principle. There is no absolute beauty; everything is relative. There is not one principle of beauty, but hundreds and, if we penetrate far enough, perhaps thousands. The situation is analogous to that of the traveler viewing the landscape. He exclaims, "How beautiful," meaning the net result of all operating factors. But when a scientist looks into the structure of this beauty, he finds thousands of elements, and endless variety of color, form, and perspective. A few years ago an experiment was started at Lake Tahoe in which landscape artists analyzed the beauty of this resort. On the basis of these reports, a list of things which should be seen and felt was posted. This constituted a scientific effort to teach park visitors to see more appreciatively.

Such is the function of the critical student of music. He identifies features in the musical object and shows students and lovers of music the existence of them. He realizes fully, however, that what each one will perceive or feel in that specific factor depends upon who and what he is.

Chapter 16

BEAUTY AS A FUNCTION OF MUSICAL IMAGERY

Do you live in a tonal world? If it were adequately measurable and I were limited to a single index to musical talent, I would take the record of natural capacity for tonal imagery. However, on account of the demands for objectivity, current psychology has given only slight attention to this exceedingly important factor. Let us see what the image means to the musician.

THE TONAL IMAGE

An inferior musician can hear and perform without conscious use of tonal imagery; in that case he remembers, images, or creates music in terms of names, concepts, or analogies for the different elements of a tone. A real musician, on the other hand, has the ability to reconstruct the tone in accurate detail in the form of memory images. He can imagine, compose, and hold up for detailed and objective scrutiny the tonal situation which he wishes to create. Between these two extremes, among those who begin training for music, we find a normal distribution of the ability to retain, relive, and create music without the presence of the physical sound, entirely in terms of the mental image.

There are many psychologists who claim that they never have the experience of a tonal image. There are others who maintain that their tonal images may be practically as realistic and complete as the actual perception in the presence of the physical tone. And between these two extremes, there are

_____

Based on Marie Agnew, "The Auditory Imagery of Great Composers," The Iowa University of *Studies in Psychology,* 1922, Vol. VIII, 279–287.

psychologists, taken as typical of scientific men, who range in ability about a mode showing much lower rating than the mode for musicians. This may mean one or both of two things:

First is the fundamental fact that the musical mind is born with this talent and becomes interested and active in music by natural selection. Second, the musician, living persistently in tonal experiences, cultivates this ability, whereas the scientist gravitates toward a career in which visual experiences are more dominant. The psychological fact remains, however, that the degree of possible development depends upon the degree of the inherited talent, and this degree varies greatly among normal individuals. To good musicians the auditory image is so commonplace and conspicuous that they take it for granted, just as they take for granted the fact that they can see red, taste sour, or hear a tone when it is physically present. As a result they seldom give the pupil systematic training in the critical use of images.

Let us ask again: What does ability in tonal imagery mean in actual music? In the first place the image has the same four elements as the perception, namely, pitch, loudness, time, and timbre—or, in their complex forms, melody, harmony, rhythm, volume, and sonance or tone quality. Sensitivity to each of these may be inherited and developed in a dominant way so that one musician lives more in a world of time and rhythm, another in the realm of dynamic expression, another dominantly in the consciousness of tone quality.

Second, it is perfectly clear that the degree to which a person can accumulate past experiences of a particular tonal characteristic in reproducible images is an index to the degree in which he can scrutinize his present performance in relation to these experienced goals, can create new modes of expression in his voice or instrument, and can master the tonal structure in creative music. Musical thinking is essentially the manipulation of images, of pitch, loudness, time, and timbre in various degrees of the present experience and moreover, most important of all, the emotional quality of remembered music is contingent upon the realism of the image present.

Third, this ability affects also the hearing of tones. Perception of tone is essentially an act of reconstruction in terms of past experiences; and if these come only in verbal form, they will be correspondingly empty of esthetic discrimination.

If the public music school instructor who deals with young students has a clear conception of the role of tonal imagery and can evaluate it to some degree, he can understand in large part the success or failure and the likes and dislikes of the students, and he can guide them more intelligently in their musical endeavors.

The best available test of tonal imagery is subjective and therefore requires some skill in administration, with due allowance made for lack of objectivity. Nevertheless, the tonal imagery test is serviceable and should be a part of the routine in any attempt to analyze musical talent, whether the test is used formally or informally. There are many ways in which such tests are made in the laboratory. I have treated this subject fully in a chapter of my book, *Psychology of Musical Talent*. This test as set forth there is hopefully intended to be of great value to music teachers, in the interest both of self-orientation and of evaluating the test for use with students. The test there given is in terms of the vividness of the image, and ratings are made on the scale from 0 to 6, in which 0 means no mental image, and 6 an image as complete as the actual perception. The competent teacher can extend this type of rating into specific details, in each of the various elements that can be imaged.

A constructive approach is to take the matter of phrasing, and ask the student to play over a phrase mentally in anticipation of the interpretation that he is to give on the piano or other instrument, until he has settled definitely what is to be his personal interpretation. Then ask him to play it and replay it, giving that particular phrasing. This will involve, to some extent, the modulations he has anticipated in each of the four factors. The competent music teacher can discuss this interpretation in such a way as to reveal the essential features in the anticipatory creation.

ASSOCIATED IMAGERY

The issue which comes to the front here is of course that of program music, but that has been so thoroughly debated pro and con that it is not necessary to go further into the controversy. However, I shall consider a much more fundamental issue of which program music is merely an extreme example. I refer to the fundamental psychology of perception and feeling which pertains to associated imagery.

Every impression which comes into the mind tends to result in a response, whether overtly expressed or merely operating in the subconscious. When I hear a fire siren a panorama of the town flashes into my mind, and I wonder about the location, development, and danger of the fire, its implications and the ways of combating it. The siren is merely a cue which touches off a much more elaborate thinking process.

When a friend suddenly appears and says, "Hello, Carl," there rises up the story of our past acquaintance, our good times and our bad times, our mutual dependents, and the friends with whom we have been associated. In short, even within the first few seconds after the two-word greeting, a vast panorama of the history of our past associations looms up before me with corresponding feelings of appreciation or regret.

In this, two psychological principles operate instantaneously. The first is that the response comes as if it were the response to all the elements of sense—sight, hearing, taste, smell, touch, and motor tendencies—all the senses contributing to my identification of this friend. The other is the fact that this total picture is immediately projected into the past, giving meaning to the intimate greeting.

Or as another illustration, the first time I saw the famous picture of Queen Louise in the Cologne Gallery, I fell into a sort of ecstasy, forgetful of self and yet myself acting in the situation in which she is represented as saying, "I would rather throw myself into the hands of death than into the arms of Napoleon." It aroused all my feelings of appreciation for her noble stand, it stirred my fighting instincts as if I were there ready to risk my life in her defense. There flashed through my mind the history of the period through which she lived. The mounting of the picture is magnificent, a single picture on a large wall with a maroon background. It is, of course, a masterpiece in color and form. But these things were not uppermost in my mind. It was the real living Queen Louise that came to me as I faced her.

Parallel examples in music are countless. Today there are martial music, songs of love, of suffering and sacrifice, and musical dramatizations of many situations. In all cases it is the music that touches off the emotional response, but the listener pays little attention to the detailed structure, the elements of beauty or ugliness in the music. To him, the music is but the cue arousing a rich and vibrant emotional life. Is there beauty in the favorite tunes of the Army and Navy? Call it what you will, there is certainly tremendous power; and the power is not in the music itself but in the associated imagery, the total living situation which it evokes.

"Drink to Me Only with Thine Eyes," as played on an instrument, carries musical beauty. The instrument transmits no words, but the tune brings back the words from memory, clothed in our dramatic self-revelation, self-expression, and reliving of those situations in the personal experience which might be associated or suggested. The beauty of the tune and the harmony is something in itself, but the esthetic glow which goes with it when it is genuinely appreciated pertains to the realistic personal experience which it brings to life.

Experiments have shown repeatedly that beautiful musical sketches, such as the *Moonlight Sonata,* come to the listener not primarily in terms of the historical setting of the composition. The movement may dramatize personal feelings which were as remote from the original objective setting in the mind of the composer as day is from night, and a corresponding variety of titles could be effective for naming this masterpiece as descriptive music.

There is another psychological factor which comes into operation here. It has been expressed in the aphorism "When you listen, you hear what you are." The same is true about what we see and what we do. This has been adequately described psychologically in terms of the reaction of the painter, the philosopher, the farmer, the sportsman, the scientist and others, each viewing the same natural scene, the wooded hillside on the edge of a beautiful lake at sunset. It was customary, years ago, to call the principle operating here *apperception,* which means that the new impression is set in our past total experience. It is not limited to seeing, but includes the arousal of instinctive responses, the flash-like dramatization involving thought, feeling, and action of the organism as a whole. The heartbeat is accelerated, the perception flows in fancy, and there is forgetfulness of self.

The highly cultivated musical critic or the musical esthete may pride himself on his critical insight or his absolute feeling of response. But upon self-observation both will confess that their minds wandered away from the strictly musical aspects and went about gathering meaning in live situations which were evoked irresistibly in great promiscuity by the musical sounds.

This is one of the reasons why, at bottom, all arts are one. It makes little difference whether we see, touch, taste, or eat a beautiful apple. The first instantaneous impression of the apple carries all these aspects in one. There is a unifying co-operation of all the senses, not only in perception but in the memory, imaginings, thoughts, and actions. This aspect of musical values would justify a central chapter in musical esthetics under the heading "The Power of Music." We can trace beauty in the individual tone, the measure, the phrase, the rhythm, the form, and the countless other structural aspects of music. But, far more important is the fact that the beauty of music lies in the response that it elicits.

To sum up, then, we can say that the largest and most vital part of music is not in immediate perception or apprehension and feeling for the art object as performed, but in the extension of this through strictly musical inner images which enrich and embellish the perception at the moment, and, even more, in the images of creative imagination which take the wings of phantasy with unlimited dramatic license and carry the music far beyond the realms of the actual message from composer or performer. To that we add that these images of memory and imagination are not restricted to the music proper but attach most significantly to the live impulses in our own personal experiences which are enacted, in a skeletal way, by the music so that they revive the total personality through memory images and extend this personality as a personal implementation of the music.

Chapter 17

BEAUTY AS A FUNCTION OF MUSICAL INTELLIGENCE

ANALYSIS OF MUSICAL INTELLIGENCE has been a bogey of the musical profession, the butt for scurrilous remarks, and an occasion for exhibiting general ignorance about the nature of intelligence. Here we must face the poser: Are musicians, as a class, intelligent? Let us consider this question from three points of view: (1) Why has the question arisen? (2) What is intelligence? (3) How do musicians rate?

THE ISSUE

The question has arisen as a result of a number of outstanding aspects of the musical situation. We may outline these aspects as follows:

Musical education. Until recently, musical education has been narrow, formulated, and controlled from an artistic point of view alone. This has been regarded as necessary because the highest achievements in music have been gained often through the sacrifice of other education. It is illustrated in the character of music scholarship, music teachers, musical degrees, and musical leadership. The nonmusical world has, therefore, made the pronouncement that musicians as a class do not get the privilege of an intellectual life, do not develop sympathies with science, history, or philosophy, or marked ability in these fields. In this there is a large element of truth; but the situation is being redeemed by the modern restoration of music to a legitimate place in the academic curriculum such as it had in ancient Greece.

Adapted from *Music Educators Journal,* March 1938, and R. Seashore and Gross, *Journal of Applied Psychology.*

The esthetic attitude. The lifework of the musician is creative art. He lives in a world of images, imagination, fiction, and fancy, as contrasted with the rest of the population which, supposedly, lives in a world of facts and objects. This is to a certain extent necessary and commendable, but there is danger of its counting against intelligent behavior.

Poetic intuition. Insofar as a musician exhibits insight and learning, he tends to develop a life of poetic intuition. It is generally admitted that great poets express profound truths which often transcend the realms of science or philosophy. These truths are reached through inspiration, and they are expressed in figurative language, the effectiveness of which depends upon the outsider's ability to put himself into the artistic mood and to give reality to the imaginative revelation. Insofar as this is to a certain extent true of the musician, it may be justly regarded as an indication of his superior understanding of some part of the world in which he lives. It tends to make him lonely and to capitalize his feeling of superiority as the keeper and master of great artistic truths.

Life of feeling. Musicians as a class are of the emotional type. Their job is to play upon feeling, to appreciate, to interpret, and to create the beautiful in the tonal realm. To be successful, the musician must carry his audience on a wave of emotion often bordering on ecstasy. While this involves intelligence and intelligent action, the medium through which he works is feeling, not factual material objects or abstract philosophies. This, again, is to a large extent necessary and commendable, for the musical mind comes into the world with a hereditary bent in this direction.

Social detachment. As a result of the above four situations, the musician is often found to be impractical, unadapted to business, industry, or logical pursuits which have social significance. He specializes so highly in emotions, both for arousing group responses and in managing his own affairs, that he becomes the butt of criticism from those who regard themselves as successful in practical life. This is one of the penalties of specialization; it should be borne with patience but hardly with pride.

Musical prodigies. It is a well-known fact that some children are born with a flair for one-sided development which results in the astonishing exhibitions of certain types of musical skill, entirely unsupported by ordinary intelligence, reason, or ability to make practical adjustments. History reveals records of musical prodigies who, from the point of view of intelligence, are correctly classified as morons. They are found not only in institutions for the feeble-minded, but in all society, even that of the successful public entertainers. These are sports. Although rare, they throw much light on the matter of musical talent and the marvelous resources which nature exhibits for self-expression.

Musical genius. We speak of a musical *prodigy* when music exhibits itself as a spontaneous outbreak in the life of the child and results in exceptional achievement. We speak of musical *genius* when the same type of spontaneous exhibition is carried to a higher plane, even beyond that usually obtainable by the most highly educated. While the term genius may be applied to a life developed in balanced proportions, as that of Paderewski, the most conspicuous geniuses of music have been one-sided, unbalanced, and impractical. Such geniuses are likely to exhibit technical skill in performance, but it rarely appears at the creative level. They live a life of isolation which often brands them as lacking in common intelligence, in spite of the fact that their achievements are superintelligent.

Temperament. All the above characteristics seem to come to a focus in musical temperament which may be characterized as a life of impulse and feeling, extreme sensitivity, and capacity for a high degree of specialization. It frequently results in frictions and clashes with the established order. The musical temperament is essential to the musical life, but it is often cultivated artificially. Most of the opprobrium attached to it results from this affectation which may penetrate into every aspect of the musical life. Jastrow, in his *Qualities of Men,* gives a masterly analysis of this problem.

THE NATURE OF MUSICAL INTELLIGENCE

In answer now to the primary inquiry, it is necessary for us to ask: What constitutes musical intelligence? There is great diversity of opinion as to the meaning of intelligence. There are scores of definitions and terms, each of which represents some more or less limited aspect of the function. According to Stoddard and Wellman's most recent analysis, a person is intelligent to the extent that he is given habitually to behavior which is characterized by: (1) difficulty, (2) complexity, (3) abstractness, (4) economy, (5) adaptiveness to goal, (6) social value, and (7) emergence of originals. Let us apply these criteria to the intelligent behavior of the musician.

Difficulty. All intelligent behavior pertains to the solving of problems, not only the problems in abstract, logical situations, but all sorts of problems in daily life which pertain to effective adjustments. The capacity, will, and persistence shown in attacking difficult problems is a mark of intelligence. As a rule, the more intelligent a person is, the higher the degree of difficult problems he is ready and willing to tackle.

Complexity. A problem may be difficult but simple. The ability, willingness, and success in dealing with problems of increasing complexity through sustained deliberation are marks of intelligence.

Abstractness. The successful solution of problems of increasing difficulty and complexity is characterized by the ability to deal with them in abstract symbols, ordinarily spoken of as concepts and judgments in the act of reasoning.

Economy. The ability to accomplish the most mental work in the least time is a mark of intelligence. Intelligent behavior is not a matter of trial and error; it consists in the economic and logical utilization of insight resulting in premises based upon previous experience.

Adaptiveness to goal. Seeing the problem, anticipating the solution, and adhering to the blueprint, figuratively speaking, are marks of intelligent behavior.

Social value. Limiting the pursuit of problems to those which have social value is a mark of intelligent behavior which is distinguished from equally difficult, complex, abstract, economic, and planned activities in all degrees of insanity or irrational behavior.

The emergence of originals. The discovery of new and fundamental truths by a process which is verifiable is the highest achievement of intelligent behavior.

INTELLIGENCE AS A TALENT FOR COMPOSING

Gross and Robert Seashore have contributed interesting experimental evidence on this issue. They took three hundred students of composition, within the larger Chicago area, who were studying composition seriously. Each student was asked to submit ten original melodies of from eight to sixteen bars each. Then six professional musicians were asked to rate these in order of merit. From this order of merit, two groups were selected: the ten best and the ten poorest students. Next, the co-operation of ten professional composers well known for their published and performed compositions was secured. Thus three groups of subjects were obtained: (1) the leading composers, (2) the ablest students, (3) the poorest students of composition. Each member of these three groups was then subjected to a series of experiments, of which I shall mention only those that have a direct bearing on intelligence in composition.

As a measure of a type of intelligence that seemed appropriate, the Seashore and Eckerson's vocabulary test, which is well standardized, was used. They chose this on the assumption that words are names for concepts that the individual knows and that the number of concepts the individual commands is an index to the scope of his intelligence. In these tests it was found that the professional composers averaged in the ninth decile, which is the next to the highest decile according to norms for university students. The successful students of composition averaged in the eighth decile, and the inferior students in the second decile.

Bearing in mind that composition is not primarily a verbal subject and that musicians are herein compared in general intelligence rather than in musical intelligence with a selected group in the total population, we find these figures unusually significant. The trained musicians would of course rank higher in musical intelligence than in this type of general intelligence. The successful composer, whether professional or student, ranks high in general intelligence. The rather shocking showing for the poorer students indicates that parents and teachers may well take general intelligence into account in guiding music students to or away from composition.

The same three groups were also given the six Seashore *measures of musical talents*. It has been shown repeatedly that in the general population the correlation between these basic musical capacities and general intelligence is low, which means that these capacities are not in any significant degree an evidence of intelligence. This was here confirmed.

Chapter 18

THE MUSICAL TEMPERAMENT

TELL A MUSICIAN that he is temperamental, and he will take offense. Yet, perhaps the thing in his personality of which he is most proud is the possession of a musical temperament. This characteristic inconsistency has a basis in the psychological fact that the exhibition of artistic temperament frequently leads to attitudes and actions which the rest of the world may criticize and view with amusement. On the other hand, without the possession of an artistic temperament, the finest expressions of musicianship would perhaps be impossible.

Many persons who pass as musicians are neither temperamental nor musical. A great many of those who ply the art of music do not have musical minds in any basic sense. Their art consists of certain skills built into a purely matter-of-fact organism. I therefore see no reason why people in the musical world who do not show any artistic temperament have any reason to boast of the fact.

I have delved into biography and autobiography of great musicians with an eye toward discovering the outstanding mental characteristics of a great musician. As a rule, the literature on this subject is emotional and unscientific, yet the psychologist can glean from it certain analyses which may be made fundamental in building a scientific psychology of the musical temperament. Let me here name merely a few characteristics which I find prominent in the great musicians.

PHYSIOLOGICAL IRRITABILITY

The highly gifted musician is usually sensitive to sound stimuli, because he has inherited a genetic constitution which is

Enlarged from *Music Educators Journal,* March 1939.

anatomically and physiologically exceptionally responsive to sound. In other words, quite apart from consciousness of sound or thought of music, his physical organism responds to acoustic stimuli of all kinds, keeping nerve and muscle in a state of tension. This tends to create a state of unrest and irritability. Without leading to actual hearing, it may arouse associations of a dreamlike or dramatic nature which may play a large role in the conscious life. It may create a state of well-being and happy associations, or perhaps more frequently, a sense of irritation and emotional eruptions. The sounds may come from a squeaking chair, the sizzling of a kettle, the song of a bird, the cry of an infant. Most frequently sounds affecting the organism in this way are inconspicuous in the environment; but they may often be strong, as, for instance, the rattling of a train or the chattering of a crowd. The musician may not become conscious of these, although he may be physiologically irritated.

TONAL SENSITIVITY

All great musicians are highly sensitive to sound in all its elements. They respond to musical sounds in three ways. First, they make a definite critical discrimination naturally. Second, the recognition of tonal elements or complexes always tends to be affective, arousing responses of attraction or repulsion. Third, these discriminations carry musical meaning. In other words, the great musician hears fine distinctions in tones, he likes or dislikes them, and he tends to give them musical meaning.

With the musician the issue is not so much true pitch, smooth dynamics, metronomic time, or uniform tone quality. His interest is in the artistic deviation from these, because his entire art lies in the capacity for artistic deviation from the true, the rigid, the uniform. In judging or expressing these artistic deviations under fine control, he works in part according to rules, but in larger part to satisfy his own emotional ear for the moment and to express his individuality in interpretation. This is, of course, a finer achievement than mere acuity for these tonal elements.

Thus, in all the variants, combinations, and modulations of pitch, loudness, time, and timbre, the musician hears, feels, and gives meaning to subtle distinctions. This capacity is inborn and is in itself enough to make the musician different from other people. At this level, temperament shows itself in exceedingly fine responsiveness to tones which may be a matter of utter indifference to the unmusical. This is the first evidence of a musical temperament.

THE TONAL IMAGE

All genuine musicians have superior auditory imagery, that is, they can recall a tone so realistically and objectively that it can be scrutinized in all its detail just as in actual hearing. The composer of any consequence conceives his themes and carries out details of composition without access to physical tone in instruments. He first hears mentally in realistic auditory imagery the thing he attempts to set down on paper. Therefore to interrupt his musical thinking, whether it be in the act of formal composition, snatches of musical thinking, or musical reveries, is just as serious an interruption to him as if it came during his actual playing before an audience. This gives him the reputation of being distrait and oblivious to elements in the environment which to others seem significant. In other words, the genuine musician is engaged in music a great deal more through the avenue of vivid memory and creative imagination than in actual hearing or performance.

In hearing actual music as well as in performing, this imagery supplements the physical stimulus and furnishes a sort of matrix or setting which personalizes the overt tones in an artistic interpretation. The musician has extraordinary resources for pleasure in the reliving and in the mental creation of sound which the nonmusical mind does not have. He really lives in a dissociated tonal world by himself, where, in tense moments, he may approach a state of ecstasy. Therefore, he may be annoyed because his pleasures or displeasures are not shared by others. This leads to impatience, fastidiousness, and eccentricity often recognized as part of the musical temperament.

ARTISTIC LICENSE

To the trained musical individual sounds heard are not the same as they are to the average listener. The hearing of pitch, loudness, time, and timbre is not in the ratio of $1:1$ with the physical sound, but always runs into artistic analysis, and interpretation with artistic license. The musical interval, the dynamic phrasing, the rhythm, and the tone quality are all heard in this way. The pitch value varies with the quality of the sound. Time may be a substitute for stress and vice versa. A subjective rhythm is richer and far more realistic than the physical rhythm. The quality of tone is heard in relation to its musical meaning. To the musician, the hearing is not so much a question of true pitch, formal accent, temporal rhythm, or vowel quality as it is a matter of musical balance and a recognition of artistic deviation from the true. Meticulously exact performance of a Bach score would be musically intolerable. Notes are frail symbols. The performer must interpret even the shortest rhythm measure or single note value. Thus, while fine sensory discrimination in all the aspects of sound is essential for correct hearing and tone production, the ability to play with artistic power, producing artistic balance and deviation from the rigid is more essential. In this artistic balance and deviation, the musician may be guided by certain artistic rules, but his direct emotional interpretation is far more significant. In this interpretation lies individuality.

Thus, in all the variants, combinations, and modulations of pitch, loudness, time, and timbre, the musician hears, feels, and gives meaning to fine and subtle distinctions, many of them quite divergent from the physical tones. At this level, temperament shows itself in exceedingly fine responsiveness to tones which may be a matter of utter indifference or impossibility to the unmusical. This capacity is largely inborn, both in the way of sensitvity to sound and a general nervous, if not neurotic, disposition, and is in itself enough to make the musician different from other people. Artistic license as a medium for self-expression is, therefore, clear evidence of a musical temperament.

THE ESTHETIC MOOD

The musician is in search of the beautiful and therefore he responds unfavorably to the ugly. His professional life is, in the main, emotional as distinguished from the intellectual life of the scholar in other fields or the action patterns of men of affairs. Whether he is a virtuoso, a creator of music, or a director, he is working on emotions through emotions. The musician tries to recreate for his listeners the feelings with which he himself is imbued. He lives so intensely and habitually in this activity that he becomes recognized as highly and persistently emotional. This extreme emotionality in the musician's daily work places him in contrast to the matter-of-fact mind. We say of the intensely artistic person in action that he burns himself out. The emotional life is expensive and flitting; it flashes and explodes, and it is in danger of running out of control.

This emotionality tends to transfer not only to other forms of art but to everyday matters, such as money and clothes, sometimes evidenced by a Bohemian flair. The musician may spend all his wages on payday and starve the rest of the month in utter complacence, and withal his life tends to be set at high tension.

EXHIBITIONISM

There is an accretion to the musical temperament in the form of a hierarchy of defense reactions which may be characterized as exhibitionism. The musical mind is on a leash, as it were, trying to drag more or less resistant and incapable minds into its own beautiful emotional life, and the musician feels the drag of the resistance. Therefore, he becomes impatient, and he resorts either to withdrawal from the world or the opposite: display. To the musician, countless means of personal display justify their end, the glorifying of his noble art. Therefore, we see the musical temperament in this artistic form in the manner of living, eating, dress and sleeping, and in the demand for hero worship.

SYMBOLISM

The main function of the great musician is to make his music symbolic. He must take the listener out of the humdrum attitudes of life, through the avenue of musical feeling, into a state of abandon and obliviousness to material surroundings and facts. The devices of program music give the musician only meager aid. His function is to enable the listener to live the art emotionally while the musician lives it symbolically. In this respect the musician differs from the sculptor and the painter who, while cultivating this symbolic attitude, are held closely to the necessity of utilizing objective realities. It is not easy for the musician to take himself out of this mood. Whether he talks of music or business, the symbolizing habit is constantly pressing in upon him. Through his mastery of the symbolic life, the musician feels rich, exclusive, powerful, and self-contained; to some people this seems queer.

PRECOCITY

Since, as a rule, the musically gifted are proportionately precocious, they may begin early in childhood to realize their peculiar gift for performance, musical appreciation, and individual interpretation. This tendency to become a prodigy is inherent in musical precocity, but the tendency makes the child conspicuous, and it interferes with his adaptation to the behavior of the common man. Musical precocity leads to a specialization and an intensification of those skills which result in approbation and hero worship on the one hand, and ridicule on the other.

What, then, is the musical temperament? It resembles the behavior found in all artistic pursuits; it arises partly from heredity and partly from training and environment. Musical temperament includes high sensitivity, dominant ear-mindedness, emotional strain, lopsided education, pursuit of esthetic goals, leadership, hero worship, and often a forced precocity.

This type of analysis could be carried further, but the four items mentioned should be sufficient to show that artistic temperament in a musician is an essential gift demanded by the nature of the art. The temperament may be good or bad, inborn or cultivated, genuine or simulated, and often it is the cause of personal eccentricities. Nevertheless, we should be eternally grateful to the Muses for their great gift: the potentially good musical temperament.[1]

---

[1] For further analysis of musical temperament, see Chapter V in the author's *Why We Love Music*, Oliver Ditson Company, Philadelphia, 1941.

Chapter 19

ARTISTIC TALENT

THE GROWING RECOGNITION of the nature and significance of individual differences is one of the achievements of modern science. The conception of talent is therefore coming to play an important role in education and practical life. Educators are taking into account the natural endowments of the child in the guidance of mental development. Society, industry, and art are becoming alert to the problem of finding and encouraging the individual according to his fitness for the job.

THE RESOURCEFULNESS OF HUMAN NATURE

Selection in the hereditary constitution. At the moment of conception, literally hundreds of thousands of human beings are represented by the sperms available, each in itself a hereditary pattern; but only one survives by entering the ripened ovum. By this mechanism one hereditary organization survives, while thousands which might presumably have been equally complete and competent carriers of family hereditary traits are rejected. Only one of the many thousands of possible variants of the species survives to determine the hereditary constitution of each individual conceived and is a carrier of all that can be transmitted through heredity. Here is the first step in the emergence of the *individual* as different from all other individuals.

Degeneration or destruction of many of the elements in the genetic constitution by forces in the environment of the embryo wreak havoc upon many of the resources of the individual as launched in the germ cell. At birth the resources of the infant are much more restricted than they were in the original hered-

From *School and Society*, 1942, 55, 169–173.

itary endowment. While some elements in the hereditary constitution have been reinforced by favorable conditions, others have been weakened or destroyed by an unfavorable prenatal environment.

Yet, at birth, the normal child is endowed with a marvelously rich constitution in the form of a psychophysic organism more or less ready to function in all aspects of human power. For every organ or element of an organ in the body, there is a mechanism providing for its function and a corresponding tendency for its development.

Environmental reinforcements. At birth, a process of selection and rejection begins, determined in part by the strength or weakness of the inherited trait, but directed mainly by a reinforcing or restricting environment. Only a minute portion of the fabulously rich resources for human development are selected and favored in progressive determination of the personality of the growing child. The law of survival of the fittest here begins to operate.

It would be quite possible, by a process of intensive child development, to favor any one of hundreds of lines of specialization in development, if that were desirable. It would thus be possible to develop, in the normal child, an extraordinary mathematical ability, a fabulous proficiency at a given type of memory, an astonishingly early development of artistic talent and judgment, or the physical power of a contortionist of extraordinary vigor and muscular skill. Within such general fields of human capacity, there are countless lines of specialization which may be selected for development by the sacrifice of other elements in the organism as a whole. Fortunately for the development of the normal child such distorting pressures rarely operate; but, when early talent manifests itself, there is a strong tendency to reinforce it by favorable recognition and opportunity for exercise in a favorable environment.

Environmental restrictions. A more significant factor that regulates talent is of a negative character. The normal child, we may say, has hundreds of thousands of possibilities for personal development; but due to environmental restrictions only a comparatively small number of these "seeds" are given opportunity to root and to come to foliage and fruitage. This is true not only of the very narrow range of outlets in primitive life but also of the higher culture levels. At every turn in the child's environment, there are restrictions upon the exercise of imagination, intelligence, logical memory, emotional adjustment, social adaptation, good taste, and will power.

The value of selection and restriction. Environment is not to be blamed too much because, even for mere survival, a radical process of selection is necessary in order to prevent chaotic and self-destructive conditions arising from attempted overdevelopment. One of the advantages of environmental restriction in development is that it makes it possible for the child to adjust himself to the restricted spheres of life which operate at his culture level or in his racial group.

Take, for example, the advantage of a limited memory. The organism has the capacity for registering every environmental impression made upon it through the senses and every association centrally initiated. But the ability to raise these experiences to the conscious level and to store them in conscious memory would result in instant insanity. It is a blessing that we do not remember everything we hear, see, think, feel, or do. Natural law restricts our conscious memory of those things which have survival value for the life of the individual. This law operates in the selection for survival of all human capacities. It is a beneficent provision of nature that, of all the possible aspects of achievement, only a workable number develop in any one personality that is adjusted to its environment and is not overtaxed by strain or confusion.

In brief, nature preserves the species, *Homo sapiens,* through a wonderfully organized hereditary endowment, the completeness and impartiality of which are guaranteed through the operation of the unconscious forces of life; in no sense do these forces remain subject to the direction of voluntary control by human effort. At birth many of these resources have already been lost, and yet, in the newborn child, the endowment of possibilities for human life is enormously rich and varied. After birth the environment, through conscious effort and, more frequently, through the operation of unconscious forces, selects for investment a comparatively small portion of the individual's natural resources. This selection and specialization of a comparatively limited number of natural resources are conditions for survival and development, especially for the development of the higher human life.

THE NATURE OF TALENT

The normal well-balanced mind is capable of development along countless specialized channels. If there are no hereditary or environmental impediments, extraordinary achievement may be attained, through training and other favorable environmental influences, within any one or more of a wide range of specific patterns of ability.

But if an urge or a spontaneous development occurs early in childhood indicating a favored outlet for mental development, we may speak of this as talent to the extent that it is exceptional. On the other hand, when there is early evidence of marked weakness or the presence of serious impediments for a certain *type* of achievement in a child, or when education and other selective environmental influences are exerted positively, and when marked inhibitions, incapacities, and limitations of various sorts block progress, we may speak of such an individual as untalented.

Since selective development is a condition for achievement, absence of achievement is not in itself an indication of the absence of talent. As a result of the necessary selection and specialization, there are hundreds of potential abilities that a child does *not* develop for each one that he does develop. Absence of achievement is therefore most frequently merely an indication of absence of opportunity. By well-directed experiments it has been shown that the presence of a high order of talent can be discovered in individuals who are not themselves aware of its existence and whose associates have observed no evidence of it. Such individuals are often wrongly dubbed untalented.

We may define talent as the *native capacity for exceptional achievement in various degrees,* and lack of talent as *exceptional native limitations on the possibilities of development in a particular line of achievement.* These two extremes are exceptions to the balanced distribution of capacities in a given population; between these extremes lies the wide range of *average* capacities of the normal child. Such is the normal range and distribution of human talent which may be cultivated by the environment and brought to fruitage through a process of maturation and training.

Qualifications of this definition. The distinctions implied in this definition have far-reaching bearing on the education and the appraisal of the developing individual. We must therefore call attention to certain practical qualifications and clarifications of the issue.

First, the distinction between inheritance and environment, as sources of talent, is made arbitrarily. Necessarily it must be somewhat theoretical, because, when a hereditary trait can be clearly demonstrated, it is already in the stage of being influenced by the environment. For this reason, there is no object in being a staunch defender of either heredity or environment. Everyone must admit that both are factors in the situation; one without the other would lead nowhere.

Second, we must clarify the conception of talent and trait. For example, in talent for poetry, an intricate hierarchy of native forces co-operate; forces such as the natural endowment of creative imagination, natural power of insight and logic, verbal memory, introvert or extrovert tendencies, emotionality, and native or acquired drives. The ability to write poetry is therefore not the exhibition of an isolated talent, and the inheritance of poetic ability is not one talent but a vast complex of native dispositions. This must be borne in mind when we speak of a person as having talent for poetry. Nevertheless, no one would deny that a great poet must be born with a poetic nature —a gift for poetry, however intricate or fragmentary its constitution.

Third, experimental psychology has demonstrated that the magnitude of individual differences in talent is proportional to the specificity of the element of talent selected for observation and measurement. Musicality, for example, involves such a complicated range of activity that important links in capacity may be missing and yet not missed in a social group. But, when we measure a specific factor such as the sense of rhythm, it can be demonstrated that one normal child may have a hundred times the native capacity for rhythm that another has. Yet in the unanalyzed musical situation no such extent of difference can be observed. However, when the trained musician is apprised of the extent of the specific talent he can trace corresponding musical effects in the musical performances.

Fourth, when the hereditarian speaks of the fixity and unchangeability of an inherited trait, he does not imply that each of the conceivable elements entering into its structure is an isolated, independently functioning, and unchangeable factor. He means rather that a demonstrated native gift for poetry, or utter lack of native ability in poetic power, for example, was present before the environment undertook its development. The hereditarian means also that this fact should be recognized under all environmental influences. The educator's neglect of such a gift is like throwing away a precious gem. His ignoring fairly fixed limitations for poetic power is as we should have said a few years ago, like attempting the transmutation of metals. We can now make gold out of lead, but the process is an expensive one which hardly competes with the digging of nature's gold. In other words, native resources count.

Fifth, it follows from these four considerations that the assaying of organic human ore is an exceedingly complicated process which can never be more than a partial isolation, and a measurement of some specific factors in a given talent hierarchy. The experimenter sacrifices wholesale solutions which are relatively meaningless. Instead, he fractionates the task so that the factor under observation can be described, measured, repeated, and given predictive value.

THE SIGNIFICANCE OF TALENT

On the basis of the above-stated conception of talent, we may ask: What significance does its recognition have? And this raises numerous questions for most of which we have only hypothetical answers. In education we have been asking: Does the achievement quotient, AQ, tally with the IQ? And the answers have been numerous in both experiment and theory. We may generalize by saying that, while there is a general tendency for the AQ to correspond with the IQ, there are countless reasons for exceptions, the fundamental fact being that IQ is only one of the factors which determine achievement. Among other factors are the number and quality of facilities for progress in a given line of achievement, degree of competing drives, susceptibility to emotional upsets, the will to work, and the general state of health—which are seldom thoroughly and accurately measured.

While outright prediction before the beginning of training is limited and hazardous, it has great possibilities if it is on both the negative and the positive sides, analytical and progressive and if applied at various stages during development. If, for example, there is available a series of approximate measures of native capacity in the form of a profile, this will have great value in the interpretation of success or failure. If a child has an excellent profile of musical talents in a few of the fundamental and essential qualifications for musicianship, he should be apprised of it and should be encouraged in his musical interests, especially in those directions indicated by the profile. The profile may serve also as a guide for adjusting facilities for growth to the degree and kind of talent, and as a basis for awarding praise or criticism for the devotion and the degree of energy exerted by the individual. On the other hand, a markedly negative profile may prove an adequate basis for the interpretation of failure or the relative paucity of success in proportion to facilities available and energy exerted. In other words, prediction should be progressive and interpretative of both success and failure in all stages of training. Herein lies the principal significance of a talent profile. The profile should never be used in a fatalistic prediction of either success or failure; it should be utilized persistently in the understanding, evaluation, and future direction of success or in the avoidance of failure. Our army has taken full advantage of these tests, particularly in determining the fitness of men for flying duty. Intelligent evaluation of fitness here has saved the lives of many and has saved millions of dollars.

Concerning the measurement of talent, the late George Eastman asserted in relation to the Eastman School of Music: "Knowledge of the existence or nonexistence of talent has saved the school vast sums of money by basing the educational facilities upon the degree of probable presence or absence of capacity for achievement," and he added that "the recognition of this principle has been a means of giving vitality and inspiration to a promising student or relieving the suffering and waste of energies of the nongifted student. Thus it has served not only to protect the institution but, what is far more important, to guide the musical investments of each individual student."

While the concept of talent is of primary significance in education, it is coming to assume a central position in all practical efforts to fit the individual for his job. In these efforts there has been previously an enormous waste of effort because of no clear concept of what constituted talent; improper assignment of credit to heredity and environment; failure to control factors in tests of measurement; limitations and qualifications of the possibilities of prediction; inability to interpret success or failure; lack of a basis for awarding praise or criticism; and inadequate motivation for work.

Chapter 20

MEASUREMENT OF MUSICAL TALENTS

THE SEASHORE MEASURES of musical talents were designed about thirty years ago, and after an approved period they were issued in the form of phonograph records. Since at that time they were drawn from the blue sky without any precedent in that testing field, it is rather remarkable that they remained in extensive use for twenty years without any revision.

REVISION OF THE SEASHORE MEASURES OF MUSICAL TALENTS [*]

During this period a great deal of experimental work has been done in psychological laboratories and in numerous musical situations in the schools, both in this country and abroad. In the revision of the measures effort has been made to review all the literature on the subject critically and to bring experimental procedures in the laboratory up to date, both for the purpose of determining the wisdom in the choice of talents to be measured and for refinement in the technique of measurement. Musicians and scientists who have employed these measures will therefore be interested in knowing the main features of the revision, which are described briefly as follows:

Improved recording. The measures have been recorded by the most recently available technique in the RCA Victor recording studios, as is exemplified in the Red Seal records.

The stimuli. With the now available tone generators on the electric principle, it is comparatively easy to produce tones of

Saetveit, Lewis and Seashore, Revisions of the Seashore Measure of Musical Talents. University of Iowa Press, 1940, p. 62.

specified quality and to control the measurements of pitch, intensity, time, and timbre with precision.

Elimination of the human element. Twenty-five years ago all the stimuli had to be controlled by the human hand. In the present revision, all the four factors which can enter into recording have been controlled mechanically. Stimulus stencils, similar to those of piano-playing records, were prepared so that in the duration of tones and the duration of intervals the absolute and relative intensity and the timbre in pure and complex tones were controlled to a high degree of mechanical precision. Psychophysical principles of perception and discrimination of tone as developed in the laboratories were applied.

Three test series. The revision provides three sets of test material: Series A, for an unselected group, such as the schoolroom class; Series B, for a musical group, such as candidates for membership in musical organizations; and Series C, for most refined measurement in individual testing. The difference in the three series lies in the range covered. Thus, for pitch, Series A has a wide range from 17 vibrations to 2; B, from 8 to 0.5; and for C the conditions are provided for making psychophysical measurements on any single step in the B series of the four basic measures.

Increase in reliability. These three series will, of course, vary in reliability from A to C, with C giving the highest reliability by laboratory methods. The increase in reliability is due largely to the elimination of large increments which have but little functional value. Reliabilities, norms, and other statistical data are furnished in the manual which accompanies the records.

Item analysis. A complete item analysis was made with the preliminary recordings, and different recordings were judged until it was found that each item functioned satisfactorily. In general, the items are arranged in order of difficulty.

The records. There are six measures. Each measure is recorded on one side of a 12-inch (4½-minute) record. Series A consists of three double-faced records, and Series B, of three other double-faced records. For Series C the B records are used. While the A and the B series may be purchased separately, experimenters will usually want the six records so as to be able to adapt the measurement to the three types of testing situations.

Shortening the test. The shortening of the records has been accomplished by placing all the test material for each measure on one side instead of on both sides of the record as in the original. This does not limit the number trials, because each face of the record may be played as often as desired as long as the key is not given out. Thus in most of the records a single playing will give fifty trials; two, one hundred; and three, one hundred fifty, with results as satisfactory as if they had been repeated in actual recordings as in the original. With this shortening, it is feasible to make all the six measurements in any one of the three series in a fifty-minute period when only one playing is given for each record in either the A or the B series; but half-hour periods are recommended.

Choice of measures. Five of the original measures (all except consonance) have been continued on the basis of satisfactory experience. Many other measures could have been added, but in view of the typical testing situations, it seems desirable to hold the number down to the original six.

Consonance has been eliminated in the revision because, after extensive experimentation in the effort to avoid the criticism which is justly leveled at this measure, we have not succeeded in setting up satisfactory conditions for it, although consonance is highly significant in the measurement of musical talent. We have therefore substituted a measure of timbre, which has many elements in common with consonance and has the advantage of being highly adaptable for test purposes. This measure, designed by Dr. Don Lewis in the Iowa Laboratory, is destined to be used for many years on the ground of its high precision in measurement and its evident musical validity.

Significant changes in each measure. For pitch, pure tones having a frequency of 500 are used. For intensity, pure tones in decibel steps are used. For time, duration of the pure tone is substituted for the original time intervals between clicks. In timbre, the harmonic structure of the tone is changed in a complex tone having the same amount of energy in each of the first six partials. The change in timbre is produced by shifting energy from the third partial to the fourth. In tonal memory, the minimum interval of the changed note is a whole tone step instead of a semitone. In rhythm, a short tonal impulse is substituted for a click, and the rhythmic patterns are graded in the order of difficulty.

Quantitative and specific. In accordance with scientific procedure, each measure represents a single and isolated factor which functions in the musical situation. The results are expressed in exactly defined quantitative terms. For pitch, it is frequency; for intensity, the decibel; for time, the one-hundredth of a second; and for timbre, the decibel change in energy of two partials. This feature is in striking contrast to the procedure in tests which deal with undefinable complex situations.

The revision is the joint undertaking of Dr. Don Lewis, Dr. Joseph Saetveit, and the writer, all working in the Iowa Laboratory. For the purpose of guaranteeing stability of the project, the revised measures have been made the property of the psychological laboratory of the University of Iowa with the provision that all earnings from sales shall be used for further experimentation in the area of musical talent. The records were produced in the RCA studios, and they are available with a manual of instructions in all the RCA offices, both in this country and abroad.

VALIDITY IN MEASUREMENT OF MUSICAL TALENT

The validation of tests is usually treated in a simple way by correlating the factor measured against a judgment or another factor without analysis of factors involved. That latter factor is often less reliable than the test itself. There is a tendency to make quantitative correlations without taking into account the operation of numerous potent variables in the conditions involved. A critical analysis often strikingly reveals that mere figures may lie.

The employment of specific and definable measurements, as in the present case, presents favorable opportunities for analysis of the situation. The better the conditions are controlled in an experiment, the easier it is to unravel operating factors. Findings in the conditions here under consideration apply in principle to the validation of tests in general; but the following is an attempt to reveal what sort of factors operate qualitatively in the validation of the measures of musical talents in particular.

Instead of considering all the six measures together, or in turn, let us limit the discussion to one, namely, the sense of pitch, for the purpose of simplifying the problem. The assumption may be made that what is found for the sense of pitch applies in principle to the other five measures in the battery individually, and, to some extent, to the battery as a whole. The principal issues involved are indicated below.

In what respects are these measures to be validated? This question may be answered by recognizing certain principles which clarify the situation.

(1) Each measure is a specific item in itself and must be validated as such; for example, pitch is to be validated not against musicality or musical performance as a whole but only for the role that the sense of pitch plays in the musical situation.

(2) It is not assumed that a good sense of pitch in itself is predictive of musical success. All that we have a right to assume on the positive side is that a person who has a fine sense of pitch ought to be capable of a corresponding control of pitch in musical achievement, other conditions being favorable. Difficulty in pitch intonation may, however, be of purely motor origin.

(3) The measure is most significant in its negative aspect in that, when properly established, a low rating should be taken as a preliminary indication of corresponding difficulties which may be encountered in musical pursuits.

(4) The sense of pitch is a measure of the basic ability to hear pitch. It therefore applies not only to the hearing of

pitch pure and simple but also (though in a diminishing degree) to the hearing of pitch in its complex forms and in its integration with other aspects of tone in music, both in hearing and performance. Pitch discrimination is, of course, a standard unit of measurement in numerous fields of scientific work, and when so used it must be validated against the purpose to be served. In taking this measurement from the laboratory we have called it *measure* in order to indicate that it is something different from paper and pencil testing, and, for the battery, we speak of *measures* in the plural to indicate their individuality. Generically we may, of course, speak of these measures as tests.

(5) Justification for isolating pitch as a factor to be measured lies in the fact that, both from the point of view of physical measurement of the sound wave and the most elementary psychological and musical analysis, pitch is universally recognized as essential to adequate musical hearing. There is therefore no ground for attributing this selection to some person's speculative analysis of the musical mind as a whole, nor for the charge that it represents a species of "faculty psychology" or that it is contrary to the scientific approach to an integrated personality.

(6) These statements apply in principle to each of the six measures in the present battery. The choice of these particular measurements rests in part on relatively low intercorrelations, indicating that they measure different things. It follows that the ranks for the battery should not be averaged as an index to musicality as a whole but should yield a partial profile. Here we see an analogy to the medical procedure in which measurements of blood pressure, temperature, heart action, metabolism, etc., are indications of specific conditions in a state of health; but, to diagnose the case, the physician must take a great many other factors into account. Users of these measures are therefore constantly warned to employ them as specific serviceable aids only in connection with case histories, auditions, and other specific measures and, above all, to employ them with a reasonable modicum of musical insight and common sense before assigning general predictive values to them.

In view of these demarcations, we must refuse to validate these measures against unanalyzed judgments about musical achievement. In the spirit of scientific method in the laboratory we must turn to the more technical analysis of the factors involved for the purpose of gaining insight into the nature of the processes involved, even at the sacrifice of broad generalizations and ultrapractical simplification.

Does the test measure what it purports to measure? This is the first question which might be asked in attempting to validate any test. Pitch discrimination is measured in terms of the least perceptible difference in pitch under relatively optimum conditions. We have come to call this the "sense" of pitch, because it is the basic measurement of capacity for hearing pitch. Whether or not the measurement is valid from this point of view must be determined in terms of the extent to which pitch is isolated and varied for measurement while all other factors are kept constant.

As we have seen, the stimulus is a pure tone at 500 cycles about 40 decibels above the threshold of hearing sound at standard intervals with a duration of 0.6 second. Thus the standard pitch, the timbre, the duration, and the loudness of the tones are kept constant, and measured deviation from the standard pitch is the only variable.

The pitch discrimination varies within a wide range with register, loudness, duration of tone, duration of intervals between tones, timbre, and many other factors. This is particularly true for tones in the actual musical progressions, but the procedure described gives a basic measure in a standardized condition. This standard measure becomes a neutral scale for comparison of individual differences, a point of reference for all of the measures of ability in hearing and use of pitch, and a tool for many other purposes in the actual musical situation. Thus, this phase of validation is answered positively: the test measures what it purports to measure. The accuracy of that measurement is expressed in terms of the coefficient of reliability.

Are individual differences in the sense of pitch of such range as to be significant? It is a general rule that the more specific the measurement of a capacity or ability is, the more exact the measurement will be and the larger will be the individual differences found. This is the reason why we find, for example, that of two equally intelligent persons possessing so-called normal hearing, one may be a hundred times as *pitch sensitive* as the other. The quantitative establishment of such a range of individual differences cannot be seriously questioned. We must judge in terms of analysis of musical situations whether or not they are musically significant. Such features must speak for themselves in answering our question.

Do small differences in pitch function in music? Through the use of phonophotography, we are now able to record in minute detail exactly how pitch is executed for each and every note in vocal or instrumental rendition. If we turn, for example, to a performance score of Lawrence Tibbett's singing of *Drink to Me Only with Thine Eyes* (see Chapter 5), which we may accept as an example of good singing, or the performance score of any other good singer, and follow the graphic tracing of the pitch, we find abundant evidence of the use of fine distinctions in pitch for artistic interpretation. There is artistic deviation from true pitch of various types and in various degrees from the beginning to the end of the selection; and it is through such fine pitch modulations in intonation that the artist reveals individuality in his phrasing. This intonation correspondingly augments or diminishes tonal intervals, and the hearing of the mean pitch imposes the same demand as the hearing of rigid pitch. The modulation of the vibrato is a continuous play upon fine pitch differentiation.

A performance score of this kind becomes a mine of riches if one takes time and knows what to look for. It is the mark of of a good singer that he does not stay on rigid pitch even for a moment; his pitch is flexible, rich in variety of artistic forms, and thus contributes toward beautiful tone quality. The point to be emphasized is that the demand upon a fine sense of pitch lies not in the mere ability to hear or intone in so-called true pitch but primarily in the ability to hear and employ artistic deviations from true pitch. Performance scores for band and orchestral instruments reveal the same principles. We see them in the best refinement in the performance score of the great violinists. If the performer's measured sense of pitch is known, we have here a means of checking its operation in each and all of the numerous types of situations in which artistic effects in pitch function. Correlations between pitch-hearing and pitch-performance can thus be established quantitatively in a great variety of situations.

Is there a direct relation between a person's standard sense of pitch and his functional hearing or performance of pitch in actual music? The notion that small differences in pitch do not function in music arose from the observation that the threshold of pitch-hearing in actual music is much wider than in the standard measure. A person whose sense of pitch is expressed in terms of 0.01 of a tone, for example, may not observe distinctions finer than 0.10 of a tone in the actual musical progression. This is due primarily to the fact that in music there is a quick succession, often of short notes, and there is no time left for a critical judgment of pitch. This fact also gives us a tolerance for a comparatively wide deviation from true or intended pitch in singing and playing.

The significant thing in this situation, however, is that from a great variety of observations a close correlation between a sense of pitch as measured in the standard situation and the same in the musical flow can be observed. Common-sense observation in daily musical life asserts this fact. We say of a musician that he has a fine ear (pitch), and we judge that by the fact that he observes significant facts about pitch both in hearing and performance. If he does not, we say he has a poor ear. No one seems to question that.

Objective proof may come from a variety of sources in experimental evidence. For instance, there is the fact that successful musicians, almost without exception, reveal a fine sense of pitch; that a good or a poor sense of pitch at the beginning of musical education usually predicts correspondingly good or poor progress in the mastery of pitch; that persons with a fine sense of pitch are correspondingly critical in the judgment of pitch performance; that there is a tendency for persons with a fine sense of pitch to succeed with musical instruments that demand it; and that an unsatisfactory sense of pitch frequently accounts for musical failure and discouragement. Scattered objective records on all of these points are available, and any one of the records can be treated statistically if statistical proof is needed. In any such situation the observed fact is that there is a relationship between the measured standard sense of pitch and the functional performance or the ability to discriminate in the musical situation.

Another factor bearing on this issue is that, in actual music, the appreciation of pitch is not so much a conscious discrimination for pitch, note for note, as it is a musical feeling for tonality, the satisfactoriness or unsatisfactoriness in musical feeling. This direct feeling, of course, tends to conform more closely to the standard measure of capacity.

Can the sense of pitch be validated for measurements in fields other than music? Pitch discrimination is a standard psychophysical measurement in laboratories and field activities which deal with acoustic problems of pitch. Thus, it is one of the oldest psychophysical measurements. The measurement has been well standardized, and its principle can be used for a great variety of purposes in purely scientific work. The present form of the measurement is a concession to the need for group measurement and the saving of time. What has been here shown to apply to music has almost exact parallel significance for speech. Comparative psychology employs this measurement in a comparison of sensitiveness to pitch and adjustment to environment among animals. Anthropology employs it as one of the measuring tools which serves as a starting point for a comparison of racial musical traits. In industry it has predictive value analogous to that in music. In all such cases a standard measure must be validated against the purpose which it serves.[1]

---

[1] In World War I the measurement of musical talent assumed military significance. As described in Chapter 34, submarines were located by an acoustic device which depended upon the observer's ability to hear the direction of sound from the submarine in terms of an auditory illusion. The medium was a normal illusion due to binaural phase in hearing, and it was demonstrated that the ability in locating U-boats varied with the degree of possession of certain musical talents for hearing, primarily the sense of pitch, loudness, timbre, and musical memory. The selection of U-boat listeners thus became one of the vital war services.

Can a battery of measures be validated as such? No matter how many members we have in a battery, each remains a specific measure; that is, the technical validation must be made in terms of the factor measured in each one. The more members of basic significance there are in the battery, the larger command of the situation will be given. This is called the *specific theory* of measurement as opposed to the *omnibus theory* which aims to validate the battery against the total situation in musical performance.[2] The adoption of the specific theory limits the usefulness of the battery in predicting musicality as a whole; but the sacrifice is worth while, and this sacrifice is the only possible procedure on scientific grounds. Since the predictive value of the battery depends upon the comprehensiveness with which the battery covers the situation, the more members of basic significance there are, the better. This is particularly true for the analysis of difficulties encountered in musical education.

The question of whether these six measures are enough to be of value in the prediction of musical success is therefore a relative one. As analysis of talents progresses, there will be more and more of such measures, but, even at the best, these measures will be only a partial solution to the problem of prediction, just as there are corresponding numbers of the physician's measurements in the diagnosis of diseases.

In the Stanton report, the validation of the measures themselves is complicated somewhat by the inclusion of an intelligence test in the battery. Stanton's assumption was that the intelligence test was a part of the battery. If, however, anyone wishes to validate against success in musical education the six measures by themselves, or, better still, each measure in turn, the data covering a period of ten years are available. Where the measures are used for the assignment of instruments, selection for group activities, diagnosis of unfavorable conditions for musical education, effective use of capacities in speech, industry, and many other fields, evidence is accumulating to the effect that a battery of such measures tends to predict what it has measured. When factor analysis applied to batteries of this kind is carried

---

[2] See *Psychology of Music, op. cit.*

far enough, we may be able to improve the selection of items and weight them for specific purposes.

General conclusions. On the basis of many years of experience in the scientific measurement of tone relationships in musical ability, we may submit tentative answers to some of the fundamental questions raised in the attempt to validate these measures, with emphasis upon the qualitative insight into the relations rather than upon a quantitative index.

(1) Does the test measure what it purports to measure? Yes, precisely.

(2) Are individual differences in these capacities large enough to be significant? Yes, decidedly.

(3) Do small differences in pitch function significantly in music? Yes, in tone and interval intonation and especially in the psychological and artistic deviations from true pitch which are a medium of artistry.

(4) Is there a correlation between the standard measure of the sense of pitch and the ability to hear and to intone pitch with precision? Yes, but the relationship is exceedingly complicated.

(5) What is the principal value of efforts to validate such correlation by scientific measurement? The most significant gain is qualitative insight into the structure and function of the operation of precision in pitch-hearing and intonation in actual music.

(6) Do the features involved in the validation of the sense of pitch apply to the validation of the other five measures? Yes, in principle.

(7) Does a fine sense of pitch operate in fields other than music? Yes, in industry, art, sport, and other fields involving acoustic operations.

(8) Is there significant predictive value in a battery of specific measures? Yes, to the extent that they are basic, sufficient in number, fair samples, and the factors predicted are the factors measured.

TWO TYPES OF ATTITUDE TOWARD THE EVALUATION
OF MUSICAL TALENT

One attitude toward this problem was expressed in the aggressive and lucid formulation by James L. Mursell in the November 1937 issue of the *Music Educator's Journal*. Accepting the courteous invitation of the editors, I take pleasure in giving my reaction, as one of the spokesmen for the opposite attitude and theory.

Professor Mursell's article should be read by anyone considering the validity of the arguments from the two sides on the basis of specific facts. He gives the key to his theory in one sentence: "There is only one satisfactory method of finding out whether the Seashore tests really measure musical ability, and that is to ascertain whether persons rating high or low or medium on these tests also rate high and low and medium in what one may call *musical behavior*, that is, sight singing, playing the piano, getting through courses in theory and applied music, and the like."

The idea seems to be this: any test or battery of tests must be validated against behavior and success in all musical situations—"musical behavior" of the types that he mentions "and the like." If this is true, his entire argument can be maintained; if not, the whole argument based thereon fails.

Let me designate his theory as the omnibus theory and mine as the theory of specifics, somewhat on the analogy of the distinction between cure-alls and specifics in drugs. Since his view was stated specifically, in part, against my six *Measures of Musical Talent*, now available on phonograph records, I may simplify my argument in the limited space by speaking only of the issue involved in these six measures.

(1) The measures represent the theory of specific measurements insofar as they conform to the two universal scientific sanctions on the basis for which they were designed; namely, that (a) the factor under consideration must be isolated in order that exactly what is being measured may be known; (b) the conclusion must be limited to the factors under control.

Each of these six tests purports to measure one of six capacities or abilities for the hearing of musical tones. There is little overlapping in these functions, and their isolation for the purpose of measurement has been criticized only in the case of one. In testing we ask specifically, "How good a sense of pitch, of intensity, of time, of rhythm, of consonance, of immediate tonal memory has this person?" The measurements are stated in terms of centile rank, and they well may be the first and most basic items in a musical profile that may have scores of other factors, quite independent and equally measurable. I deliberately coined the term *measure* for this type of procedure in order to indicate its scientific character and to distinguish it from the ordinary omnibus-theory procedure.

(2) The tests have been validated for what they purport to measure. This is an internal validation in terms of success in the isolation of the factor measured and the degree of control of all other factors in the measurement. When we have measured reliably the sense of pitch, that is, pitch discrimination, in the laboratory, and we know that pitch was isolated from all other factors, no scientist will question the fact that we have measured pitch. There would be no object in validating against the judgment of even the most competent musician. We would not validate the reading on a thermometer against the judgment of a person sensitive to temperature.

(3) The tests are subject to criticism on the ground of relatively low reliability; but it must be remembered that the phonograph records are a makeshift for the purpose of securing a dragnet group test of an unselected population in a limited period of time and without training for observation. When such requirements are made, we cannot expect high reliability. We should also note that these recordings were designed when there were no precedents for this type of instrument construction, and when recording was relatively inferior to what it is today. Careful revision of the re-recording has been made.

In actual testing it has been shown that all ratings in the upper half of the group may be counted as reliable for individual diagnosis. Those showing low ratings must always be re-investigated before any conclusions can be based upon them. The ideal condition is, of course, to use the original measuring instruments of precision. For a responsible experimenter working with laboratory instruments and testing a single subject under controlled conditions, the reliability of each of these six measures runs in the high 90's. I would, therefore, admit that the six measures at present are makeshifts, but maintain that the principle of measurement for guidance involved is right and highly reliable.

(4) The tests should not be validated in terms of their showing on an omnibus theory or blanket rating against all musical behavior, including such diverse and unrelated situations as composition, directing, voice, piano, violin, saxophone, theory, administration, or drums, because there are hundreds of other factors which help to determine job analysis in each of such fields.

In view of this, the ratings found in the formidable table compiled by Professor Mursell are unwarranted. I have been bombarded all these years by the omnibusists for this type of validation, but have persistently refused on the ground that it had little or no significance. The two experiments by Brennan in that table which emanated from my laboratory were performed during my year's leave of absence under the direction of an outsider inexperienced in testing and against my protests.

For the same reason, I have always protested against the use of an average of these six measures, or any other number of the same kind, and have insisted upon the principle of a profile in which each specific measure stands on its own. Again for the same reason, I have insisted that even the most superficial rating for selection or placement in musical training or adjustment should be based upon a careful case history and a reliable audition with the profile of measurements in hand. That has always been the procedure in the Eastman School. The experimenter works with the attitude of physician who takes note of blood pressure, heart action, and metabolism.

It is easy to show that we cannot find a good violinist who does not have a good sense of pitch; or a good pianist who does not have a good sense of intensity, which is the *sine qua non* of touch. But it does not follow that goodness in these capacities alone will make a good artist.

Validation of pitch against the violinist's artistic performance in the actual musical situation would require that the sense of pitch be correlated with objective records of musical performance in *pitch intonation* or ability to hear *artistic pitch deviation* in the musical situation—not with the countless other merits or demerits that the violinist may exhibit. The same principle applies to any other scientific measure, such as the correlation of the sense of intensity with artistic touch by the pianist.

(5) The tests play primarily a negative role in musical adjustment. If a person has the urge, the facilities, and the support for a particular type of achievement in music, the purpose of these measures is to see whether or not a given measure indicates any probable impediment. Great musicians may rate low in one or more of these six and many other equally important capacities. The musical guide must use his head and consider whether high or low record in a specific capacity has any significance in the specific situation before him.

There is, however, a positive use, just as there is in dragnet surveys in a school system, a social center, a musical organization, or any other group. A relatively good profile may lead to case history, to further measurement, and to auditions for the purpose of discovering and encouraging talent. The main point is that a good profile is not in itself a guarantee of musical success, but it may furnish a good lead and may become a basis for encouragement.

(6) The application of these tests is relatively limited by the restriction that the conclusions shall be limited to the legitimate implications of the factors measured. This self-imposed limitation is one of the fundamental characteristics of scientific procedure. It does not permit of wholesale solutions and therefore cannot meet the demands of the popular clamor for a single index or universal practical guide.

If a person makes a record of 99 on the centile scale for pitch, the conclusion is not that he is musical but that he has a very high capacity in one of the numerous qualities that function in music. The problem of application is then to find out in what types of musical situation a keen sense of pitch discrimination actually functions, as in the hearing of pitch, in the control of pitch, and in the feeling for pitch. It may also be worth while to inquire to what extent a keen sense of pitch functions in the hearing of melody, of intervals, of harmony, and of tone quality. The guide has in hand a verifiable fact, and he must use judgment in determining what application is to be made of it in the analysis of a given situation.

(7) The tests have suffered much from popular and superficial advertising and propaganda. I have often paraphrased the aphorism: "The Lord protect me from my friends, I can protect myself against my enemies." Among these friends there are many who assume a blanket validity of these tests on the omnibus theory and have therefore sold the notion on a large scale. This has also been the basis for many journalistic stunts, and many wrong applications have been made.

I have here tried to state the basic issues involved in the theory of specific measures so that comparison may be made with the omnibus theory. Musical guidance is a new and complicated procedure. I agree with Professor Mursell that we should beware of easy solutions. I am glad that he has made the cleavage in the issue so clear and that he has sounded a warning to his followers against the use of my specific measures of musical talent in his omnibus theory. It is my humble opinion that no creditable test of musical talent can be built on that theory.

Chapter 21

THE INHERITANCE OF MUSICAL TALENT

MUSICAL TALENT probably lends itself better than any other talent to the investigation of the laws of mental inheritance, for it does not represent merely a general heightening of the mental powers, but is recognized as a gift which can be fractionated into its constituent elements, many of which may be isolated and measured with reasonable precision. Therefore, the inheritance of musical talent may be studied not only for itself alone, but also for the bearing that it has upon the inheritance of mental traits in general.

Yet, in approaching the investigation of musical talent, we are forced to face certain complexities which tend to make the work difficult, and which may at first seem insurmountable. Frank recognition of them, however, is the first step in scientific procedure.

MUSICAL TALENT NOT ONE BUT A GROUP OF HIERARCHIES OF TALENT

The musical person may be distinguished in voice, in instrumental performance, in musical appreciation, or in composition; each of these talents is an independent field in which one may gain eminence without giving evidence of marked ability in the others. Then, within each of these four large avenues of musical life, we find numerous independent variables. Voice, for example, is a physical capacity which may be distinguished in volume, range, and timbre; these three variables are quite independent, and they are not necessarily associated with the musical mind.

Adapted from *Scientific Monthly,* 1940, *50,* 351–356; and *Music Educators Journal,* May 1939.

On the sensory side there is a threefold division of the content of music as it is heard: tone, time, and intensity, each forming a hierarchy of its own which is quite independent of other talents. Each hierarchy of capacities runs as an independent branch, not only in sensation, but through memory, imagination, thought, feeling, and action. Each branch of this family tree throws out similar clusters of capacities. For example, the powers of imagery, creative imagination, emotional warmth, and logical grasp tend to appear in all three of the branches, except where they are excluded by the limitation of fundamental capacities for hearing one or more of these attributes.

In the investigation of inheritance we must therefore abandon the plan of merely calling persons musical or unmusical. We must isolate and observe such isolable traits as the inheritance of the sense of pitch, creative imagination, motor imagery, a large register of the vocal cords, excellence in motor control, or musical intellect.

CAPACITY VERSUS ACHIEVEMENT

The investigator of inheritance is not interested primarily in the degree of achievement attained; this is usually a circumstance of fortune or misfortune in environment. The investigator has to do exclusively with the valuation of inborn capacities. The term *capacity* is used in psychology to denote inborn power, whereas the term *ability* is used to denote acquired skill in the use of a given capacity. Skill or achievement is significant only insofar as it gives evidence of native capacities. It is manifestly unjust to attempt to trace musical inheritance in terms of distinguished achievement in music. Wherever we find achievement we count it as evidence of capacity; but we must employ ways and means of rating undeveloped capacities fairly in comparison with capacities which have been given natural outlets for development into achievement.

This point of view is fundamental and must be taken seriously. As long as we rate the presence of musical talent in terms of musical achievement, we shall be dealing mainly with the superficial sociological and pedagogical phenomena of opportunities and scope of musical training, or the effect of inhibiting circumstances on spontaneous self-expression in music.

Investigation of inheritance has been made possible for the first time by the introduction of methods of psychological examination by means of which we can discover, measure, and rate the existence, kind, and extent of natural musical capacities, regardless of age (beyond infancy), training, or musical performance of the subject. Most of us die "with all the music in us," but modern methods make it possible to observe and record the extent to which this is true.

THE NORMAL MIND VERSUS THE GENIUS
AND THE DEFECTIVE

The normal mind is musical, and the normal body is the instrument for adequate expression of music. As has been seen, whether or not the person with a normal mind and body will distinguish himself in music is largely a matter of opportunities for development and absence of suppressing forces.

Investigation of heredity will naturally center first on what are thought to be the most tangible cases, that is, on the one hand the genius and on the other the defective. But this distinction is not as simple as it might seem at first, for musical genius may be of various kinds, many of which are due to unrelated causes. Thus, there may be the genius in composing, in performing, or in interpreting music, one quite independent of the other, and each classification subdivided further. Likewise, musical deprivation may be due to faulty hearing, inadequate association, or inferior intelligence, and within each of these and similar categories may be various types, many of them entirely unrelated. Therefore, not much comfort will be found in thinking of the genius or the defective as representing peculiarly tangible cases, for, even here, it will be necessary to deal with specific factors in analyzed concepts.

The normal mind is the average mind. But the average does not represent a single dead level for all the various human capacities. Thus the two cases A and B, represented in Figure 1, may be regarded as typical of "average" musical minds, yet they are radically different as may be seen by a comparison of the charted capacities. It is not illuminating to call them "normal."

What is here illustrated in musical capacity is equally true for other human endowments. This is saying only, "We normal people are so different." If, for example, we rank capacities on the scale from 1 to 100 per cent, the so-called "normal" person may be found to be endowed with a superbly high faculty in one capacity, and in another, equally important, markedly defective; in one he may rank 99 per cent, and in the other 2 per cent. There is nothing gained by speaking of this as representing the average; each person must be considered by himself. Other persons who may be said to be relatively unmusical, have one or more capacities through which proficiency in music may be realized, provided the more favored capacities are hit upon in the narrow available form of musical achievement.

Therefore, it will be necessary to phrase the concept of normal, superior, or defective in terms of specific and isolable talents upon which musical achievement must depend. When this is done the popular distinction of genius, normal, and defective loses its significance, just as the term "insanity" has come to be merely a legal term, while the psychiatrist deals with specific causes and symptoms of mental diseases and finds all sorts of interweavings between sanity and insanity.

GENIUS AND IMPULSE

We must distinguish between the talented person and the genius. The most distinctive trait of the musical genius is the fact that he finds in music a dominant interest, is driven to it by an impulse, and burns to express himself in music. The musical genius is driven by an instinctive impulse or craving for music which results in supreme devotion to its expression. The talented person, on the other hand, gives evidence of unusual powers which may or may not be motivated by an instinctive impulse. To view genius merely as a talent is to view the waterfall in terms of measures of water or height instead of regarding it as water in action, falling, working, entrancing. The imposing manifestation of grandeur in the giant veil of

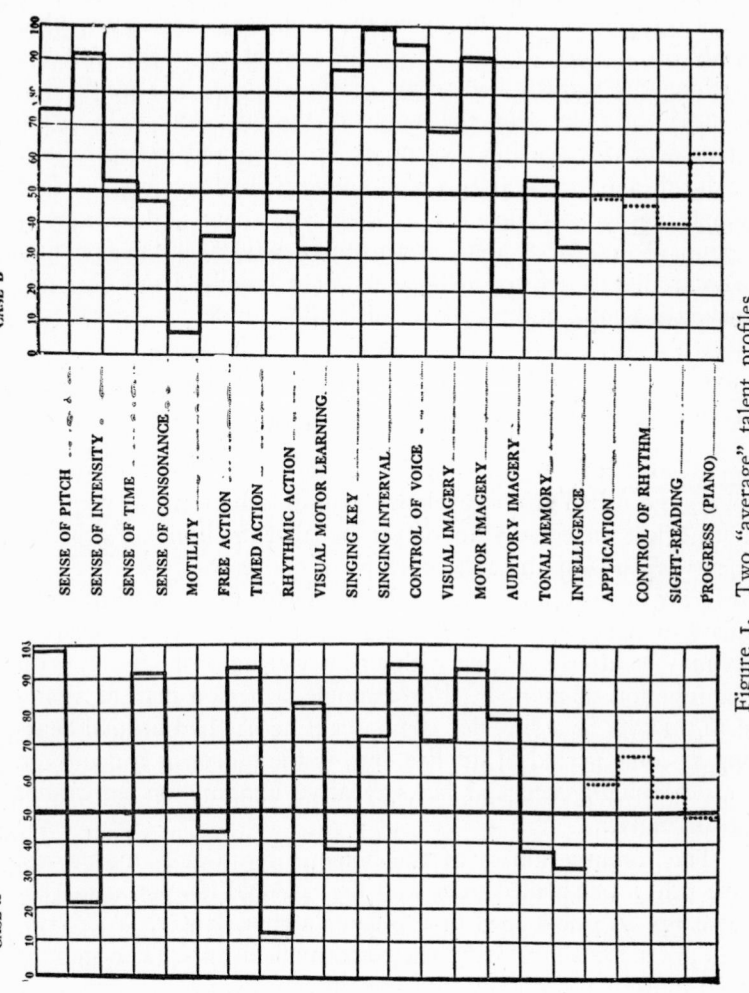

Figure I. Two "average" talent profiles

water is a reality. But there would be no fall were there no gorge, no water, no high shelf. The functioning power is implied in the structural composition. So, in music, the impulse to live the life of music owes its existence to the possession of other musical talents. In laying the foundations for a scientific study of heredity we may therefore content ourselves with describing the waterfall in terms of the shape of the gorge, the quantity of water, and the height of the fall; that is, in terms of capacity for sensing, executing, imaging, and feeling music.

In all art forms, it is a well-known fact that we often find people desperately devoted to their art, that is, drawn by a dominant impulse to a given art object, who never achieve and who are finally spotted as hopeless. The impulse itself does not make the genius and may be a misleading guide.

VERSATILITY AND PLASTICITY OF THE
HUMAN ORGANISM

In stressing the classification in terms of inborn capacities as distinguished from developed skill or achievement, we must not neglect the equally important fact that the limits of achievement depend on the relationship of one capacity to another. Inferior or medium capacities in one factor may constitute adequate support for excellence in a dominant capacity, and a capacity may be utterly lacking without interfering prohibitively with the function of another. For example, a person may be stone-deaf and yet be a superior composer if he has had normal hearing at some period of his life, but, if the person is a genius in musical intelligence and lacks creative imagination he cannot create music.

The resourcefulness of the human organism is marvelous. Recently a one-armed man won the national honors in marksmanship. A one-legged man became a rope dancer. War cripples are astonishing us by their accomplishments. The same is even more true mentally, because the mind is more complicated and plastic than the body. Therefore great insight is required to distinguish real achievement reached after the overcoming of handicaps from the possession of talent. Such achievement, under handicap, is favored in music by the fact that the material of music is manifold and the avenues of expression are many. A person without a voice may play; a person with a small register of voice may have beautiful quality; a person lacking sense of tone may excel in the rhythmic aspects of music; a person lacking the sense of time may dwell in the tonal aspects; a person lacking emotion may excel in the more abstract processes of composition and musical criticism.

In all such cases it will be necessary to deal with specific gifts, either unusual excellences or marked absence of excellences, and in all cases to rate natural capacities as distinguished from the acquired skill or ability.

This point of view throws a flood of light on the analysis of likes and dislikes, character of performance, and character of creation in music. Thus, a distinguished singer was found to be inferior in the sense of pitch, and in this was the explanation of the fact that she had failed several times in music before she hit by chance upon folk songs. Now she appears in solo and, without apparent extravagance, takes advantage of the artistic liberties which folk singers take with their melodies. She has a beautiful voice, wide compass, and a beautiful face, so that appeal to the eye dominates the esthetic appeal of the tonal message.

Persons who lack a sense of time or a sense of intensity are common in musical circles. The relative absence of feeling, imagination, or intellect in persons who have attained distinction in music is a notorious phenomenon. Many persons prominent in musical circles perform in a certain mechanical way, and are always pronounced unmusical by the connoisseur; the voice lacks life, the rhythm is mechanical, the tone is cold. In any investigation of heredity we may have to call these highly trained persons unmusical on the basis of ratings in natural capacities.

ATTITUDE OF THE ARTIST

Mental tests can be applied to rate the capacities of soldiers under military command, and the soldiers must accept the consequences of the rating whether it be favorable or unfavorable.

In the schools there have been established a variety of systems of tests by which the "gifts of nature" in the pupil are thrown into relief for the guidance of the educator. Children are coming to look upon the intelligence quotient, mathematical rating, and the learning curve as matters of routine like measures of height, weight, and lung capacity. The prospective musician in the music school is eager to secure his talent chart as a basis for the organization of his course, the identification and analysis of encountered difficulties, and the forecast of prospects in a musical career.

But when we attempt to follow up the individuals in a family of musicians with all its collateral branches we encounter prejudices, fears, scruples, and other negativisms, born of ignorance —ignorance quite excusable in this ultramodern movement of applied science. Apart from this, there is, in the very warp and woof of the musical temperament, an attitude of mind which, by its esthetic glow, is opposed to cold scientific procedure. This aloofness of the artist is also partly justified by the fact that the necessary procedure for the scientific investigation of musical inheritance is still crude and has not yet become a recognized custom.

ABSENCE OF ESTABLISHED BIOLOGICAL THEORY

This reserve of the artist is further justified by the lack of established biological concepts of the physical mechanism by which mental traits are transmitted through the germ plasm. For some time to come, there must be a patient procedure by trial and error to try out the best working hypotheses available. There is little precedent for the application of Mendelian principles to mental traits. But, from the point of view of modern psychology, the prospect of drawing analogies from related experiments in plants and animals is very hopeful. Indeed, that is the only logical and economic way to proceed. We may accept the Mendelian hypothesis as a general working basis, and proceed to ascertain what determiners in the germ plasm function for musical talent; which are dominant and which are recessive; which musical dispositions are carried on the same determiner; and which are carried on determiners charged with nonmusical factors, etc. In psychology, these problems will be virgin soil for investigation.

APPARENTLY OF ONLY THEORETICAL SIGNIFICANCE

It would be difficult, at the present stage, to convince the musician who regards everything artistic as something almost beyond nature, at least very ethereal and sacred, that the biological theory has any practical bearing. Yet, if it should prove possible to identify heritable musical traits, as we believe it is, and if the laws of the operation of this inheritance should become common knowledge, it is conceivable that the gain for the development of artistic resources would be as far-reaching for musical art. The knowledge of such laws already is proving useful in conservation of favorable and the elimination of unfavorable traits in animals and plants. And this may come about without any eugenic infringement of the finer sensibilities of esthetic man in human evolution.

THE DISCARDING OF THE LITERATURE ON MUSICAL INHERITANCE

The above facts, and many others like them, prove conclusively to those acquainted with the literature of the subject that little or no help can be obtained from works now extant on the inheritance of musical talent. The mass of music biography and autobiography is expressed in terms of loose and utterly unscientific concepts. True, when we adopt a scientific terminology it may be possible to identify specific factors in previous compositions, published musical criticism, and a variety of other objective evidence of the presence of similar traits in successive generations of certain musical families. But it will be difficult to determine how much to attribute to nature and nurture respectively. Even then it will be like counting only the ships that come in, for we can get only scant information about the musical nature on the maternal side. The male musical genius has often come from a mother whose extraordinary talent has passed undiscovered until it has appeared in the career of a son. To trace inheritance, all the members of a family of blood relations including certain collaterals must be counted, and there must be as much significance given to the rating of talent which has found no outlet for expression as to that which has found expression. This has not been done in musical biography because biography deals primarily with achievement.

In the few biometric studies of inheritance traits in which musical inheritance has been taken into account, the data obtained and the technique developed are of little value because none of them deal with specific capacities. To those who are not trained in the technique of individual psychology of biometric experiments, this discarding of the contributions of the past may seem sweeping and even arrogant; yet such is the process of clearing away the rubbish before breaking ground for a scientific venture in this field.

THE EXPERIMENTAL METHOD ESSENTIAL

Where there is no experiment, there can be no science. Scientific investigation of musical talent had to wait for the appearance of the scientific psychology of music. Only in comparatively recent years have we seen the beginning of such a science. This science is still restricted to laboratory and to other technical work and has not yet invaded musical thought to any considerable extent. The investigation of musical talent is still in the inceptive stage, and the investigator of heredity must, therefore, content himself with the few aspects of musical talent which have been reduced to experimental control, and deal tentatively with those aspects which can be isolated, measured, and described with precision. To the investigator it is no sacrifice to abandon the hope of tracing the inheritance of musical talent as a whole. He prizes the opportunity of dealing with one specific capacity at a time.

MEASUREMENT OF FACTORS IN TALENT

The whole subject of the analysis and measurement of musical talent is treated, as fully as the material available at the time of publication permitted, in my book *The Psychology of Musical Talent*.[1] The methods, means, and significance of the measures, ratings, and records here recommended are described in that volume.

Among the measures of specific factors in musical talent now available for use in quantitative procedure, I would mention the following:

The basic sensory capacities. Beyond question the first step is to measure quantitatively the four basic capacities: the sense of pitch, the sense of intensity, the sense of time, and the sense of timbre. For these we have a standard of procedure, instruments, and norms readily available. Each factor represents a primary branch in the family tree of musical talent. Each should be followed further into its branching. The measurement of these factors will reveal the actual psychophysical capacities for the hearing of music, because all musical sounds are perceived in these four forms. Complex cognitive factors, such as the senses of rhythm, of consonance, and of volume, are composed mainly of the four basic factors, but have distinctive musical values and should each be measured with this in mind.

The basic motor capacities. When considering natural endowment for musical performance, the two large divisions, singing and playing, must be separated at once, and the latter must be considered in its various forms. Ultimately it will be necessary to employ distinct measures of aptness in singing and in playing different instruments. We may measure the capacity for control of pitch in terms of accuracy in the reproduction of pitch of a standard tone with the voice. For control of intensity we may measure natural precision in "touch" as shown in producing a tone of the standard loudness by pressing a key while guiding the loudness by ear. For control of time, accuracy in keeping time is measured with a set standard. For each of these, standardized instruments and methods of procedure are available. It is evident that each of these three capacities for action rests upon its corresponding capacity for hearing.

---

[1] The Silver Burdett Co., Boston, 1919.

Musical imagery. While we relive and create music through images in all the senses, two are essential and characteristic of musical life: auditory imagery and motor imagery. Auditory imagery must be determined because it is in terms of this that we relive music we have once heard and express new music in creative imagination. Motor imagery, that is, the subjective sensory experience of action in association, is also a basic factor, because it is the taproot of emotional expression and is really an index of musical emotion. For each of these we have serviceable introspection measures.

Memory. There are many vastly divergent aspects of musical memory which may be measured, but for the present purpose only one will be selected: memory span; that is, the capacity for grasping and retaining for a moment a group of musical sounds.

Musical intelligence. Since the character of the musician is determined largely by the character of his general intelligence, quite apart from music, the so-called "intelligence quotient" test for children may be used to obtain a rating of intelligence in terms of mental age. For adults, corresponding tests are available and may be adapted for musical purposes.

THE RATING OF FACTORS NOT MEASURED

The development of experimental technique has led to clearness of analysis and critical procedure in the observation and recording of factors which cannot be put under experimental control. Such observation and rating of factors, with reasonable precision, must furnish valuable supplementary information for aid in the interpretation of the quantitative measures. Among the items to be observed in examining an individual are the voice quality as to its register, volume, evidences of training; general motor control, as in the use of the hands, grace and precision of movement, and general alertness; evidences of rhythmic tendencies; vividness and fertility of imagination; characteristics of memory; musical centers of interest and stock of musical ideas; the expression of musical feeling, temperament, and artistic attitudes when off guard; physique, health, and physical development.

Significant biographical data in the form of case histories should be gathered, including striking ancestral traits, hereditary diseases, social and vocational status, educational opportunities, impediments which have stood in the way of successful education and achievement, and other significant facts of the life history. No set form should be followed, but alertness and skill in observing the essentials are desirable.

In these ratings and case histories, the experimenter should not fill out forms or record sheets but should take the same attitude that the physician takes. The physician has in mind the generally recognized diseases and their symptoms, and he takes notes of anything which, in his judgment, may appear to be relevant. The examiner should not pad formal records but should collect relevant facts.

One factor which cannot be measured but may possibly be observed systematically for the purpose of tracing transmission through heredity, is musical impulse as shown in a natural craving for music, sustained interest in its pursuit, and a deep feeling of satisfaction in things musical. This impulse, when genuine, rests upon a natural bent of mind due mainly to the possession of capacities, but including a general artistic disposition or temperament. The best that we can do, at the present time, is to record all observable evidences of such a driving impulse apart from artificial stimulation and simulation. Undoubtedly interesting relationships will be found between these impulses and the power to achieve. It is desirable to learn to what extent such an instinctive impulse may be lost through untoward circumstances in early life. It will also be interesting to see to what extent a dominating impulse of this sort is related to lack of capacities or absence of interest in other activities.

POSSIBLE WAYS OF ORGANIZING INVESTIGATION

The laws of the inheritance of musical traits must ultimately be determined by actual experiment with carefully selected matings in which the measurements may be repeated for successive generations. Such an undertaking could be fostered only by an agency heavily endowed; it would have to be on a nationwide scope, and it would have to adopt a thoroughly standardized procedure which could be sustained for many years.

In general, it would seem feasible to follow, in an investigation of this sort, the same methods that have been followed so successfully with plants and animals, that is, to isolate and observe, under experimental control, one factor at a time in all the progeny from a given pair for a certain number of generations. There need be only the one restriction, in view of the fact that we are dealing with human beings, namely, that we cannot breed successive generations for this specific purpose. This, however, is not serious, because we can adopt the device of selecting from among volunteers in whom the factor under control is mated in a known way, and examining them and their children and their children's mates in successive generations. Since this process would be elaborate, perhaps several factors could be measured in the same series. The advantage of taking only one factor at a time lies mainly in the fact that it would then be possible to start a pedigree in each case with conspicuous matings of the same capacity. In some cases two or more factors might be found sufficiently conspicuous in the same mating. Full ratings through systematic observations and case histories could be kept quite complete. This is undoubtedly the method of the future. It involves not the slightest infringement upon reasonable sensibilities or proprieties; on the contrary, it should constitute a fascinating co-operative search for truth.

A more direct procedure would be to examine large numbers of parents and their children, taking into account the transmission of factors in one generation. We would have the alternative of spending time and effort in selecting conspicuous matings for a given capacity, or of taking families at random and depending upon large numbers of measurements to yield reliable data. The former of these alternatives would undoubtedly be more desirable.

A third method may commend itself for a pioneer effort in the field of inherited musical traits: a family or families in which conspicuous musical talent has appeared could be studied; the children and their mates, and possibly their grandchildren, would have to be reasonably available for visit and examination, and records of achievement and descriptions of talent in their ancestry would contribute largely.

POINT OF VIEW

This scientific point of view does not conflict with the artistic and philosophical points of view, both of which regard these same phenomena of inherited musical traits from entirely different angles. The artist, in successive attitudes, may regard his life from each of these three points of view. As an artist he finds himself in esthetic *rapport* with nature. As a philosopher he reasons about the relations of this life of music to the life of nature as a part of beauty and truth, and weaves this relationship into his world view. As a scientist he turns upon the same phenomena objectively, and he expresses interest in particulars, causes, conditions, and mental laws.

The point of view here presented is that of the naturalist. Musical life is made up of phenomena in nature, all operating according to determinable laws of nature; these laws are analyzable, describable, explainable—knowable and worth knowing.[2]

INTERVIEWS ON MUSICAL INHERITANCE *

Bring together all the thoughtful questions that have occurred to you in regard to your heredity, and you will find answers to nearly all in Scheinfeld's book, *You and Heredity*.

What made you male or female, tall or short, quick-tempered or stolid, red-haired or black-haired? To scores of such questions the author brings the answer of science in a fascinat-

[2] The above article was written in 1918, and is of interest in that it represents a step in pioneering in what was, at that time, a virgin field. The article served as an effective protest against the then prevailing questionnaire methods, uncontrolled observation, and loose biographical procedures. In the following I shall report two notable studies made from that scientific point of view. Then as now massive materials were accumulated for interpretation—notably family relationships, anthropological records of primitive races, Mjoen's studies on European races, the Eastman School of Music records for entering students, and the numerous records of siblings in public schools.

* Adapted from a review in *Music Educators Journal*, May 1939, of *You and Heredity* by Amram Scheinfeld, assisted in the Genetic Sections by Dr. Morton D. Schweitzer, F. A. Stokes Co., New York, 1939.

ing style. Two chapters are devoted to the problem of the inheritance of musical talent. They are based on a remarkable series of personal interviews.

He dealt with three groups of musicians:

(1) Thirty-six of the outstanding musicians of the world, including for example, Barbirolli, Bauer, Bodanzky, Brailowsky, Busch, Bustabo, Damrosch, and Elman (named in alphabetical order).

(2) The entire cast (thirty-six) of the Metropolitan Opera Company, including Bampton, Bori, Branzell, Burke, Cigna, Fisher, and Flagstad.

(3) Fifty selected graduate students in the Juilliard School of Music.

Table I, from Scheinfeld, p. 259, gives in epitome the nature of the inquiries and the quantitative answers to each. Table II summarizes the findings in regard to musical pedigrees. Let the figures in each of these tables speak for themselves. They tell a significant story.

TABLE I

SUMMARY OF SCHEINFELD'S GENERAL FINDINGS
ON THE THREE GROUPS

	Virtuosi Instrumental Artists (36 in all)	Metropolitan Opera Singers (36 in all)	Juilliard Graduate Students (50 in all)	Totals for All Groups (122 in all)
Average Age Talent Expressed	4¾ yrs.	9¾ yrs.	5¾ yrs.	6 yrs.
Mothers Talented or Musical in Some Degree	17 (47%)	24 (67%)	37 (74%)	78 (64%)
Fathers Talented or Musical in Some Degree	29 (81%)	25 (69%)	29 (58%)	83 (68%)
Brothers and Sisters, Total	110	103	72	285
Talented or Musical in Some Degree	55 (50%)	43 (42%)	51 (71%)	148 (52%)
Number Reporting Talent in Additional Near Kin	13 (36%)	16 (44%)	37 (74%)	66 (54%)

TABLE II

SUMMARY OF SCHEINFELD'S GENERAL FINDINGS ON THE
EFFECT OF TALENT MATINGS

	Where Both Parents Had Talent		Where Only One Parent Had Talent		Where Neither Parent Had Talent	
	Number of Other Children*	Number With Talent	Number of Other Children*	Number With Talent	Number of Other Children*	Number With Talent
Bros. & Sisters of Instrumental Virtuosi (26 families)	31	22 (71%)	35	21 (60%)	27	4 (15%)
Bros. & Sisters of Metropolitan Singers (26 families)	42	26 (62%)	16	8 (50%)	25	2 (8%)
Bros. & Sisters of Juilliard Graduates (32 families)	21	19 (90%)	20	14 (70%)	14	4 (29%)
Totals for All Three Groups	94	67 (71%)	71	43 (60%)	66	10 (15%)

* In addition to the artists themselves.

This is the most representative array of data now available by the method of interview. Musicians will turn to the book itself for the author's qualifications, interpretations, and personal histories.

As an example of how a specific factor may be traced in studies of heredity, the author shows the occurrence (Figure 2) of *absolute pitch* in Kirsten Flagstad's family. Absolute pitch is a specific factor suitable for scientific measurement. But it may occur in vastly different degrees, ranging from the ability to name any note sounded on the piano to the ability to recognize a deviation of one vibration from international pitch without reference to any means of comparison. In the future the student of heredity will measure and indicate the *degree* of the possession of this factor.

The author makes a bold effort to apply the theory of genes in the chromosomes of the inherited cell to the inheritance of musical talent in the same way that it applies to the inheritance of stature, hair, blood-type or any other specific and measurable factor. In this he presents a series of novel ideas regarding the probable nature of the mechanism. This is an intriguing problem to the geneticist. The alarming difficulty which both musicians and scientists encounter here lies in the uncertainty of identifying specific measurable traits which can be isolated and traced from generation to generation. This cannot be done by the method of interview, but by objective checks, as given above.

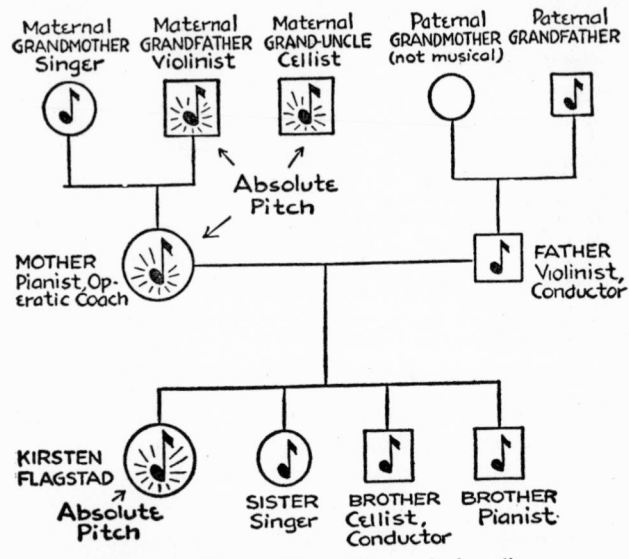

Figure 2. Kirsten Flagstad's musical pedigree

The author is undoubtedly right in holding that inheritance of musical talent eventually must be expressed in terms of the mechanisms of genes as are other forms of heritage. But it yet remains to be shown that musical traits are as specific as the genes by which they are to be identified. Is the sense of *absolute pitch* one? Is the more general *sense of pitch* one trait? Is *ear-mindedness* a single trait? In a word, the difficulty now is not with the theory of heredity as a principle, but with the psychological description of the musical mind in terms of musical traits that may be inherited.

Chapter 22

TWO PHENOMENAL ASPECTS OF
MUSICAL HEARING

As EXAMPLES of psychological experiments which have significant practical application in musical esthetics two significant results in two areas are here reported: first, the distinction between
absolute and relative pitch and, second, the operation of the law
of presbycousis.

ACQUIRED PITCH VERSUS ABSOLUTE PITCH

If a good musician should say, "I do not have absolute pitch,
but I have a very serviceable and rather accurate memory for
all the tones in the musical scale," he would be describing accurately the commonest situation among good musicians. My
purpose here is to crystallize this distinction and to encourage
its adoption both in musical and in scientific terminology.

The original and technical meaning of absolute pitch was
that it represented an extraordinary memory for pitch which
was inborn. The term thus conveyed three ideas: that it was
inborn, that it was extraordinarily fine, and that it was therefore
a rare occurrence. In current terminology and practical thinking, however, absolute pitch has been confused with fairly serviceable memory for the notes or intervals of the musical scale.
In this type of memory we note three characteristics: that it is
acquired, that it is in terms of musical steps, and that it is a
fairly common achievement among outstanding musicians. Let
us clarify our thinking by giving this type of memory a specific name, *acquired pitch.*

Thus we recognize three fundamental distinctions between
absolute pitch and acquired pitch. First, absolute pitch is an

From *Music Educators Journal,* May 1940.

inborn predisposition which manifests itself early in childhood, usually before musical education has begun, and is strikingly immediate and spontaneous; whereas acquired pitch, although based on a favorable hereditary predisposition, is acquired through training and tends to be more reflective. Second, absolute pitch is extraordinarily fine, involving errors of a small fraction of a semitone; whereas acquired pitch operates and is thought of in terms of steps in the musical scale. Third, absolute pitch is rare and not essential to musicianship, although it may prove very valuable; whereas acquired pitch not only is a fairly common musical skill in some degree but is essential to the highest order of musicianship. A word of caution is needed for each of these distinctions.

Both absolute and acquired pitch are forms of memory. Both rest upon a favorable hereditary capacity or predisposition. Both are influenced by training, but absolute pitch only to a slight degree; whereas acquired pitch can be cultivated to some degree by any person with a good sense of relative pitch, and it is dependent upon knowledge of musical notes and steps. This ability can be rapidly improved by specific training. The person who has absolute pitch will quickly attain extraordinary skill in acquired pitch; whereas the person who is not born with absolute pitch probably cannot acquire it. The term *absolute pitch* does not refer to perfection but is used in contrast to the term *relative pitch,* which is pitch discrimination or the sense of pitch.

As to the degree of accuracy of free tonal memory for pitch, we find a gradual transition from the very finest absolute pitch through all degrees of accuracy down to crude forms of acquired pitch. But it is convenient to make the distinction that absolute pitch may involve accuracy to a small fraction of a semitone; whereas acquired pitch is usually thought of in terms no finer than semitones or the sharp or flat of an interval.

Absolute pitch is so rare and so distinctive that it seems to stand in a class by itself. It is found occasionally in musical prodigies and musically precocious children. It is a specific talent combining a fine sense of pitch with an extraordinarily faithful memory for pitch. A musician may be highly distinguished in any field of music without having absolute pitch, but the possession of it enriches and sharpens his musical experience. Absolute pitch is not necessarily associated with high intelligence—even idiots have been reported to have it—but acquired pitch is associated with good logical memory and feeling for tone.

The above-mentioned lines of demarcation between absolute and acquired pitch are not rigid or without exception. They should be regarded rather as a practical guide. It is therefore clear that in accepting this classification, distinguishing roughly between absolute and acquired pitch, we still have the privilege of noting exceptions or qualifications. Thus, a person who lacked early spontaneity and has acquired skill through training is classified as possessing acquired pitch, but, in certain situations, he may have about as fine a tonal memory as if he had absolute pitch. Recognizing the term *acquired pitch* as a generic name, the classification may be qualified by a word or phrase indicating either some specific aspect of superiority or some characteristic limitations. The main object is to distinguish acquired pitch from absolute pitch in the historical sense.

In a recent investigation of absolute pitch, Dr. Bachem [1] found that 43 out of 103 cases investigated had relatives who possessed absolute pitch. It is probable that this inheritance follows the Mendelian law. The effects of practice and of necessity for use are illustrated by the fact that absolute pitch occurs relatively more frequently among blind persons. It has often been noted that violinists exhibit this trait more frequently than pianists, but that may possibly be accounted for by the principle of selection.

Both absolute pitch and acquired pitch vary with a large number of factors, in various degrees and ways, including the quality or kind of tone, place in the musical scale, loudness, duration, auditory imagery, voice, instrument, length of retention, fixed pitch associations, and methods of exhibiting pitch. For facts about such variables, see Petran.[2]

---

[1] A. Bachem, "The Genesis of Absolute Pitch," *Journal of Acoustical Society of America,* April 1940.
[2] A. Petran, "An Experimental Study of Pitch Recognition," *Psychological Monographs,* 1932, Vol. XLII, Monog. 193.

There are important theoretical distinctions, both physiological and neurological, between the two types of tonal memory. At the present time, however, there is no generally accepted theory of absolute pitch. This is a field which calls for rigorous experimentation with modern instruments and methods. Many of the earlier reports of absolute pitch are probably exaggerated, because in those days accurate means of measurement had not been developed.

CHANGE OF MUSICAL HEARING WITH AGE: PRESBYCOUSIS [*]

Many years ago when Madame Gadski and her daughter were visiting our laboratory and observing various tests and demonstrations in hearing, I tested the upper limit of hearing for the daughter and found it was well above 20,000 vibrations per second. In testing the mother, a great artist, I found that she fell short of this by more than one octave, about 10,000 vibrations. It seemed incredible to the mother that her daughter who was not a musician should hear such a wide range of tones which she, the artist, could not hear at all. The experiment was therefore verified most carefully, and the first findings were confirmed.

When I explained to the mother that this was a normal change in hearing that takes place with age and that it meant not only that she could not hear these high tones in nature or in music but that she could not hear the true quality of her own voice as she had heard it when younger, Madame Gadski seemed amazed and pointed out that she had never noticed any change in her hearing of music.

Her case probably represents the typical situation and attitude of aging musicians. They are not familiar with the law of a progressive lowering of the upper hearing limit with age, and the change comes upon them so gradually that they have no means of comparison by which they can determine the change in tone quality which follows.

---

[*] This section is quoted from *Music Educators Journal,* May 1938, and is based upon investigations made by Dr. Noble Kelley as Eastman Fellow in the Psychological Laboratory of the University of Iowa.

The author's personal record is an example at first hand. When I was half as old as I am now, I had superior hearing throughout the entire register, reaching about 20,000 vibrations. I cannot say exactly how much because the methods of measuring the upper limit at that time were not as reliable as they are now. Now at the age of eighty with a very accurate measurement, I can hear a moderately loud tone as high as 4,000 vibrations per second; but when that tone is made softer and softer, the upper limit falls lower and lower so that a pianissimo tone may not be heard at 3,000 vibrations. Yet my hearing below 3,000 is about as keen as it was in youth. In my own case at the present time, I cannot hear the highest two notes on my piano played *mf*.

I have cited these two cases because they are typical of what happens to all of us, whether musical or unmusical, as age comes on. In order to establish this point, an adequate sampling of the hearing of persons above fifty years of age was made in our laboratory by Dr. Noble Kelley. Having found persons of this age who were intelligent and interested in taking the test, the experimenter subjected them to an otological examination to determine, first, whether or not there was any serious loss of hearing in the lower register, and, second, whether or not loss of hearing at any register was due to disease or illness of any kind. He rejected all those who had significant loss of hearing in the lower register and also those who had any loss of hearing due to past or present disease or any other form of injury, so that the statistics which he collected would be based upon intelligent observers who had not suffered any deteriorating disease of the ear and whose hearing in the lower register was not seriously affected.

The subjects were divided into four age groups: (1) 50-59, 60 ears; (2) 60-69, 80 ears; (3) 70-79, 22 ears; and (4) 80-89, 6 ears. The results of these measurements are shown in Table I. For each age group and each octave, the top number shows the average amount of hearing loss in terms of decibels, and the figure in parentheses below this shows the average deviation from the average for the group. These data are plotted in Figure 1, which gives us a clear picture of this law of degeneration in the ear which is known technically in otology as *presbycousis,* meaning "loss of hearing due to age."

The normal hearing of youth is represented by the heavy zero line at the top of Figure I. The normal young ear can

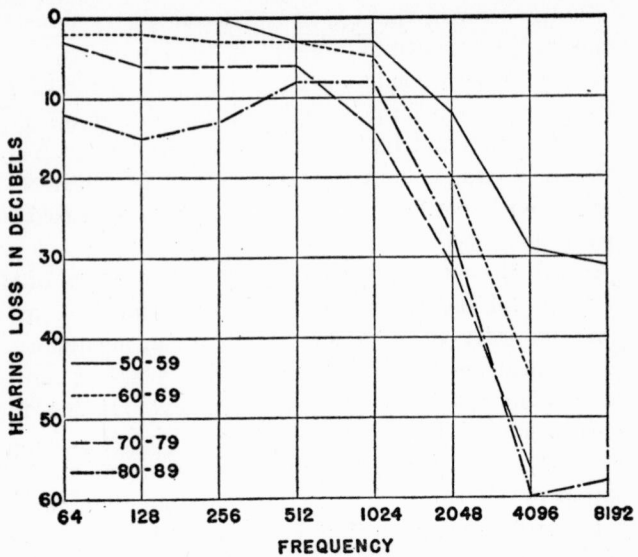

Figure I. Loss of hearing with age

hear tones in all these octaves in all the degrees of amplification indicated. If this rectangle were extended up to 20,000 vibrations and the curves were all carried up to the maximum amplification, which is 60 decibels above the normal threshold, we could envisage what happens to us as we grow old by seeing that there is a marked progressive loss of hearing from somewhere around the 1,000-vibration level up to the 20,000-vibration level. The actual loss would be shown quantitatively by the area above and to the right of these curves, and the retained hearing by the area below and to the left of the curve.

This represents a tremendous loss and a radical change in hearing. It not only limits the hearing of the fundamental pitch of high tones and distorts their loudness when heard; but,

TABLE I

Loss of Hearing with Age

Frequency	60 Ears Age Group 50–59	80 Ears Age Group 60–69	22 Ears Age Group 70–79	6 Ears Age Group 80–89
64	0 (3)	2 (4)	3 (6)	12 (5)
128	0 (3)	2 (5)	6 (6)	15 (5)
256	0 (3)	3 (5)	6 (6)	13 (3)
512	3 (4)	3 (5)	6 (6)	8 (5)
1,024	3 (5)	5 (5)	14 (9)	8 (6)
2,048	12 (9)	20 (11)	31 (16)	27 (14)
4,096	29 (13)	45 (18)	57 (17)	60 (15)
8,192	31 (16)			58 (5)

The upper figure in each bracket denotes hearing loss in terms of decibels, and the figure in parentheses below it gives the average deviation from the average for the group.

Twenty-seven of the 168 ears could not hear the 8,192-vibration tone at maximum amplification, 60 decibels, above the normal threshold.

even more significantly, it radically changes the quality of the tones that we hear by the elimination of the higher overtones.

To test this hypothesis, we performed a very interesting and exacting experiment. A violin was played by an automatic device so as to produce a rich tone of superior quality on the open A string. Then electrical filters were introduced, which eliminated in turn all partials above 2,000, 4,000, and 6,000 vibrations. The filtered tone was then sounded for comparison with the full tone. Normal young persons listening invariably heard the difference and were able to identify the filtered tone due to the absence of the higher partials; but each old person failed to distinguish the full tone from the filtered tone when he reached the limit of audibility indicated by his hearing curve.

Here, then, is a very definite law, a quantitative statement, of what happens in our world of hearing as we grow old. This law is of great significance in the hearing of music, as it is also to some extent for speech. In this loss of capacity for discrimination of tone quality, age has no respect for professional standing, training, or knowledge. It is a physical law representing the degeneration of the harp structure in the ear. This specific law is an accordance with the general biological law of degeneration; degeneration of function begins with the most recently acquired and most delicate structures.

It is comforting to know that the register which remains practically normal is the region in which the fundamentals of most of our musical tones occur and within which speech sounds are most significantly differentiated. The loss comes upon us so gradually that we make corresponding adaptations in hearing, and radical as it is, we may not be aware of it in ordinary experience.

I confess to feeling a little like a bull in a china shop in bringing this law to the attention of artists who are enjoying a rich musical life in old age. The greatest comfort lies in the realization that our subjective hearing, as in the case of deaf musicians, still plays a very important role. Also, one reassuring feature is established in this same investigation: loss of hearing within the lower serviceable register does not follow as a result of age. If it comes, it is not presbycousis but is due to some specific or general organic disease affecting the ear. Old persons are not necessarily hard of hearing in the lower register.

PART FOUR

HISTORICAL BACKGROUND AND EDUCATIONAL APPROACHES

Chapter 23

THE SONG OF THE CANARY

MODERN PSYCHOLOGY has turned increasingly to the study of the behavior of the lower animals: monkeys, guinea pigs, rats, cats, dogs, birds, and insects. With animals the conditions are simpler and more easily controlled than in human behavior. Animals frequently exhibit the same biological principles demonstrated in human behavior. This is strikingly true in the study of heredity and the effect of environment—fundamental problems of nature and nurture. Experiments on the fruit fly, for example, have resulted in an array of fundamental biological facts, many of which are as basic to man as they are to the fly. Even such an esoteric subject as musical esthetics may find in these experiments a solid foundation, as I propose to show in this chapter.

Metfessel, now Professor of Psychology in the University of Southern California, had his graduate training in our Iowa laboratory, rising after three years of study for the doctorate and three years of postdoctorate study to the position of full Professor of the Psychology of Music and Speech. For a decade he was one of the most effective leaders and contributors to the Iowa research program.

Metfessel's research in Iowa centered around the recording of speaking and singing voices of celebrated artists. In 1927, while in Berlin, Germany, he purchased a number of records of bird songs to take into the laboratory for re-recording and analysis by the same methods employed for artistic and primitive music.

Based on Metfessel's *Relationships of Heredity and Environment in Behavior*. Presented as the Seventh Annual Research Lecture in the University of Southern California and published in *Journal of Psychology*, 1940, *10*, 177–198.

When he transferred to the University of Southern California, he was impressed with the local importance attached to the song of canaries. In southern California annual canary contests are held, and more than a dozen experts make a profession of judging the quality of the songs in competition. Pedigrees of the birds are registered as carefully as those of race horses, and high prices are paid for birds with a fine quality of song.

I was there at the time, and was introduced to a lady who exhibited a canary that sang with wonderful precision such melodies as *Silent Night* and *Yankee Doodle*. At Christmas the bird was taken to a number of churches to sing *Silent Night*. The only difficulty was the danger of his lapsing at any moment into another tune such as *Yankee Doodle*. The canary made a tremendous impression on the Christmas audiences.

As we were then in the midst of our studies on the vibrato, we were particularly impressed with the fact that this bird had a beautiful vibrato in his song, and the question arose whether the vibrato was a hereditary trait or had been learned from the trainer who possessed the same general type of vibrato. Metfessel measured the rate of the vibrato of the bird and the trainer, and found them strikingly similar.

He began immediately to make recordings of birds of this kind, and that led to the setting up of a long-time program, which was interrupted, unfortunately, by the war. His intention was to answer two questions: To what extent are the characteristic songs of the canary inherited, and to what extent are they learned through training or environment? These questions presented a fascinating problem in the psychology of music, and opened a way for a basic biological approach to the issues involved in problems of the inheritance of musical talents. Metfessel was particularly interested in finding a biological explanation for the human vibrato.

The psychological laboratory was located in a tower of a central building on the university campus, and the top two floors of this tower were isolated and set aside as a scientific sanctuary for the housing and control of singing canaries. By consulting with experts he found that the song of the canary, as exhibited by the best singers, is limited to about twenty types, called *tours,* of which the ten most frequent are listed in Figure 1.

THE HEREDITY EXPERIMENT

Metfessel took up first the problem of inheritance. The question was: How many, if any, of these specific tours will the bird exhibit if hatched and reared in a soundproof cage until

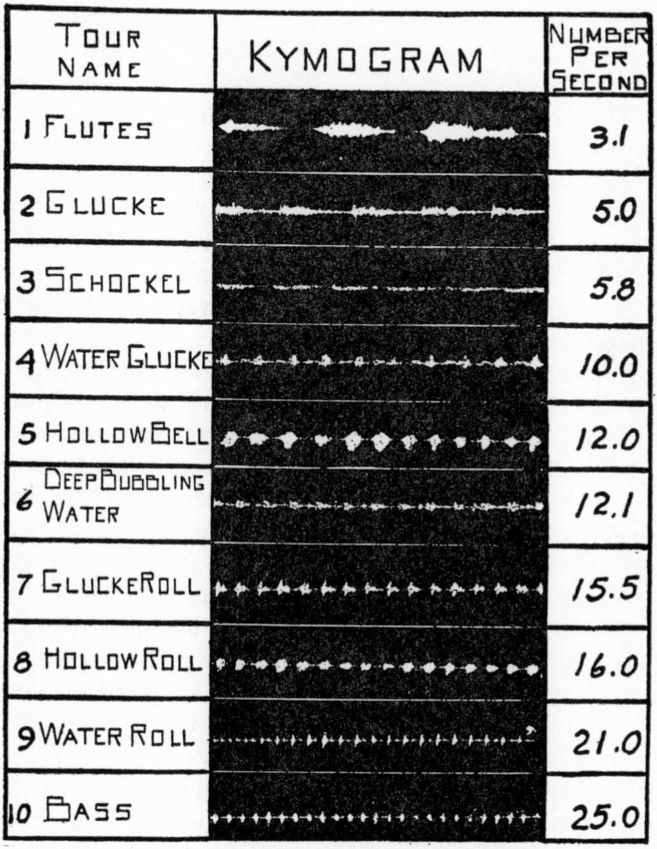

Tour Name	Kymogram	Number Per Second
1 Flutes		3.1
2 Glucke		5.0
3 Schockel		5.8
4 Water Glucke		10.0
5 Hollow Bell		12.0
6 Deep Bubbling Water		12.1
7 Glucke Roll		15.5
8 Hollow Roll		16.0
9 Water Roll		21.0
10 Bass		25.0

Figure 1. Tours of roller canary song

Ten of the most important tours of roller canary songs, showing the name and the average rate of pulsation for each tour. One second of each tour is represented and reveals the characteristic number, form, and temporal regularity of the pulsations in each tour.

one year old? This involved, of course, the determination of the extent to which the spontaneous song would be clearly typical of the recognized tours. Each bird was hatched and reared in complete isolation. Microphones were installed in the cages, and adequate recording devices registered the relative loudness and the time of each pulsation, so that, for each bird, adequate sample records of all the sounds the birds made in daily sample periods were recorded.

During the first six years of the experiment, seven male birds were hatched and matured in such isolation that they could not hear the song of their species. The problem was to determine through continuous daily records for a year to what extent these birds would develop the song characteristics of their species. The records are of permanent character, report a complete series of daily samples for each bird, and are available for intensive study. Each of the daily records was transcribed into patterns as in Figure 1. The pitch, not shown in the figure, was found to vary between 1,000 and 10,000 vibrations per second. The most striking showing of the figure is that there is a periodic recurrence of pulsations as indicated by numbers at right.

Metfessel's first report was based upon the computations of 143,297 pulsations. From these he drew the conclusion that it was not necessary for a male canary to hear the species' song in order to produce it; the song was a product of his organism. It would not have to be taught, for a canary would develop it by himself in the process of maturation. Each bird developed a significant number of characteristic tours which the fanciers regarded as good and as typical of those exhibited by famous singers. However, they did not develop as many tours as those exhibited by the pedigreed parent birds. Each one also developed some extra tours which the canary fanciers classified as undesirable. Apparently there is a process of selection in the exhibition birds by which undesirable tours are eliminated. It was believed from the evidence that the song of the isolated birds would be classed as better than that of wild birds, but not equal to that of their pedigreed parents.

Here, then, at the first stage of this investigation, is a fundamental demonstration of the inheritance of musical talent and its development into beautiful song in complete isolation from the singers of the species and absolutely without training.

WHAT WAS INHERITED?

One of the most promising results of this investigation was that it established data which will enable us to analyze the achievement of the birds in order to discover exactly what was inherited and, to some extent, why it was inherited. Here I shall depart from the plan of reporting facts and instead set up a hypothesis for the utilization of some of these data. The fundamental question is: What are the survival values in the spontaneous activities of the isolated canary which tend to determine racial types of performance? Among these, I wish to point out seven, and indicate how they may operate separately or together, in the preservation of a racial musical trait.

Similarity in the psychophysical musical organism of the species. It is a well-established fact that with the inheritance of an organ goes a tendency to use that organ. While probably all birds have in common some kind of vocal equipment, it differs widely in the various species, as we may judge from hearing the canary, the cuckoo, the owl, and the parrot. Each has a characteristic and predictable register within which the voice can operate. Each has a characteristic volume control. Each has its muscular load which affects the temporal characteristics. Each has different resources for harmonics. Each vocalizes for specific purposes of attraction and repulsion in its specific environment. In other words a given species has a characteristic vocal organ, an instinctive tendency to exercise it, and similar observable devices for its perpetuation and protection. All these are marked limitations upon what a particular species can do in song.

Periodicity. There is a well-established biological law to the effect that in the central nervous system the nervous discharge of the muscles is periodic, the rate of discharge usually being the minimum rate that will result in a steady muscular response. This principle operates in the swing of the golf club, the movement of the tongue, and the maintenance of a smile. Within each of these basic periodicities for an organ is a series of higher frequencies, probably due to the co-ordination of complex musculature. Industry has adopted this highly economical principle of periodicity, for example, by using alternating current in electric lighting systems. The same steadiness of light is obtained from alternating electrical impulses as there is from a direct current giving continuous discharge. In animal life this periodicity has survival value because it is economical. The rate varies with the size and complexity of the musculature that is to be controlled. Here, then, is one basic factor which is common to all birds of a species, and which limits the temporal characteristics of tours.

Only four variables. All vocalizations of birds have pitch, intensity, time, and timbre. The songs of canaries can differ only in these four respects. That fact is, of course, conducive to a similarity in performance which would not exist if there were more or an infinite number of variables. Each species of birds has a tendency to emphasize one or more of these four elements. In the canary, time and intensity play dominant roles. All canaries are recognized by their high pitch and dominant rhythms.

Ease of production. There is a law of inheritance to the effect that instinctive tendencies in action tend to appear in the order of their complexity, ease of production, and basic value. For example, the exhibition of pitch in the song of the canary comes most naturally as a monotony within its register. Although the situation is not as simple as that, presumably new tours could be formed by having for each pulsation a rising pitch or a falling pitch. Then might come a sequence of rise and fall, or a circumflex modulation, and at the highest stage there might appear a trace of design, as a melody. In the same manner it is conceivable that, while the dominant pattern is mere periodicity, there would gradually develop rhythmic patterns through combinations of long and short, loud and soft pulsations. This tendency toward ease and simplicity is of course conducive to a similarity of patterns in the species.

Low versatility. No one would think of saying that human songs are inherited. The versatility of the human mind is so great that there is small chance of a musical theme being inherited, although even here the organic resources for certain inflections favor similarity in song. The features inherited in the human voice are certain types of feelings in the realm of a great variety of pleasures and pains. Musicians find that there are tonal mechanisms which characterize the expression of these feelings. But in a bird there is a very restricted resourcefulness due to instinctive stability of pleasures and pains and the relative absence of creative power. A definite restriction to the range of performance is of course conducive to the appearance of similarity within the limited instinctive range of performances.

Esthetic appeal. In spite of limited resourcefulness, the bird has characteristic ways of expressing pleasure and pain in his song. In man we say the esthetic appeal may be purposeful, whereas in the bird it is purposive; that is, it serves a purpose more or less automatically. Nevertheless, the pleasures or the pains determining the character of the song may constitute genuine esthetic stimuli and lead to likes and dislikes, both on the part of the singing and the listening bird. On the side of pleasure there is a tendency among canaries to have a rate of pulsation of six or seven cycles per second, which is the same as in the human vibrato. We may hazard the suggestion that there is a limit of tolerance in the rate of pulsation for musical satisfaction of the bird, as there is for man. When a bird sings beautifully, it is not out of question to assume that the bird gets satisfaction in a rate of pulsation which stays within the limits of tolerance for rate in a tone beautiful to him. The same is true for richness of tone, insofar as richness of tone may characterize natural urges. Even such a musical variable as preference for harmonic structure may operate instinctively, and simple tendencies to modulate in loudness may set limits to the dynamic structure of the song.

Emotional drives. Within the range of pleasures and pains the bird has basic drives of a more or less fixed character. The wooing song makes use of elemental acoustic mechanisms of attraction; the fighting song comes out of parallel mechanisms of repulsion. We may even assume that the bird sings merely for exuberance in self-expression, but in all these the range of expression is limited by all the above-mentioned limitations of his neuromuscular organism and his musical mind.

Here, then, are some armchair hypotheses about how nature may operate to conserve and exhibit specific types of song in the canary and to limit the range of variability in the song. Analysis of the Metfessel records now in hand may contribute significantly to the identification of factors of this kind, but such hypotheses should lay the foundation for detailed experimentation on birds in the effort to isolate and identify the mechanisms of inheritance of a mental trait in animal behavior. Such experimentation should contribute largely to our understanding and appreciation of inheritance in our human esthetic behavior.

THE ENVIRONMENT EXPERIMENT

It is well known that birds can be taught actual human sor.gs as far as pitch, intensity, rhythm, and tone quality are concerned. It is also generally assumed that young birds profit by association with good canary singers, by imitation of the human voice, and possibly by persistent sounds in the environment. It is now desirable to make a scientific demonstration to show that the natural song, as exhibited in the principal tours of the canary, can be modified by training for a specific adaptation that can be measured and evaluated statistically.

Since the song of the canary may give a clean-cut exhibition of the vibrato, the experimenter undertook to see if he could change this vibrato in some specific characteristic by training. For this purpose he isolated good singers and set the experiment so that he could not only demonstrate the success of such training, but even determine the rate and the limits of development.

It has been shown statistically that typical singers raised in isolation delivered between two and three per cent of their songs with a pulsation rate of approximately seven cycles per second. To see whether the environmental changes would have any influence on this rate, he put two birds in isolation cages, and delivered to them a musical tone of 1,100 vibrations per second, with the pitch pulsations a semitone in extent, and a rate of seven pulsations per second. The stimulus tone was recorded on a phonograph record which was played at stated periods daily in the cage. The experiment showed that in this manner he could change specific parts of the species' song to conform to their environment. Both birds gravitated significantly to the rate of pulsation in a stimulus tone.

In another experiment he substituted a stimulus vibrato of fourteen pulsations for the one of seven pulsations in the preceding experiment. The result of this experiment on four male birds resulted in demonstrating again that the expected song of the species was modified so that there was a tendency to conform to the stimulus pattern. Three of the four birds developed a fourteen-pulsation-per-second vibrato to a significant degree. Thus it was demonstrated that, in a specifically selected and technically measurable element of the song, the species was changed to conform to the song of the environment. This finding offers an explanation for the slight differences found in the song of birds of the same species in different localities.

These experiments clearly prove that canaries learn by imitation of their environment, and, where the environment is controlled by experiment, a specific quality of the song may be cultivated. In this case the rate of the pulsation in song, which corresponds to the vibrato, could be changed so as to deviate from the inherited tendency and make the tour either more or less desirable by training.

For technical details of the experiment and additional observations made by the experimenter, the reader must turn to the original report. What is gleaned here are the positive answers to the original questions, namely: first, some particular tours of the canary are inherited; and, second, inherited patterns may be altered under experimental control of training in the environment. The technique developed gives great promise to the geneticist for the use of birds such as the canary as "guinea pigs" in determining exactly what is inherited, and for relating this to the mechanisms of inheritance.

Chapter 24

MUSICAL ANTHROPOLOGY

MUSICAL ANTHROPOLOGY is at this time entering upon an epoch of development attributable to the availability of new instruments for recording and preserving musical material in field work on an extraordinarily comprehensive scale, and the development of a scientifically and musically significant performance score.

PHONOPHOTOGRAPHY IN FOLK MUSIC [*]

This section will be devoted to a pioneering experiment in the collection, transcription, and interpretation of American Negro songs. From the original collection of thirty-two songs, six are reproduced here as fair samples of scientific field work. These samples contain mines of information which the musician and scientist alike can interpret in the light of his point of view, technical knowledge, insight, and interests.

The experiment reported was a piece of pioneer work which was undertaken for two purposes: first, to substitute motion picture films for the traditional phonograph; and, second, to introduce the performance score (at that time it was called pattern score) and technical laboratory transcription as scientific media through which to preserve and interpret collections of musical material.

In 1926 the University of Iowa, in co-operation with the University of North Carolina, undertook a project for recording Negro songs in their natural setting. The Laura Spelman

---

[*] Based on *Phonophotography in Folk Music,* by Milton Metfessel, published by the University of North Carolina Press, and reprinted by the State University of Iowa in 1928, 181 pp., with musical scores for all the songs. The first 17 pp. contain my introduction to this investigation.

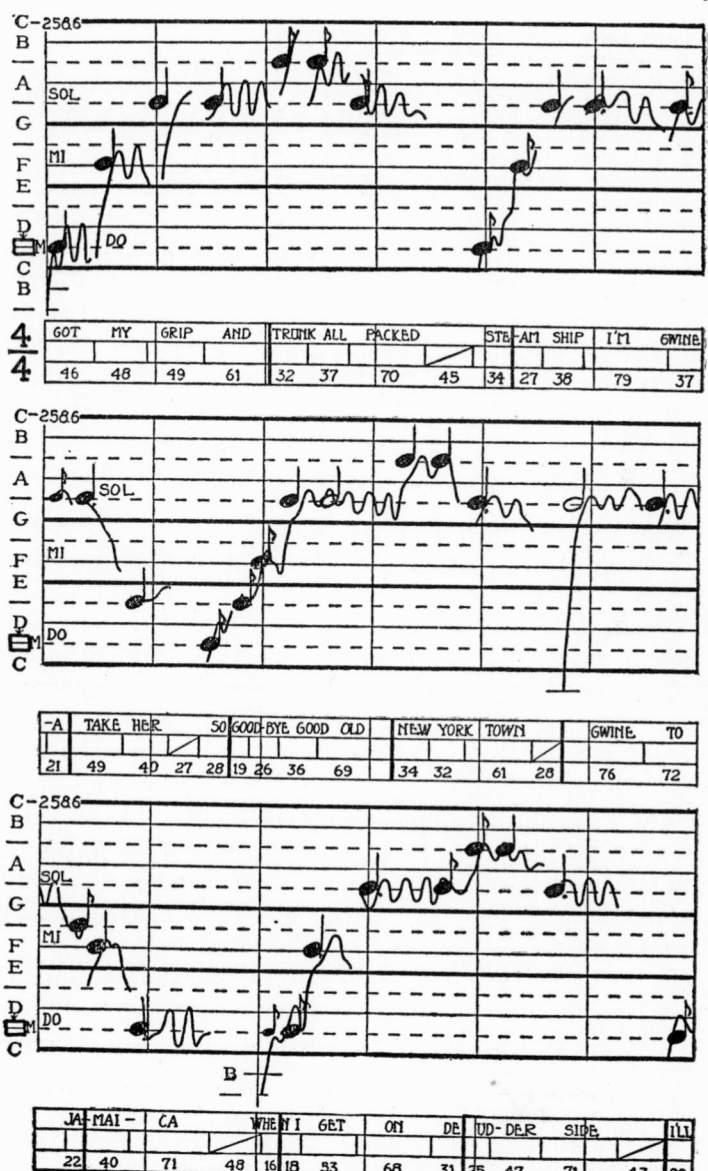

Figure 1a. *West Indies Blues*

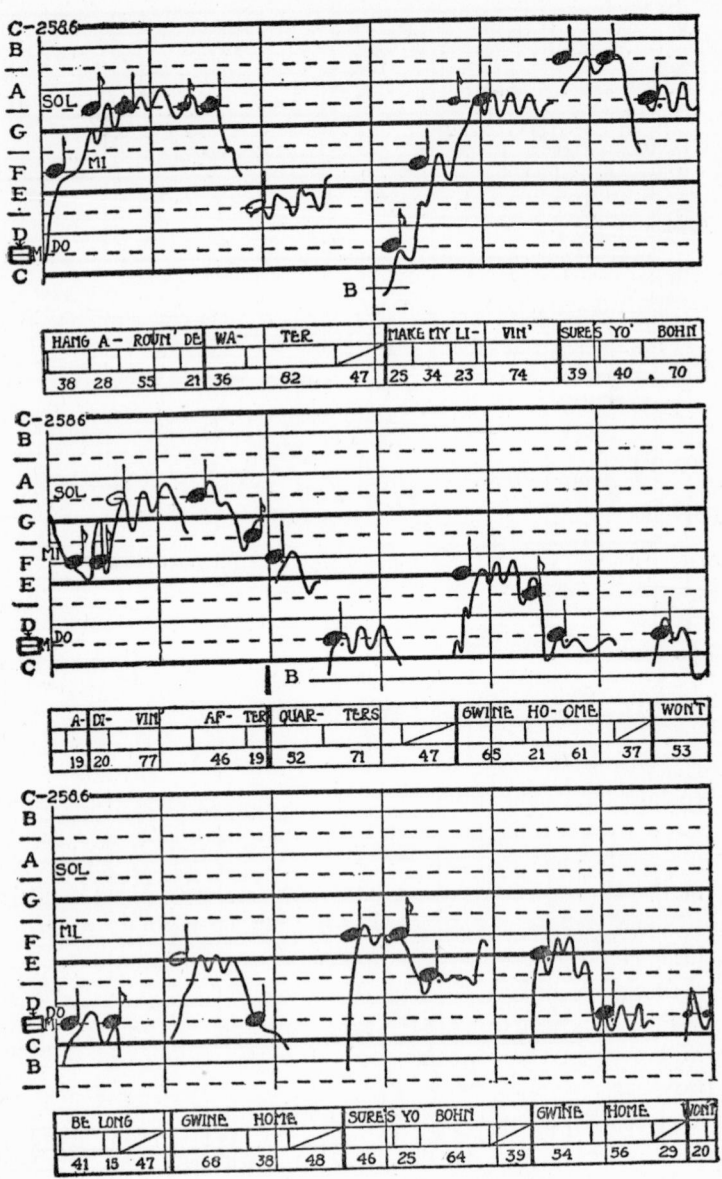

Figure 1b. *West Indies Blues* (cont'd)

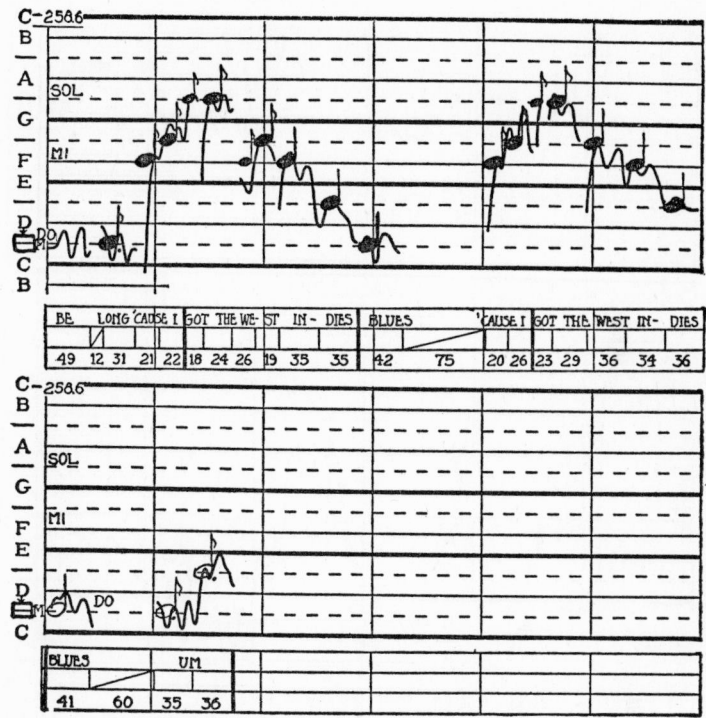

Figure 1c. *West Indies Blues* (cont'd)

Rockefeller Foundation had placed a subvention for the collection of Negro music at the disposal of the Institute for Research in Social Science of the University of North Carolina, under the direction of Professor H. W. Odum and Dr. Guy B. Johnston, authorities on Negro music. In the pursuit of this project, these investigators were hampered by the shortcomings in the methods of musical field work, and became interested in the new developments at the University of Iowa. In turn, we at the University of Iowa had developed techniques of recording, transcription, analysis, and description of the performance of musical artists, and were anxious to extend these techniques into the vast field of musical anthropology.

It was agreed that the men at the University of North Carolina were to use part of their special fund for this purpose,

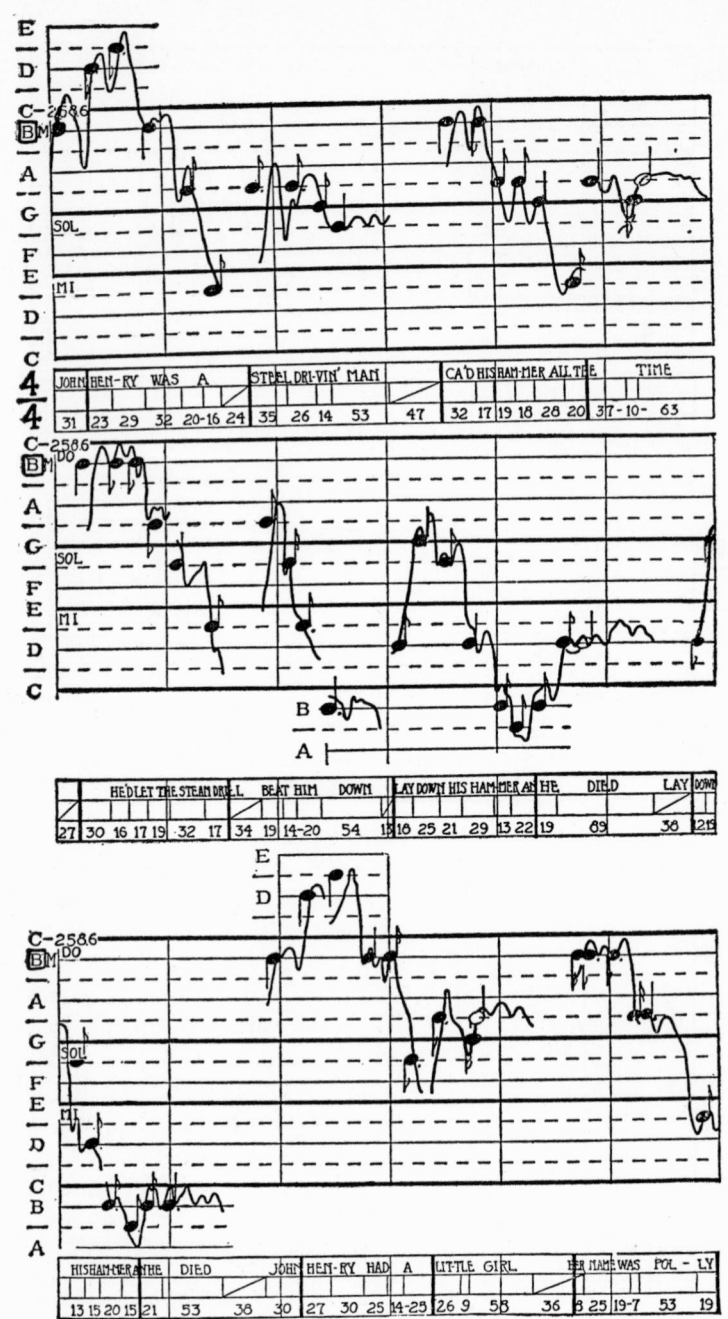

Figure 2a. *John Henry*

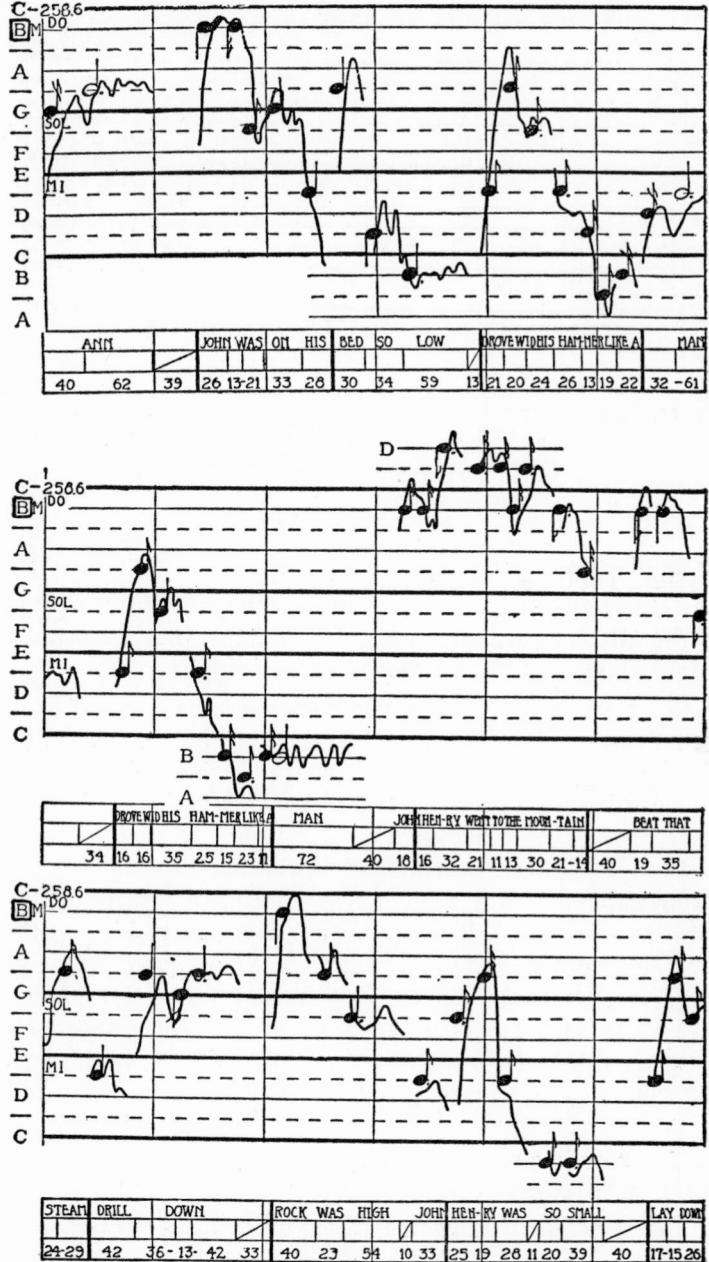

Figure 2b. *John Henry* (cont'd)

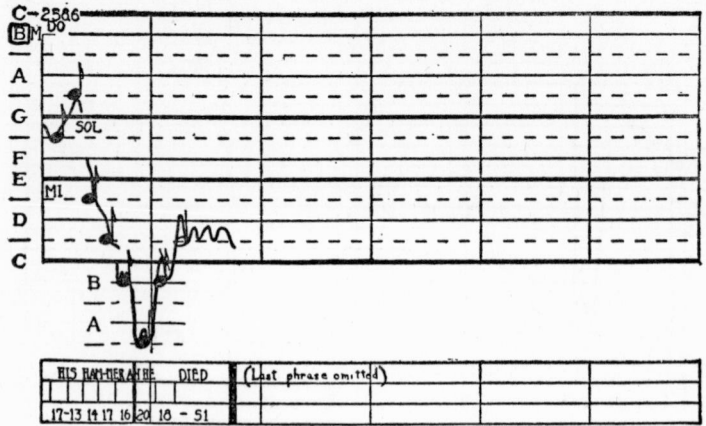

Figure 2c. *John Henry* (cont'd)

selecting significant singers and standing the cost of publication. The University of Iowa was to furnish the technical apparatus, do the actual field work, transcribe the films into performance scores, and report the findings in a monograph.

Dr. Milton Metfessel, a National Research Council fellow from 1925 to 1928, had taken a strong lead in the development of laboratory techniques and was chosen to pursue this project. This was before the sound film had been adapted for field work, so that we had to design and build a camera especially for this purpose. In order to camouflage it, the camera was built into a suitcase which was represented as being a moving picture camera. This was to keep the singers unaware of the fact that their singing would be recorded. The Negro workers in the field were delighted to have their pictures taken, but they might have been embarrassed had they suspected that their voices were being recorded. However, motion pictures were taken of the performers, as in Figure 1, where the singer is represented in his emotional attitude in singing after he had worked himself into a trance-like religious inspiration which he considered necessary for singing.

The principle of the performance score has been illustrated in earlier chapters of this book. Suffice it here to say that the

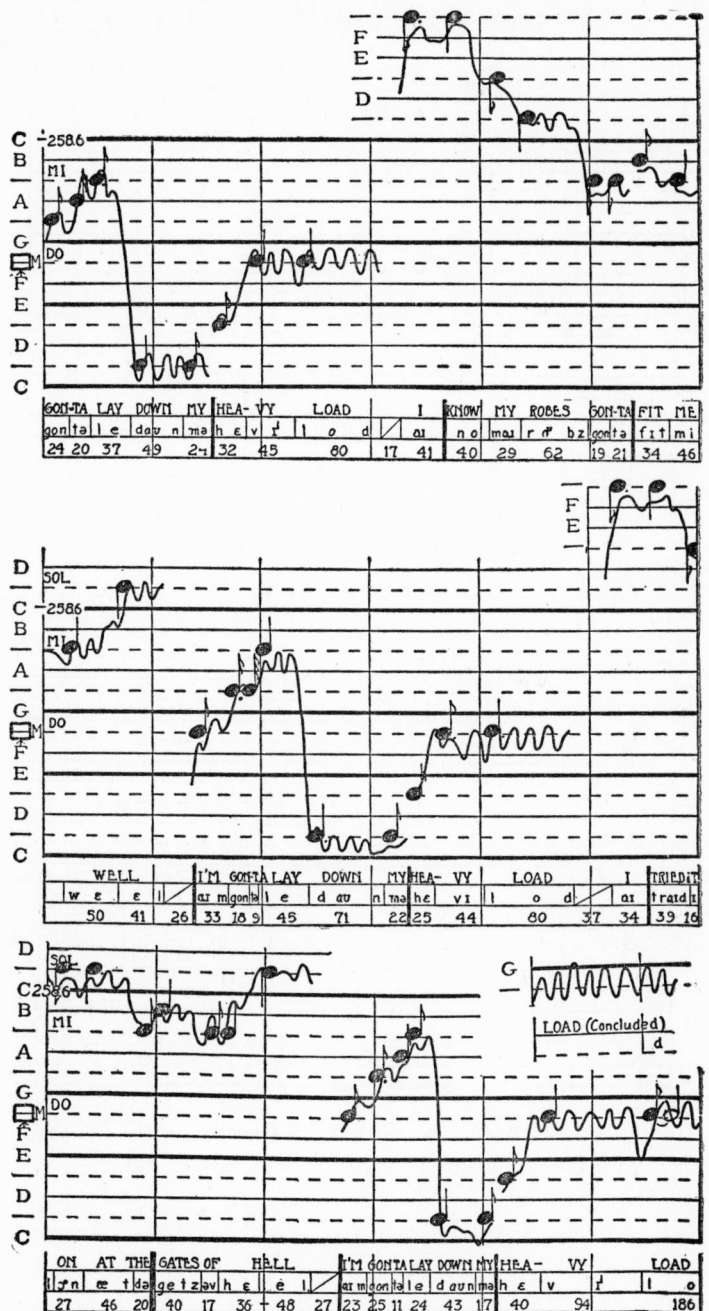

Figure 3a. *By and By*

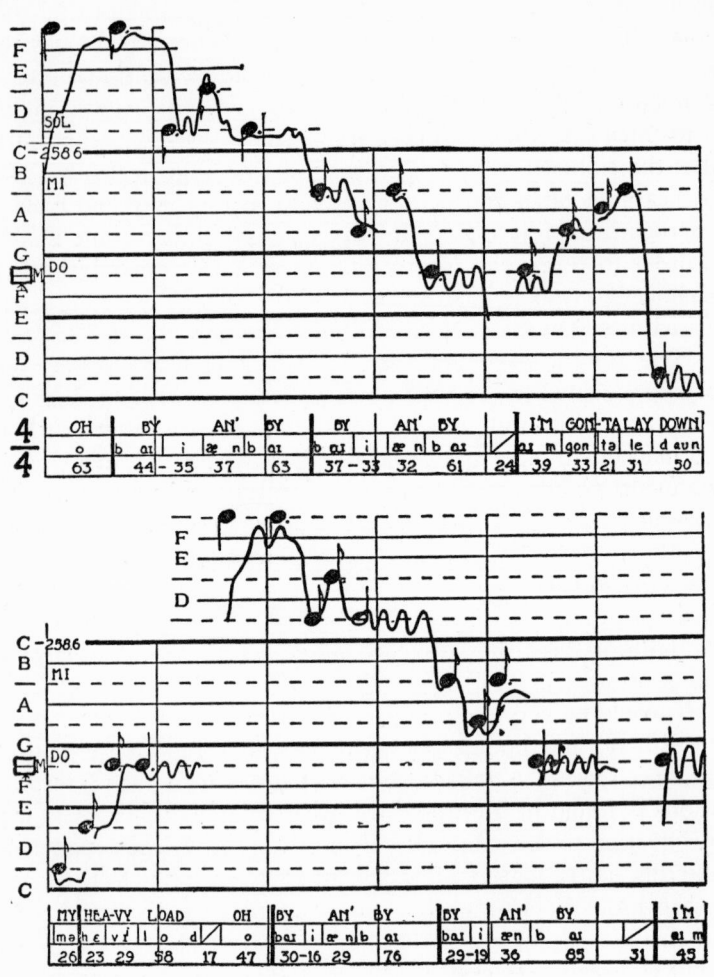

Figure 3b. *By and By* (cont'd)

score consists of graphs showing in exact detail the intonation as to the pitch, and time relations of each sound, on an adapted musical staff. Each note is represented by a graph showing the actual pitch and time in the performance. Through the assistance of Professor Philip Greeley Clapp, the conventional musical notation is interpolated so as to indicate the theoretical goals as to pitch and time. This is important because it represents what the cultured ear tends to hear in listening musically. No one hears the pitch, for example, exactly as it is sung, but makes generous interpretation in the direction of the harmonic goals. In order to reveal the Negro dialect the words are interpreted in phonetic symbols, and below these the approximate duration of each note is expressed in terms of a hundredth of a second.

Here for the first time we have a language of musical recording, adapted to the conditions of field work, which is exact, definable, and meaningful. Compare that with the former loose and inadequate reporting in field work. At the time this record was made, no adequate means were available for measuring the dynamic phases of the performance in terms of intensity of tone; nor did we have any field instrument which recorded the sound waves in sufficient detail for harmonic analysis to reveal the tonal spectrum of each note. With the instruments now available both of these can be recorded and represented in performance scores.

It would be very tempting to engage here in a discussion of the esthetic and nonesthetic principles involved in these performance scores. A fairly extensive treatment of such interpretations is found in Metfessel's original volume, *op. cit.,* and my introduction to the same. But I must here leave each reader to take this source material and put his own questions to the facts before him. Some objective and quantitative answers occur, but this was a pioneer work, and performance scores like these could be greatly enriched today by adding intensity and timbre to the pitch and time here recorded. The reader may also bear in mind that all the complex forms of audible expression are reported in terms of the four basic aspects of musical hearing, which correspond to the attributes of sound waves. We have

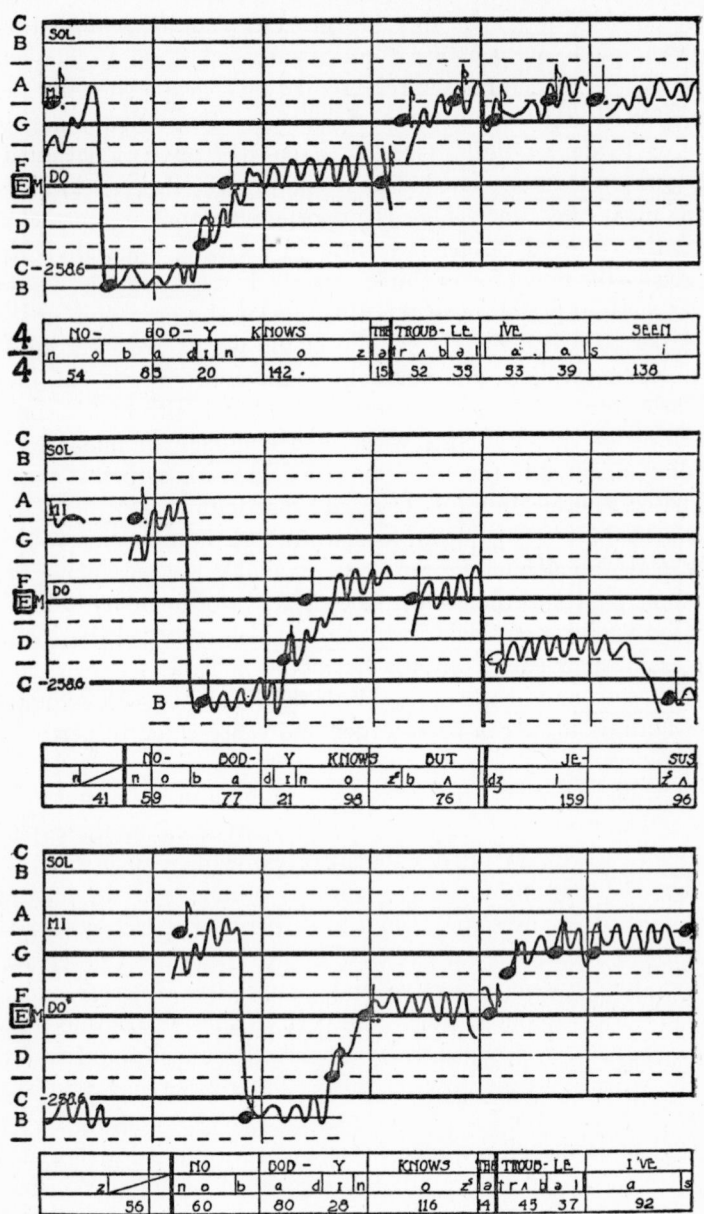

Figure 4a. *Nobody Knows the Trouble I've Seen*

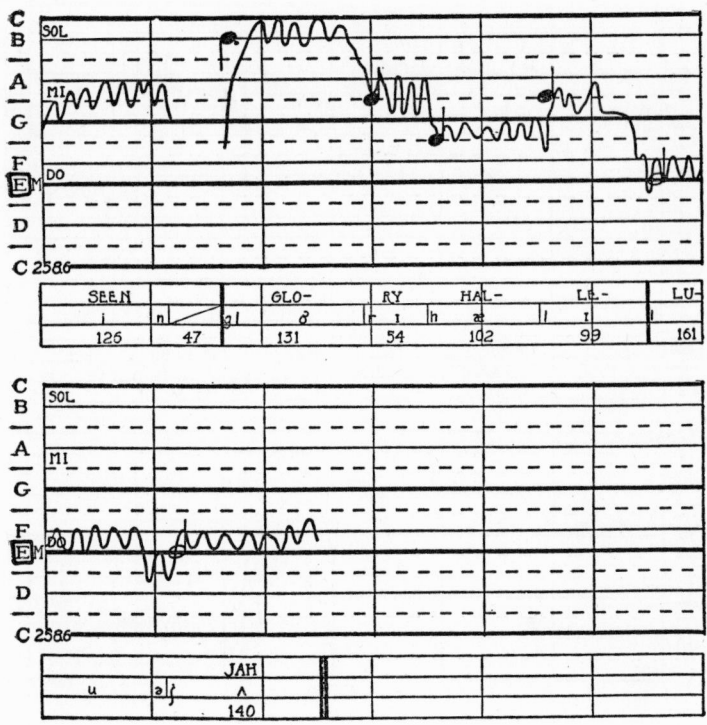

Figure 4b. *Nobody Knows the Trouble I've Seen* (cont'd)

here a blueprint for procedure in musical anthropology of the future.

This experiment was made in 1926. Since then marvelous progress has been made in the development of instruments and techniques for the recording of music. Indeed, musical and scientific material of extraordinary value is accumulating in the laboratories of the motion picture industry. Committees for salvaging this material are co-operating with the industry, but as yet little has been accomplished by this means. I therefore present in the following section of this chapter a definite plan for accomplishing one part of this job.

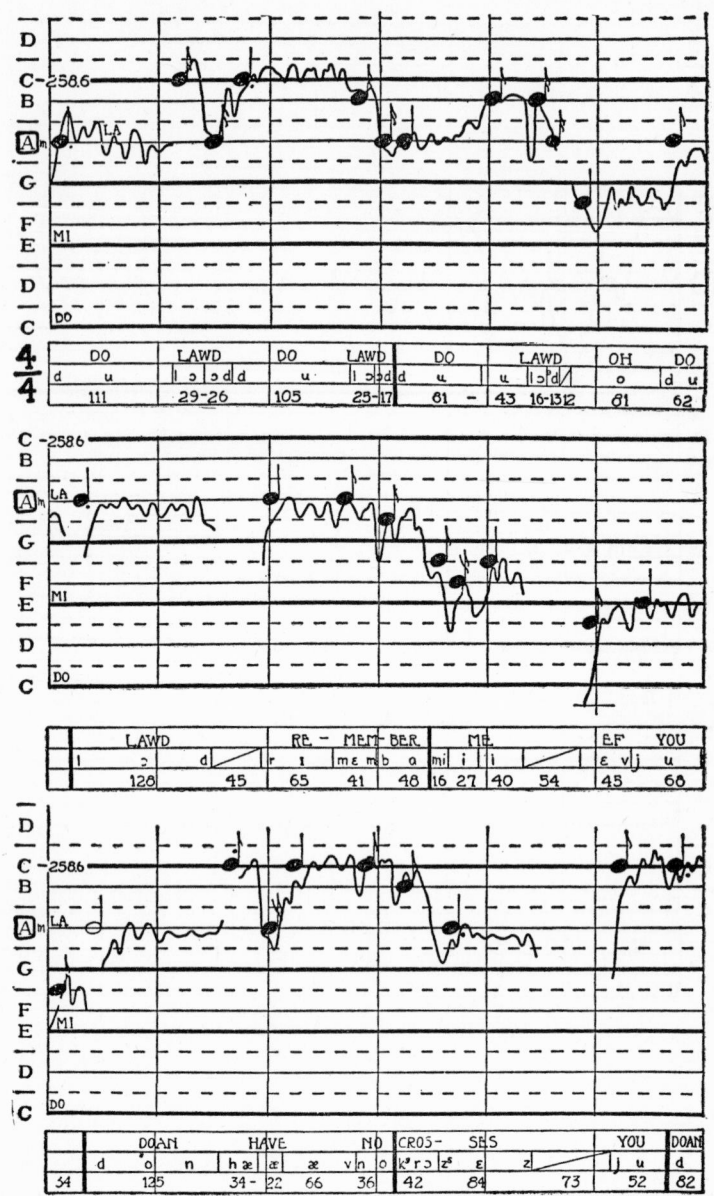

Figure 5a. *Do Lawd*

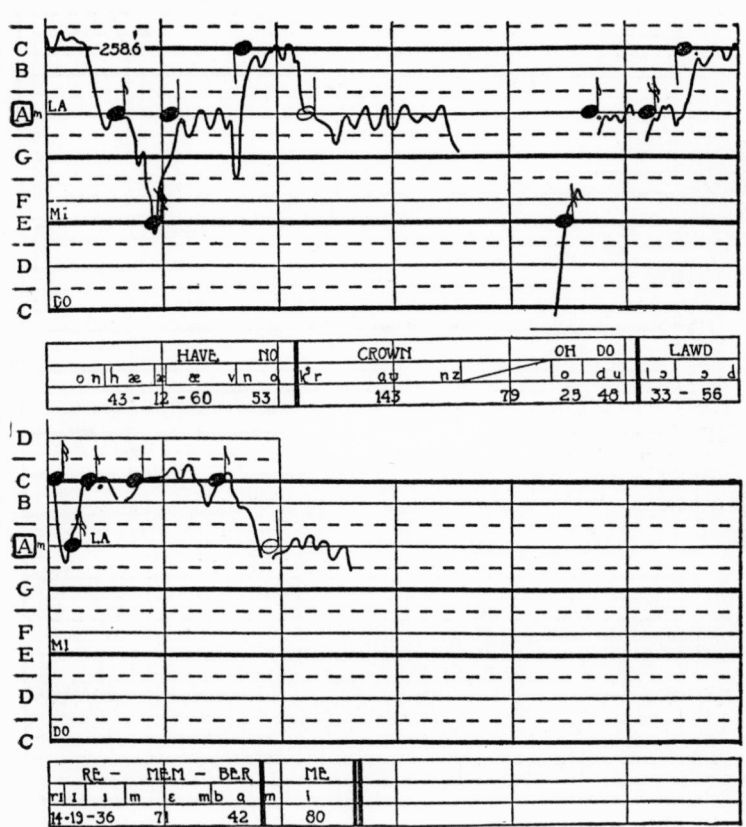

Figure 5b. *Do Lawd* (cont'd)

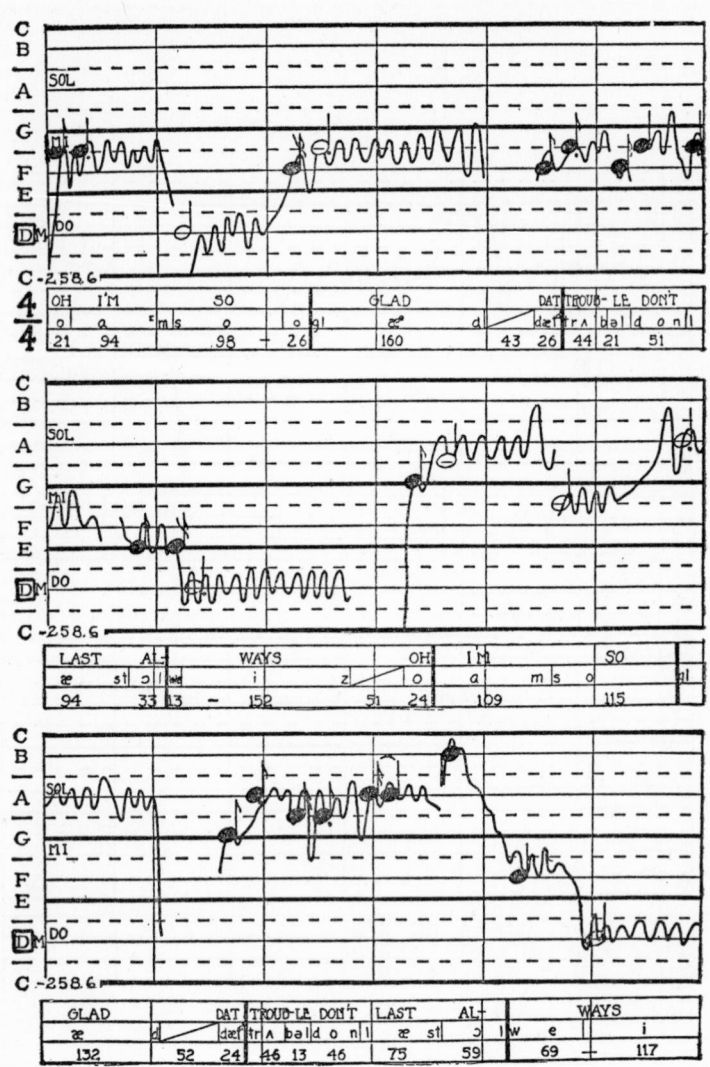

Figure 6a. *I'm So Glad Trouble Don't Last Always*

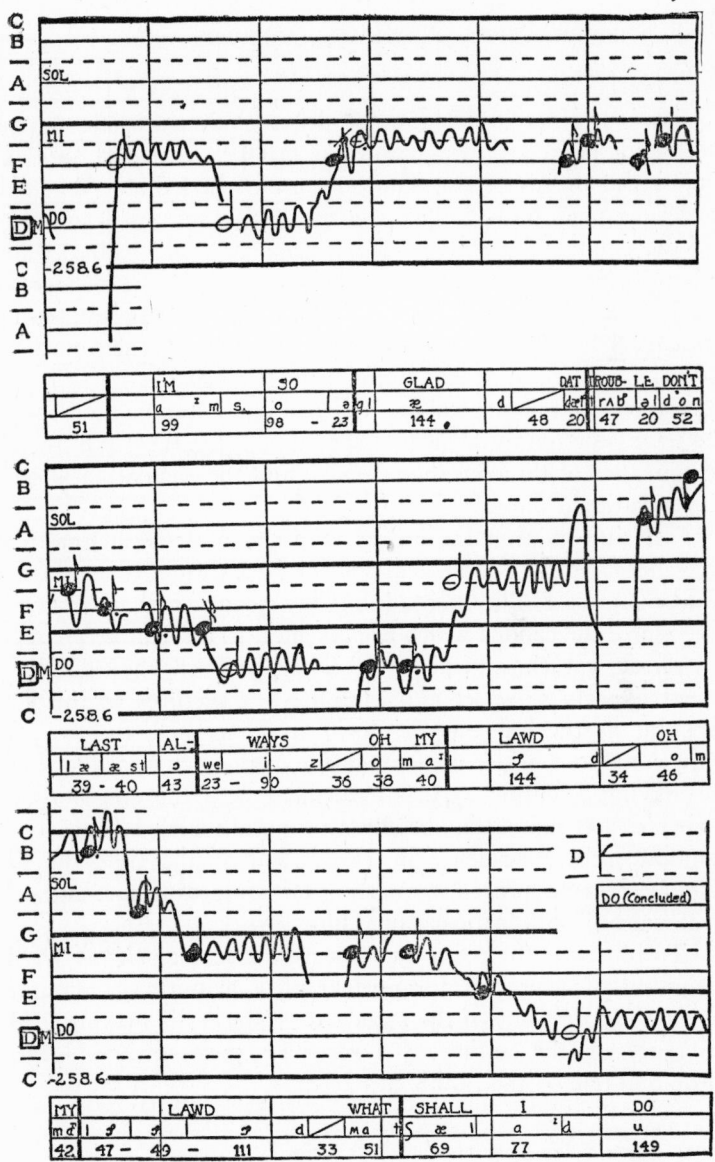

Figure 6b. *I'm So Glad Trouble Don't Last Always* (cont'd)

CO-OPERATION OF SCIENCE AND ART WITH THE
FILM INDUSTRY *

Acoustical engineering, especially as exploited by the theater, has made great progress within the last few years. It has revolutionized means of communication, enriched the art of public entertainment, and changed the economies, interests, and tastes of the public. The acoustical engineer has dealt primarily with the physical instrument and its environment; the theater has dealt primarily with the problem of merchandizing amusement. But each has left an equally large field of approach quite untouched. The acoustical engineer must reach out into the psychological and phonetical analysis of human hearing and feeling as they function in music and speech, and the theater must take cognizance of the educational value and the factual basis of its informational films.

The informational value of amusement through tone films has increased the educational power of the theater to an extraordinary degree. But in so doing the producers have failed to recognize the canons which are essential to a scientific approach to music, speech, and pictures. They have engaged entertainment experts to select and organize the pictures in the field. Insofar as the interests of music are concerned, the time has now come to consider the factual side of the picture at the source by having scientific experts associated with the entertainment experts. Let me outline briefly a proposal which I made to the motion picture academy in Hollywood at the time the film *Trader Horn* appeared, requesting faithfulness to fact and educational utility in informational films.

To illustrate the point by a concrete case, let us consider the planning of a project for portraying a primitive community. Let us say that one of the standard producers is making a film to represent the culture of a relatively pure strain of savage people in one of the South Sea Islands.[1] To secure correct and

---

[1] The same principle would apply to the filming of racial characteristics of music or racial life in general, not necessarily primitive, such as the music of the American Negro or Indian or any national folk music.

---

* From *Science,* 1942, *96,* 263–265.

effective representation of the resources, characteristics, and uses of music, and dance and speech in this primitive group, the producers should send a competent musical anthropologist to the locality a year or two in advance of the actual photographing. Among the qualifications and functions of such an expert for the study of primitive music would be the following:

(1) He must be well grounded in the psychology of music, the history and theory of music, and the anthropological and ethnological literature bearing on primitive music and allied arts, such as the dance, the drama, speech, and magic. This is necessary in order that he may have a well-organized matrix of facts and theories into which he is to set new facts and by which to classify his observations.

(2) He must cultivate the acquaintance and good will of the natives so as to be admitted to their dwellings, to their ceremonials and all their other activities in which music may play a part. In so doing, he should select unobtrusively the outstanding performers for the demonstration of the scientific aspects of this project and at the same time prepare for the cameraman by identifying interested groups which might function willingly and faithfully for the cameraman. Primitive communities are conservative, but they are interested in all forms of magic. The scientist should utilize this interest while cultivating responses which will reveal the true life of the people. For this purpose such devices as the phonograph, the camera, and motion pictures may be employed to create a receptive atmosphere for the film organizers. While the scientist is initiated into the life of the tribe or community in his two years of residence, he will lead a sort of heroic life by introducing into their play life a pattern which is in harmony with the culture level and which will lead to self-forgetfulness and revealing self-expression in all performances.

(3) Through an adequate period of intensive study of the musical life of the community, the scientist should be able to discover and isolate characteristic features of purely scientific interest and rehearse these in significant forms through his play life with the people. When the photographers arrive, he will

have a scientific program set up in the form of a series of short specific acts which will constitute a well-designed scientific collection. Producers have assured us that they would be delighted to take these pictures without cost to the scientific interests in recognition of the service rendered and donate them to appropriate collections, unretouched and freely available for study by home experts. The scientist should exercise insight into the various affiliates of music, such as dance, speech, and mimicry, and try to reveal the ethical and esthetic significance of the entire culture of this particular group. The sound films will of course be accompanied by motion pictures revealing the actual behavior and environment characteristic of the performance.

(4) In the meantime the collector will have paved the way for the organization of amusement features which will give effective cues and provide trained actors for the exhibition films. This in itself would be an adequate service for which the producers would be glad to cover the expenses of the scientist. Naturally he would serve as a consultant in the organization of the amusement features in such a way as to give them educational validity. This would give scientific and educational value to the pictures in the theater. It should in no way interfere with the entertainment value of the picture because patrons of the movies would be quick to discover that in such cases truth may be stranger than fiction.

(5) It is conceivable that the purely scientific pictures might even find a place as shorts in the standard theater. The adoption of that policy might prove a successful innovation now that education in popular science is so general in this country.

(6) The practice of advertising the backing of scientists in moving pictures has been the drawback in enterprises of this kind. But this is due to the failure to develop and follow a reasonable policy of co-operation. Both parties can now take a long stride forward in solving this problem. The two interests are so closely allied that some satisfactory solution must be found. To be effective, any plan must operate in the selection and sponsoring of the scientist and must be defined specifically in his contract. Scientists and educators should realize that it will benefit all.

(7) The first steps in the scientific work on such a collection in the field of primitive music would naturally be (a) to take the films into the laboratory and rephotograph them in a form suitable for the construction of performance scores for which we now have adequate techniques and patterns; (b) to publish these performance scores in order that they may be permanently preserved as a graphic representation of all the findings; and (c) to publish with the performance score the technical field notes of the collector.

(8) To implement the scientific use of the collection, it is essential that the various musicological, psychological, and anthropological research organizations should co-operate with their representative, not only in recognizing him as the authentic collector, but in organizing research staffs for utilizing the collection in the interests of various sciences. It is therefore desirable that the prospective collector, before he goes, should acquaint himself with the ways and means of promoting research in this field through the various professional research agencies. A one-man collection thus made could serve as sufficient research material for a large staff of workers.

In conclusion I may say that when I first broached this proposition to the Academy of Motion Picture Arts and Sciences in Hollywood, great interest was shown, and from several sources I heard the question, "Where is your man?" I gained the impression that if the right man had been available at that time, the project would have been undertaken immediately.

Chapter 25

THE EVOLUTION OF MUSICAL VALUES

THE NATURAL HISTORY of music reveals the principal rungs in the tottering ladder of its evolution. The rise of man has covered a period of at least a million years. Like the evolution of man as a whole, music has proceeded by ups and downs, in intricate ways and along divergent routes, always contingent upon the culture level of man and the rise of new urges, new purposes to be served, new abilities, new environments, and new facilities. The story of this evolution told in a few pages, it is confessed, will be oversimplified. This brief sketch will be limited to the prehistoric period as traced for us in musical anthropology and ethnology. The historic period of music is but an hour as compared with the million years in the prehistoric period. Our appreciation of the great art of today can be enhanced by an understanding and appreciation of its humble origin and natural perspective.

MUSIC BEFORE MAN

Every musical capacity had its taproots in the lower forms of animal life, where song and vocal calls of warning, attraction, endearment, and sociability tended to preserve the individual, perpetuate the species, and integrate the group. The rising need of vocal communication in the animal world resulted in the development of a physical organism essential to musical behavior, both in tone production and in tone appreciation, from the simplest phonation to highly patterned whistling, rattling, howling, and roaring militant or endearing vocalizing for the purpose of repulsion on the one hand, and on the other hand to the articulate vocal intimations of friendliness as in the fascinating love song of birds.

Like protective coloration, protective phonation has played an important role in animal life. The various forms and refinements of ear arose to serve increasing needs of attraction and repulsion. As the display of beauty in coloration developed dominant types in different animal species, so the exhibition of sounds of attraction developed along special lines. Like the display of color, the exhibition of sounds and the response to them through hearing was mainly automatic. Yet from our point of view, audible behavior rose to heights of beauty that might well be regarded as musical. The development of the ability to respond to sound applied not only to the sounds of animals but to sounds of nature. Accompanying dramatic actions arose, as in the song and dance found in the courtship of birds and beasts of many species. Much of our appreciation of musical sounds as nature lovers attaches to the musical behavior of animals in their natural habitats, such as our gardens, forest preserves, and national sanctuaries. Men visiting the Bok Tower Preserve even on a hot day are asked to wear and not carry their coats out of respect for the animal life in this sanctuary where the play of vibrant sounds mingles in harmony with the beauty of flowers and the grand carillon.

The story of musical behavior furnishes one of the most fascinating chapters both in scientific and popular observation of animal behavior. While the species from which man became differentiated may not have been outstanding for their song, there is no doubt that these species lived very largely in a tonal world of their own. Thus, before man came upon the horizon, his forebears had already developed the necessary muscular and neural organizations which, in man, made possible the development of human music. Primitive man undoubtedly carried over not only the musical organism but the instinctive forms of behavior distinctive of his parent species. But with the emergence of man, the musical organism assumed radically new functions, the development of which we can now sketch in outline.

THE SMILE

Students of origins have speculated about the possible taproots of human music. One of the plausible theories traces the beginning of musical expression of feeling to the human smile. The beginning of the smile has been conceived somewhat as follows: The primitive mother in the species just emerging is nursing her infant. When the infant is satisfied, its head drops back and, as a result of releasing the nipple, a reflex puckering of the lips takes place. The mother, seeing this repeatedly, came to accept it as an indication that the child was satisfied or pleased. Through sympathetic observation of this for generations, there gradually developed in the mother an imitation of the puckering of the lips. Thus, mother and child developed a mutual understanding—an inceptive language of feeling and meaning. This one attitude of satisfaction was gradually extended to cover a variety of experiences. When the infant was patted on the back, kissed, bathed, and played with, it responded with this one sign, the smile.

At this stage there developed a complement to the smile, the frown, which was also reciprocated by the mother. Mother and child recognized in each other two distinctive facial attitudes: the expression of pleasure and the expression of pain. Physiologists now recognize an organic basis for differentiation of these two complementary types of facial expression representing, as James said, the two basic types of behavior interchange. It was the beginning of the language of feeling in man.

LAUGHTER AND CRYING

The visual signs of pleasure and pain soon took audible forms in signs of attraction and repulsion. Thus arose the power of expression through simple spontaneous gurgles and other vocal utterances. These gradually developed into primitive patterns of laughter and crying, which were differentiated into various kinds and degrees of expressions of satisfaction or dissatisfaction. Laughter became a pleasing "ha-ha-ha" and crying came to indicate many distinct forms of distress. Through eons of cultivation of these more or less reflex sounds, certain advantages were found in the substitution of audible for visual expressions. In the primitive community, vocal communication tended to preserve life from the infant level up to more elaborate forms of co-operation and combat in adult life because sounds could be heard in the dark or at a distance. Sounds of attraction could be made pleasing and sounds of repulsion terrifying. Meaningful sounds thus became key instruments in the conscious preservation and enhancement of life. The evolution of the smile and laughter and of the frown and crying are parallel throughout the rise of man.

CONSCIOUSNESS OF MUSICAL MEANING

The rise of music in man began with a purposeful, as distinguished from a mechanically purposive, use of the medium. In the lower animals musical behavior had been essentially instinctive, however efficiently it served its ends; whereas in man it gradually became rational and deliberative. From the inception of musical behavior we may trace a progressive increase in the consciousness of music as a power and as a source of pleasure in itself. Primitive man undoubtedly could not sing and charm with music as could some of the specialized animal species of that day. He was, in the beginning, at a disadvantage in comparison with them. But man developed musically through recognition of purpose, a deliberate and feelingful pursuit of musical goals, and the attachment of meaning to musical sounds in nature and in the human voice in the control of life.

It will be observed that throughout the rise of music the form was determined by its use. The primary object of music was to serve a purpose rather than to give pleasure. Thus throughout its rise we must emphasize the ecological place of music in the evolution of human behavior. This includes the appeals to the gods which have always been one of the major functions of music. Then followed martial music designed to facilitate rhythmic action and engender emotional drives. Later came the avocational use of music as a means of passing leisure time and enjoying social intercourse, with the primary object of strengthening the social bond in connection with the dance and other group activities. Out of this grew folk music, first in the form of heroic narrative on the part of roaming singers and later in the form of group singing and instrumental ensembles, expressing the joy of living, the sorrows, ambitions, hopes, and devotions of man. Through the entire history of magic, music has been cultivated for its healing value. It is only in comparatively recent times that music has been cultivated as art for art's sake. Throughout history there has been a progressive refinement of music as a means for the expression of love—love as the expression of human bonds, love as a form of the expression of wonder, fellowship and devotion in worship, love as a nonreflective self-surrender.

MAGIC AND RELIGION

One of the earliest functions of music came in the realm of magic and mythology. Primitive man was early impressed with the idea that his was a spiritual existence, because in his dreams he found himself engaged in countless varieties of adventure and exploration in the unknown world, while his body was at rest, and he observed that this same experience was shared by others. This belief in spirits aroused in him two basic feelings: fear and awe. He began to wonder about the spirit world and gradually developed a mythology which promised him a form of immortality and aroused cravings for communication with the good spirits and the heroic friends who had passed into this region. The primary urge, however, lay in the necessity for pacifying and controlling the evil spirits. To him, the spirit world was the real world, the larger world, the world of the powers that control all nature. He therefore developed ways and means of putting himself in good standing with this world through sacrifice, incantations, and magic. These expressions rose out of his spontaneous wails of fear and grunts of hope. But he soon began to exercise them by proxy, through intermediaries such as magicians, priests, prophets, and rulers. A primary function of these intermediaries was to make sacrifices, both animal and human, which were freely given to pacify the gods. To be effective and impressive, the sacrifice had to become a ceremonial. This took the form of incantation, which made use of colorful sounds, dances, and other forms of dramatic action which would presumably please the gods as they pleased man.

The intermediaries between the gods and man thus came to provide protection and enhancement of life through their supposed control of the spirit world. Through this medium, food, rain, safety, and power of all kinds were solicited; and the right to live in a spiritual world after death was promised. In the beginning the music in these ceremonies consisted of individual performances, vocal and instrumental, with dramatic action on the part of the magician or other intermediary who supposedly had entree to the rulers of the spirit world. In the early stages these musical appeals to the gods consisted largely of mysterious and powerful noises. There was no formal melody; few, if any, words or sounds having specific meaning were used. Much later there developed group action, as in the chant and dance and rhythmic maneuvers which increased as man rose in culture and lived in larger and larger units in social co-operation.

ORDERLY EVOLUTION

Each of the numerous and complicated rungs in the ladder on which music rose represents a vantage ground from which larger and larger horizons developed in the rise of civilization and culture. We should not gain the impression that these steps are clear-cut. Music as a normal medium for the expression of feeling contained from its beginning the rudimentary elements of all that now has flowered into modern music. They were present in speech and in the sounds which were substituted for speech. They were gradually recognized in the sounds of nature and countless forms of animal life. There was a constant flux and differentiation in the progressive rise of each element in the musical medium as new sound controls and powers of appreciation evolved. Yet our story should emphasize the fact that the coming in of each element in the musical medium had a logical basis in which we can trace the increasing operation of cause and effect for the preservation and enhancement of life.

The rise of music as a medium of human expression was contingent upon the rise of man as a whole, especially the ability to discover and meet new situations, the growth of new urges for self-expression, and the rise of human ideals. It was also contingent upon the progressive evolution of society. Thus we can readily see that the growth of music was contingent upon and parallel to the evolution of the power of human beings to live together in larger and larger units pointing toward a brotherhood of man in a civilized and cultured world.

MUSIC AND SPEECH

The voice was the original instrument both in prehuman and human natural history. From stage to stage it set the pace for the discovery and invention of instruments and the development of instrumental music. Most of the elements of musical sound appeared first in forms of emotional speech. Whether music or speech had precedence in the development of the use of sound has been a bone of contention among anthropologists. They probably developed together inseparably. Speech and music have the same characteristics, such as pitch, loudness, time, timbre, rhythm, and volume. They are formed by the same vocal organs; they both serve to convey meaning and feeling. Of course, the use of words in music had to await the development of words in speech. But meaning was conveyed in inarticulate sounds long before it came to be conveyed in organic words. Music made a long stride forward when it adopted conventionalized words in place of the imitations of natural or symbolic sounds to convey meaning.

Primitive song was not, however, exclusively a method of conveying meaning; it was also a means of enriching sounds with feeling, as in the chant, which might consist of the continuous repetition of two or more words for their euphonic value. This characteristic is well represented even in the primitive music of today, where a song is not the telling of a story but a repeated play upon certain key words which have symbolic meaning and euphonic power. In its earliest stages the song was not used as a substitute for speech in conveying consecutive messages; rather it consisted of syllables or words as ejaculatory forms for the expression of feeling. Verbal intonation was first cultivated for the individual communication of feelings of attraction or repulsion. As the number of usable words increased the chorus developed, and was used in the celebration of heroic events, of plentiful harvests, in group appeals during famine or war, and in festivities to mark the rising of the sun or the changing phases of the moon, and generally in events of human relations, individual and social.

MUSICAL SYMBOLISM

From the beginning music, as the expression of emotional life not reducible to logical language, has been a medium for communicating ideals or urges as contrasted with ideas. It has been the language of mysticism, going far beyond the idealizations as expressed in poetry. It has expressed an attitude toward the gods and the spiritual world as a whole. As in the behavior of birds, it has expressed the sexual urge in all its rationalized and idealistic forms. As music for music's sake, it is a sort of dream language which carries the performer and the listener far beyond the routine of daily life.

In its inception, music operated as a sort of magic between man and the gods; it was an individual art. The magician, the conjurer, and the priest acquired great prestige through their mystic art. Participation of the social group came much later, and in this we can trace the development of musical leadership devoted to the stimulation of co-operative effort in the control of nature, in the development of morals, in the fostering of a sense of beauty, and in the offering of a common human retreat from the humdrum aspects of life. Out of leadership arose the functions of the composer who in the early stages originated musical activities which became conventionalized and perpetuated from generation to generation by word of mouth. Even the civilized composer had to await the art of writing and the gradual establishment of musical notations.

The aim of this sketch has been to trace the purpose and order of musical values from the point of view of esthetics. Using the term *music* in its broadest sense, embracing animal as well as human performance, it is evident that in both cases vocalizations were a means of communication, a language cultivated distinctly for its utility in the preservation and enhancement of life. But from the beginning these vocal signs tended to become pleasurable as tokens of success in attraction and of power in repulsion, developing into patterns in which we find the rich blossoming of musical form. Parallel to the vocal utterances and in imitation of them arose the invention and utilization of instruments. Like vocal sounds, instruments were first mainly of utilitarian value but gradually evolved through their effective appeals into independent elements of beauty in musical form. While the earlier function of music as of life preserving value has not diminished, the capstone of musical achievement even today lies largely in its purely artistic aspect—in music as a form of play with no ulterior purpose, as art for art's sake. In interpreting·this statement, we must remember that such play has had a dominant role in the evolution of man and today has a leading role in the development of the individual and society.

Chapter 26

THE MEASUREMENT OF MUSICAL ACHIEVEMENT

NATIONAL STANDARDS for progressive examinations are now feasible and highly desirable, especially for our system of musical education in the public schools. They should be formulated and maintained by an organized body of music educators who have technical competence and artistic interest in the clarification of the aims and purposes of the public school curriculum, and in the motivation of achievement by a uniform system of examination. This raising of standards and motivation for achievement is in the best interests of progress in music education. Here is a worthy project in applied esthetics.

We have now reached the psychological moment for taking our bearings in the topsy-turvy progress that has been made in the measurement of achievement in musical learning. Instead of presenting a critical review of past and present procedures, I shall boldly sketch some of the goals toward which I think we should strive in the near future. With acknowledgments to all the experts in the field, I submit a few basic principles for guidance in the construction of tests, scales, examinations, or other measures of musical achievement.

Broadly, we may recognize that musical achievement includes musical information, power of musical observation, comprehension and appreciation of music, and musical skills in performance. All of these must be interpreted in relation to the nature and extent of talents present. The analysis of skill in performance requires either a recording by phonic or graphic methods or judgment by an expert in observing individual performance.

Adapted from "Measures of Musical Achievement," in *Music Educators Journal*, February 1940.

Knowledge of notation is incidental and not of primary importance in testing. Measures of musical talents require the elimination of the element of training insofar as that is possible, and may be made a prerequisite to achievement tests. There is a wide central area of achievement that can be measured by paper and pencil tests with a standardized record or an instrument for individuals or groups; but for the present purpose I shall take as an example the measure of some of the content covered in introductory courses in sight reading. This will involve primarily the recognition and comprehension of musical scores through visual or auditory cues. The basic principles of procedure may be seen in the following outline.

(1) *The measures to be based on widely recognized objectives in musical education.* The time is ripe for undertaking the construction of a battery of tests, scales, or measures comparable to the intelligence tests and college entrance examinations which have now become highly standardized. Such a scale, or scales, should serve the following purposes: (a) the measurement of progress and status in musical learning; (b) an analytical classification of basic objectives in musical education; (c) a motivation for teacher and pupil alike by furnishing a measuring stick for the analysis and evaluation of musical progress and the need of remedial work; (d) a teaching device which, even by frequent use, will not waste time but rather be an effective lesson in critical musical experience and appreciation; (e) promulgation and encouragement of new steps and concepts in musical education through revisions at, say, ten-year intervals; and (f) development of a community of interests and a spirit of co-operation among music educators.

(2) *The content to embody a series of definable and isolable specific factors as basic and fair samples of musical achievement.* A scale should be a battery of specific tests so interwoven as to represent complete musical sentences, and yet so planned as to be identifiable for the purpose of the test directions and interpretation of records. Hence, it must be limited in scope in order that it may have the following advantages: (a) showing of exactly what has been measured; (b) provision for dovetail-

ing with multiple or supplementary scales; (c) adequate measure of the factors selected; (d) samples of factors, fair and sufficient in number, to give significance to the score as a restricted index to musical status; (e) arrangement of trials in the order of difficulty; (f) validation by item analysis; (g) norms for the battery as a whole and for each identified factor; and (h) factors so grouped as to facilitate an achievement profile.

(3) *The range to be wide enough in a single scale to cover significant levels from the third grade up to and including the high school or adult level.* The designer must provide some device by which the examiner may select the most appropriate section or sections of the scale for a given group with regard to stage of advancement, age, endurance, and kind of preparation. For this purpose it may prove expedient to divide the scale into eight, ten, or twelve levels of which one or more may be selected for each testing period. The record may then be kept in terms of per cent of success at each level, or per cent of success at the level for which a certain degree of success—for example 75 per cent right—may be designated. While age, grade, degree, kind of training, and other factors may be interpolated, they should not be made the basis for grading the steps. Such implied uniformity is neither practicable nor desirable because types of procedure in school systems vary so greatly. The preparation may be made through private instruction of a specialized character or through effective curricular and extracurricular group activities. It may even arise through a sort of intuitive and spontaneous exhibition of superior talent instead of formal instruction.

The steps should be graded in the order of difficulty so as to increase in length and in progressive introduction of musical ideas, idioms, and art principles in the operation of the factor measured.

(4) *The test material to be presented in one attractive and comprehensive booklet designed to dovetail with a single record sheet.* The entire scale should be printed in a single booklet, comprehensive in content and artistic in format. The loose-leaf method involves a great economy in time and space. The book-

let may be used with any number of groups and for any number of times without mutilation, and each record sheet need cost only a fraction of a cent. The examiner need not manipulate the pages of a volume to check the record but can use a one-page stencil for all purposes. This record can be filed and handled economically.

The record sheet should carry on the reverse side: (a) talent profile, (b) memoranda from case history, (c) blank for achievement profile, and (d) notes on incidental observations and interviews. The sheet should be at hand for conferences with the student. Ultimately such scales should be expanded so as to embrace in an organized system all the principles of musical esthetics which are regarded as legitimate objectives at this level of training.

Achievement testing began with such things as knowledge of nomenclature. In current musical instruction such knowledge may be taken for granted. Measurement of achievement has reached its highest point of comprehensiveness and validity in the performance scores of types outlined in this volume. These are, however, not adapted to the testing of groups, which procedure always will be in greatest demand in educational circles. Between the individual and group testing procedures the development of achievement tests will now lie in the isolation of specific skills in the hearing, rendition, appreciation, and understanding of esthetic principles involved. Any musical feature that is worth while as an objective of training may be identified and included in our system of measurement.

A comprehensive manual of instructions and interpretations for the examiner should contain directions, explanations, safeguards, keys, norms, data on reliability and validity, and general principles of interpretation.

This material was suggested by my happy experience in the use of the *Knuth Achievement Test in Music*.[1] Dr. Knuth is to be congratulated on his splendid achievement. Many of the ideas in this outline were derived from his work. It is without question one of the best extant procedures in the testing of

---

[1] Published by the Educational Test Bureau, Minneapolis.

achievement in music and should be in the hands of all workers in the field. It may well be regarded as an effective step in the direction of the goals here set forth.[2]

(5) *The accumulative findings in achievement records to be made a basis for progressive adjustment in nationally recognized courses and curricula.* An existing national music teachers' organization should assume the responsibility for co-operative revision of the content and the sequence of instruction in public school music. If this cannot be done a new national committee to serve the specific purpose should be organized. Such a committee should be charged with the responsibility of making recommendations at stated periods in regard to the elimination of undesirable practices and improvements based upon the records in its office serving as a national clearing house.

---

[2] In a postdoctorate project in the University of Iowa School of Music, Dr. Alafaris is now developing an analysis of high-school goals in musical training, and has recently built a splendid achievement test in terms of these.

Chapter 27

GRADUATE TRAINING IN SCHOOLS OF FINE ARTS

IT IS ONLY within the last two or three decades that fine arts have begun to gain recognition and companionship with the older graduate disciplines; but the expansion within this period has been phenomenal. It is time, therefore, that some appraisal be made of this new movement. In order to be concrete I shall make bold to cast a tentative appraisal in terms of the development in a single typical institution, the State University of Iowa, on the basis of my firsthand observations. Comparisons and adaptations can readily be made by those who are acquainted with parallel developments in other universities; but it is a striking fact that the circumstances which led to the rise of fine arts have varied greatly in different universities.

FORMATIVE FORCES

In this University the first impetus to the recognition of graduate work in the fine arts came through the establishment of the Child Welfare Research Station, the mother institution of its kind, devoted to scientific study of the normal child. One of the seven areas approved for research by the Legislature in the charter of the station was the study of fine arts in the training of children.

About this time the demand for instruction in fine arts was fully recognized by the public schools in the face of the absence

Adapted from my recent articles which have appeared in *Design,* February 1945, *Music Educators Journal,* April 1945, the *Association of American Colleges Bulletin,* May 1945, and *Journal of Higher Education,* and an article by Professor E. C. Mabie, "The Fine Arts," in the series of Baconian Lectures, 1944, University of Iowa Press.

of adequately prepared teachers. This brought a challenge to the University for advanced training of teachers of the fine arts, and led to organization of the School of Fine Arts with an administrative director. This led to an expanding building program, development of an art center and generous equipment in workshops, libraries, collections, exhibits, and superior facilities for performance.

This rising movement was most significantly enhanced through the recognition by the Graduate Faculty, in 1929, of masters' theses and doctoral dissertations in the field of practical or creative art. Creative or imaginative work was placed on a par with traditional research, and theses or dissertations may take any form of achievement that can be evaluated as evidence of creative scholarship and exhibition of artistic skill. This was the door that gave an opening to new aspirations, responsibilities, and the joy of explorations in the graduate field.[1]

The crowning feature in this groundwork for the recognition of fine arts in the Graduate College was the faculty's provision for the breaking down of departmental barriers and the broadening of training through the co-operation of related departments in this new field of research. To illustrate, it provided that the candidate for the doctorate shall take his acoustics under a physicist, his psychology under a psychologist, his education under an educationist, his anatomy under an anatomist, in addition to the basic theoretical and practical courses in specific fields of arts and the research or creative work leading to a master's thesis or a doctoral dissertation. This not only gave fine arts a graduate academic status but enlarged the research interests in these various departments for the sharing of approaches to the fine arts.

Tied up with this movement was another principle which made the School of Fine Arts responsible for the extension of its program from what might be called the traditional pure art, recognizing the growing range of applications and services in the fields of art.

---

[1] Other universities were slow in adopting this principle; but at this year's meeting of the Association of American Universities it was given approval by unanimous vote of the Deans of the Graduate Schools.

ORGANIZATION

The School of Fine Arts in the University of Iowa was formally organized in 1929. It includes three departments: speech, music, and the visual arts. The school is under the general supervision of a director, Professor Earl E. Harper, who has the responsibility for co-ordinating its general activities. While each department is autonomous, like other standard departments in the University, the director serves in a number of important capacities, such as the building of the staff, the co-ordinating of policies within the school, the general supervision of extracurricular student activities, the holding of conferences, the management of exhibits, the conduct of public lectures, the securing of art collections, and the building program.

THE GRADUATE CONSTITUENCY

Our first and largest constituency is for the integration of fine arts with the other learned subjects as a part of a liberal education at all levels from preschool through graduate college.

A second constituency is that of teachers of fine arts in the public schools. This is evidenced by the forthcoming requirement of a master's degree for such teachers.

A third constituency is that of teachers or professors of fine arts in higher institutions of learning requiring a doctor's degree, including not only the standard colleges and the graduate schools but also a variety of specialized institutions at or above the college level.

A fourth constituency is that of professional private teachers, not only traditional teachers of fine arts but a wide range of technicians in the varied fields of applied fine arts which are now rapidly expanding.

A fifth constituency is that of the professional artists. Our artists in the past have been "discovered" and frequently self-educated, but the artistically talented are now moving within the learned horizons with unlimited facilities for training at their command. In short, provision is made on a broad academic basis for the education of artists at the highest level.

Finally, there is the encouragement of training of specialists in the scientific laboratory or studio, in anthropological and archaeological field work, and in philosophical esthetics.

THE MASTER'S DEGREE

The master's degree may be of three orders: (1) a terminal M.A. degree for teacher certification, definitely organized as a one-year program, (2) the M.A. as a preliminary to the doctorate and organized definitely as the first year of a three-year schedule, (3) the M.F.A., organized as a two-year terminal program with emphasis upon performance.

The candidate must present an adequate background in general education as certified by a bachelor's degree. This may involve an undergraduate major in the specific art but not necessarily, in view of the wide range of fields of concentration open, as in history, theory, practice, and esthetics. The thesis may be of the ordinary academic type or the imaginative and creative type. It may be written in any specialized field relevant to pursuit of art. The schedule should be such as to develop artistic personality at the graduate level.

THE DOCTORATE

Before the University offered the doctorate in music, speech, or graphic and plastic arts certain conditions in each department had to be met. These were: the presence of an adequate staff holding doctor's degrees and engaged in research, the adoption of the policy of integration with other departments, the availability of facilities for research, and a satisfactory policy of publication. The candidate for the doctorate must present a bachelor's degree and a master's degree, evidence of having satisfied the language requirements and passed the qualifying examination, and an acceptable budget for concentration in a field of research. Thus a doctorate with field of concentration in a branch of fine arts should compare favorably, under ordinary circumstances with the doctorate in the well-established disciplines. The degree granted is the unqualified and conventional degree, Doctor of Philosophy.

FIELDS OF CONCENTRATION

Acquaintance with the history and theory of art in all its forms is looked upon as a key to all the higher avenues of appreciation of music, visual arts, and the drama. In it the student of art traces the surprising magnitude of the role of art in the evolution of culture, in the making of history, in the development of applied arts and a philosophy of life. This discipline has held a respectable place in higher learning throughout the historical ages and must be generalized, expanded, and adapted to the purpose of current fine arts.

But the fine arts in themselves are creative. Music must be composed, paintings and sculpture must be executed, literature must be written, and the drama must be written and enacted. Basic training in art from the very beginning of childhood is training in performance, the development of specific skills, the mastery of media. The artist must carry the ball, not merely sit on the sidelines. Art is a form of play and therefore must be played through the expression of the imaginative life. As a form of play it is a preparation for life, it continues throughout the normal life, and is one of the chief realizations of the good life.

The term "creative work" at the graduate level is now coming into vogue. We have come to feel the need of a word in the English language to cover, under one term, both "research" and "creative work." At the present time these words are used interchangeably, since all research that is worth the name is creative work and all creative work demands research as a preliminary in any field of achievement. The differentiation might be based upon the content or the point of emphasis.

In our organization the term "fine arts" is used in a broad sense on account of the prevailing departmental organization; that is, much of the work undertaken in these departments is not strictly fine arts. But the University of Iowa has adopted a policy of putting all of the oral and visual disciplines which pertain to art under the administration of the School of Fine Arts, giving the greatest freedom for interpretation of what is or is not art and at the same time subordinating all the activities of the department to the principles of fine art.

At the higher levels of ambition the artist much reach out into underlying sciences and humanities, such as specialties in physics, physiology, anthropology, archaeology, and anatomy, as well as literature, history and philosophy. In such disciplines it is now conventional to give the psychology of each of the specific arts a leading role in that the function of this type of applied psychology is to integrate and interpret the groundwork underlying each art.

Perhaps the best information in regard to the general scope of the graduate work in the University of Iowa School of Fine Arts can be gained by indicating some of the achievements in the last normal decade, the decade just before Pearl Harbor.

SPEECH

The Department of Speech is under the direction of Professor E. C. Mabie.

The term *speech* in this University replaces and comprehends a variety of areas which appeared historically from time to time under various names, such as, dramatics, fundamentals of speech, public speaking, radio, speech pathology, phonetics, and speech education. The field of concentration may be taken in any of these areas as well as in supporting areas such as education, psychology, child welfare, or even in the underlying areas of science or art. We may consider as an indication of the magnitude of the work undertaken the following figures showing the number and area of the advanced degrees earned during this decade:

	Ph.D Degrees	M.A. Degrees
Dramatics	8	141
Fundamentals of Speech	13	50
Public Speaking	13	55
Radio	1	10
Speech Pathology	10	46
Speech Education	6	44
	51	346

Another indication of graduate achievement is that of publications. Approximately 185 articles by members of the staff and advanced students appeared in many national journals. Nine textbooks were written and staff members collaborated in the writing of three others. Two of these books, one by Travis and one by Van Riper, opened a new field and have become leading textbooks in speech pathology. Editorial services covered work on nine volumes of speech and research papers and on the *Quarterly Journal of Speech and Speech Monographs*. As editor of *The Journal of Speech Disorders,* Dr. Johnson did valuable work for researchers and teachers in speech correction. Of monumental character is the Thonssen and Fatherson 800-page *Bibliography of Speech Education*. Dr. Knower's bibliographical record of research in speech in forty-three American universities during the last ten years is indispensable to advanced students. Dr. Baird was one of the editors of a two-volume book entitled *A History and Criticism of American Public Address*. The editor in chief was one of Dr. Baird's students, and contributions to the book were made by twelve other students who completed graduate research under his supervision.

To these must be added a long list of plays first produced in the experimental theater and then produced on a number of professional stages, thus giving first professional training to such playwrights as Conkle and Maibaum, Marcus Bach, Dan Totheroh, Paul Green, and Howard Richardson.

MUSIC

Music, like speech, in the graduate school offers a variety of fields of concentration. In the decade before Pearl Harbor about 200 master's degrees were granted in music. Of these about one-fourth had a major with thesis in the field of composition. Other master's theses were largely in the fields of music education, child welfare, and psychology of music. Sixteen doctorates were conferred by the Department of Music itself. In addition to these, twenty-one doctorates with major in psychology of music were granted, and more than that number of researches by postdoctorate students in the psychology of music were published. Similar support came from other departments, notably child welfare and education.

Professor P. G. Clapp is Head of the Department of Music. During this period Dr. Clapp himself developed a number of original compositions in a variety of forms. These have attracted lively comments from music critics, being pronounced as showing a fine modernity of spirit with genuine creativeness and originality of expression.

GRAPHIC AND PLASTIC ARTS

While a certain amount of graduate work had been offered in earlier years, it took new impetus with the appointment of Professor Lester Longman as head of the Department of Graphic and Plastic Arts in the middle of the decade under consideration. Graduate work may be undertaken in various fields of concentration. We may use, in part, as an index of achievement some information on advanced degrees granted. During the decade before Pearl Harbor 117 master's degrees, eighteen master of fine arts degrees, and one doctorate were conferred for original creative work in art. Two-thirds of the master's degrees were in painting—most of them in oil but some in water color, fresco, and tempera. Eleven were in design and all but nine others in various other forms of print medium—lithography, wood engraving, etching, aquatint, and silk screen.

The quality of work done during this pioneering period is evidenced by the fact that the work of Iowa students has been selected for exhibition by juries of prominent artists and critics. This has been the case in all the jury shows, including the Carnegie International Exhibition, the Pennsylvania Academy Annual, the Corcoran Biennial, two Chicago Art Institute Annuals, the National Academy Annual, and the annual exhibitions in Cincinnati, Detroit, Kansas City, Buffalo, St. Louis, and Richmond. In addition, Iowa students have been represented in the New York World's Fair Exhibition, the San Francisco Golden Gate Exposition, and the "Artists for Victory

Exhibition" in the Metropolitan Museum in New York. In a few cases Iowa students have won prizes and awards and their pictures have been singled out for praise in magazine reviews. Half a dozen students have won government mural competitions.

WHITHER AHEAD?

Looking back over the short period of this very unusual development, it is gratifying to find that, where effective leadership exists, a doctor's dissertation can be developed, representing as high a type of scholarship in the field of fine arts as in any of the sciences or humanities. What has been given here is a report of American progress in terms of one concrete case.

What does this development in a state institution symbolize? It symbolizes the phenomenal awakening of America to an interest in the cultivation of the fine arts. It parallels the rising scale of scientific, social, and industrial progress. It beckons to new vistas of American frontiers for exploration and possession. It pledges the state to the support of this relatively new and enlarged field of liberal education. It takes esthetics into the workshop and the laboratory. It implements educational theory for the cultivation of the emotional life, the higher sentiments in particular. It vitalizes the hitherto formal studies of the humanities and social disciplines. It makes art function in the home, the community, and the state. It opens new basic resources and furnishes new motives for all forms of applied arts. It denotes a new vantage ground in the maturation of the nation. The fine arts are here to stay and grow.

PART FIVE

SOME SCIENTIFIC SPECULATIONS AND CONCLUSIONS

Chapter 28

THE DEVELOPMENT OF MUSICAL SKILLS

ONE OF THE GOALS of the psychology of music is to apply scientific principles to methods of training so as to guarantee insight into the nature of the learning process, a shortening of the time of training, and attainment of higher precision and mastery than is ordinarily obtained. In this it must follow the universal requirements of scientific procedure, dealing with one specific factor at a time and employing objective standards of measurement.

Training begins in the most elementary stage by setting up efficient habits which become thoroughly fixed so that they function automatically in the actual musical situation. Fundamental requirements are that the pupil shall know exactly what element in the music he is trying to master in a given assignment, shall have an objective check on his achievement in every trial, and shall practice until this particular control is completely established as a habit.

Instruments for such purposes are fast coming upon the market and are so reasonably priced that for the price of a good piano one can equip a studio adequately. A single installation of this kind can serve a large school; the cost is not prohibitive for a music school or for a department of music in a public school.

At present, the problem is to convince music teachers of the possibilities and significance of this scientific approach to musical training. The instruments are here and more are coming. The first essential is knowledge of the fundamental techniques in the psychology of music. Courses in that subject are fast developing in progressive teacher-training institutions. The range of possibilities is unlimited when we once establish confidence in the idea that it can be done.

One of the most valuable principles involved in most of these instruments is that the sound wave is converted into a visual picture so that the moment one sings or plays a given note, he will *see* the note on a dial or some other indicator. These visual pictures of sound waves are to the student of music what the microscope is to the student of microorganisms: every element in the tone produced is enlarged; even factors not recognized by the unaided ear become clear and conspicuous.

In our round through the laboratory, I could have demonstrated a variety of instruments for this purpose. Let me here attempt to give a general picture of an elementary musical laboratory designed for training in the acquisition of musical skills. A laboratory of this kind has three functions: first, the measurement of natural talent at the beginning of practice; second, training in the acquisition and refinement of specific skills in musical performance; and third, measurement of achievement. The talent testing should include on the one hand measures of musical hearing and, on the other, measures of natural talent for motor skills.

SEEING PITCH INTONATION

This was illustrated in the section on the tonoscope in Chapter 3. The tonoscope was first used for the study of improvement with practice; for example, a number of singers who were known to flat were given organized training for the purpose of eradicating the flatting habit wherever it was not due to a faulty ear. With actual singers and players, faulty intonation was found to be due primarily to a slovenly functioning of the ear. Such slovenliness is nearly universal and is due to the absence of objective standards in training. When a singer or player standing in front of the tonoscope observed that he flatted by a given fraction of a tone, he was required to correct this immediately by sight. The correction took place with surprising rapidity and with a high degree of precision. This was, of course, accomplished by using the eye as a check on the ear to establish critical hearing of pitch to the limit of the ear's capacity.

By the same means, it is possible to improve intonation in the singing of musical intervals. The singing or playing of the chromatic scale and diminished or augmented intervals is greatly improved by this visual aid. The teacher need not be present, because the pupil is sent to the instrument and told to practice hearing and intonation until the tonoscope picture shows that a required degree of proficiency has been attained. It is like using a ruler in measuring the size of an object. Any of the pitch modulations that are not too rapid can be observed by this instrument.

One such instrument in the laboratory studio can be used for class demonstrations, the tuning of instruments, the comparison of pitch in different types of tone quality, the establishment of correct habit of pitch intonation, and as an achievement test. The instrument can be used with the teacher present; but to be most effective, the pupil should be assigned a task and allowed to work independently by the hour, simply reporting achievements from time to time.

Among the fundamental exercises should be: first, the establishment of the habit of correct intonation of an isolated tone; second, the mastery of intonation in the natural scale for the fixing of intervals; third, the mastery of the chromatic scale for the same purpose; fourth, the checking of these skills for selected notes in the actual musical situation, as in singing or playing a simple melody; and fifth, treating in the same manner the development of skills for artistic deviation from the true, as in the augmenting or diminishing of intervals and the performance of other artistic modulations in pitch. All these represent basic and positive habits which may be mastered by the beginning student so that they will function automatically at all levels of musical performance.

Such laboratory procedures represent the latest achievement for instruction in ear training. They should be dovetailed with the best conventional exercises for musical achievement.

Advanced students or artists who are found to be defective in pitch control at certain levels in the register can be given the task of eradicating these faults. This can be accomplished by specific and persistent practice on one feature at a time, keeping a record of the progress made. Each of the objectives in pitch control is studied by itself, but the habits established become interlocking and the net result is precision in the hearing of pitch and mastery of its control. At the beginning of training, the student becomes clearly pitch-conscious and develops a critical attitude. As learning progresses, he becomes less and less conscious of the specific object, and thereafter the pitch control becomes automatic so that he sings and plays with precision in the artistic mood, conscious only of the larger objectives of the art.

The tonoscope, built in 1897, was the first instrument designed for this purpose. There are now various forms of electronic instruments which serve the same purpose.

SEEING THE DYNAMIC ASPECTS OF TONE

One of the fundamental marks of musicianship is the mastery of the dynamic control of tones in all musical phrasing and interpretation. The student of this aspect of tone has been greatly hampered because he has had no defined terminology for intensity of tone, no objective standards, no units of measurement. As a result, he has been left groping for this aspect of tone in comparative ignorance and helplessness. Training for skills in dynamic control has been the barest rule of thumb procedure.

Performers, as a rule, are guided by their personal feeling of what is satisfying in terms of loudness. They have a general conception of *pp*, *p*, *m*, *mf*, and *ff*, but these vary among individuals and in the same individual from time to time. Musical scores have had no basic references; musicians have had no unit in terms of which they could express degrees of modulations of loudness in musical phrasing, the carrying power of different qualities of tone, and the balancing of instruments.

But through the science of acoustics there recently has been developed a means of measuring loudness. We now have standards of loudness, musically significant units of loudness, and scientific knowledge of the factors which influence real or apparent loudness of a tone.

Practical interest in this aspect of musical performance is in its very beginning. As far as music is concerned, this is a virgin field. Students as well as teachers must learn of the new possibilities. The decibel is the new unit introduced for registering the intensity of tones. One decibel represents approximately the smallest difference in loudness that can be heard by the average ear. It is, however, standardized in terms of units of electrical energy so that it has a fixed value for all measurements in the dynamics of sound. Fundamentally, the decibel designates physical intensity or energy in sound; but it may be converted into loudness scales, loudness being the musical correlate of physical intensity. Thus we can measure loudness in terms of physical intensity of tone just as we measure pitch in terms of the number of physical vibrations per second.

Dr. Reger, psychologist in otology,[1] has suggested that under defined conditions we might start tentatively by adopting the following scale, in decibel levels above the threshold, for an orchestra of seventy-five musicians:

ppp	20 db
pp	40 db
p	55 db
mf	65 db
f	75 db
ff	85 db
fff	95 db

The establishment of scales is the function of acoustic laboratories or bureaus of standards; it is the function of psychology to adapt these to musical needs. Scales are a fundamental requirement in all aspects of acoustics, as in soundproofing and other acoustic treatment of rooms, in abatement of noise, in testing the efficiency of industrial instruments, and in many other phases of sound production now the object of scientific investigation for theoretical and practical purposes. Once established, these scales can be recorded for training purposes so that we can hear, think, and speak of degrees of loudness in terms

---

[1] See author's *Psychology of Music,* p. 89.

of decibels, with an approach to the same precision that enables us to speak of pitch in terms of vibrations. Instruments may be devised for sounding tones in any desired degree of loudness. Within the last few years radio technicians have made great progress in standardizing and controlling degrees of loudness in tone.

For present purposes, it is not necessary to master all these technical details. The immediate objective is to make the student loudness-conscious just as he is pitch-conscious—to make him feel at home with loudness, to master the control of loudness; to form definite loudness habits, and objectify feeling values for it.

The first essential for a training laboratory in this field is a simplified output meter such as we see in use in all radio studios. There are many varieties of these, all relatively inexpensive. The essential requirement of an output meter for the training laboratory is that it have a dial on which, by the movement of a needle, the intensity of tone registered through a microphone will be indicated in terms of decibels. It is the same principle employed in ammeters or voltmeters. The instant the performer sounds a note, he can watch the swinging of the needle over the decibel scale and observe how the tone rises in intensity, how it moves in crescendo and diminuendo, and how it fluctuates in steadiness. The process is as simple as seeing the time of day by observing the hands of the clock, for the instrument can be relatively foolproof.

On the analogy of exercises in pitch, exercises in training for loudness should be organized: first, to make the student loudness-conscious by giving him complete and verifiable illustrations of observable magnitudes in the dynamic value of tones; second, to train him in the production of a given loudness, for example the standard for *mf,* just as we train in the production of a given pitch; third, to observe the function and control of loudness as an element of rhythm or stress; fourth, to master evenness in loudness desired, crescendos and diminuendos, and forms of attack and release of the tone; fifth, to balance dynamic values of different instruments; and sixth, to master artistic deviations from loudness as in the intensity vibrato.

With the output meter standing on the piano like a metronome, a pianist can see for the first time the exact details of his musical phrasing in terms of intensity. This is most significant, since the control of intensity is a key to artistic performance on the piano. The student can be assigned a task with the privilege of working by himself with the instrument and recording artistic achievement.

A musician who is not familiar with these recent developments in acoustics would be dumfounded to see how helpless he has been in the absence of these devices for the hearing, understanding, feeling, and controlling the dynamics of tone. It would be hazardous to predict what coming generations of musicians will be able to achieve through their acceptance of this type of device. The challenge to the musical educator today is to utilize this innovation for the refinement of musical performance.

SEEING THE TEMPORAL ASPECTS OF TONE

The soloist is not restricted to metronomic time nor to rigid adherence to the indicated rhythmic pattern in the measure. His artistic deviation from the regular is the principal medium for his musical interpretation. Indeed, this artistic deviation is more difficult than rigid adherence to the time indicated by the notes. It rests, of course, primarily upon a fine feeling for time; but the execution of that feeling depends upon the development of a motor skill for the purpose.

The situation is quite different in group performance of voices or instruments. Much of the distress that the orchestra conductor has to suffer comes from those who cannot keep time or differentiate rhythmic patterns.

We can now take the student into a training laboratory and measure, first, his sense of time in hearing, and second, his natural capacity for performance in time. On the basis of each of these, discriminating selection may be made for admission to the group. The scores will carry evidence of various degrees of natural aptness and will reveal cases which probably should be discouraged due to lack of such talent. On the basis of each of these two talent ratings, training in the motor control of pitch may be instituted.

The best available all-round instrument for this purpose is the R. H. Seashore rhythm meter.[2] This consists of a phonograph disc fitted with a series of variable contacts by means of which any particular rhythm may be set up and sounded through a telephone receiver. The rhythmic action consists of the tapping of a telegraph key which sounds the rhythm in another receiver. An ink stylus in circuit with the key makes a graphic record on a plain sheet of paper, cut to the dimensions of the standard disc and resting on it. On this paper, the standard pattern is indicated by reference bases, and the pattern as performed is indicated by a stylus tracing on the paper. This tracing shows exactly how the performer succeeded, measuring his deviations in terms of 0.01 of a second for any one or all members in the rhythmic pattern. If we desire to register the stress in addition to the time, the lever carrying the tracing stylus can be set to indicate degree of accent. One great advantage of this type of meter is that the record is preserved in permanent form and can be measured and analyzed at any time in full detail. Thus, from a series of such records, a learning curve can be established. There are various forms of this instrument.

The performer can see every item in the record as he hears it in his performance, or he can make a series of trials covering, for example, ten measures; after each one, he can examine his record as an exact indication of his performance. Such instruments can be adjusted for a variety of purposes, but I would suggest the following basic procedures with beginning students: first, measure the sense of time and the sense of rhythm; second, measure the capacity for keeping metronomic time and the natural aptness shown for precision in the performance of a simple rhythm; and third, with these measures of natural talent in hand, give the needed training for precision in keeping time and in the performance of rhythmic patterns with a series of two, three, or four notes in the measure.

---

[2] Obtainable from the C. H. Stoelting Co., Chicago.

SEEING THE QUALITATIVE ASPECTS OF TONE

Timbre is the most complex factor with which we have to deal in tone production. Training of students of voice or instrument for timbre or tone quality represents one of the most helpless stages in traditional instruction. Musicians have not had any objective standards or means of obtaining performance scores in timbre or sonance—the two factors which constitute tone quality. At best, the teacher has tried to explain how to produce a tone through instruction in the various elements which determine quality of tone, and has sung or played examples of the goal to be reached. Granting that the models thus exhibited are good, which is rarely the case, these procedures still involve an enormous waste of time and seldom result in a high order of achievement unless the student, by luck or natural aptitude, happens to stumble along with some degree of success.

Within the last few years instruments in the training studio have made it possible to reverse this process so that the student begins by accepting the specific goal toward which he is training, and, in working toward that goal, discovers for himself or is taught the essentials of tone production. Training begins not with exercises in tone placement, resonance, and breathing (without a goal), but in the formation of a well-defined concept of the type of tone to be reached. The pupil is then in a position to appreciate the advantage of instruction in terms of controlled hearing and visual representation of the result.

One good approach to the use of objective records in teaching voice, available to all teachers, lies in the use of the phonograph to set up a good model tone. Try this experiment: Help the student select a superior recorded song suitable to his voice and register, preferably in the legato style. Let him sing with the record playing softly so that he can hear his own voice clearly —sing, sing, and sing in his private room until he becomes familiar with both his objective and his shortcomings. Then let him fractionate the task by alternating with the master voice in singing representative tones or phrases until it begins to be a real contest. Now is the time to step in and supplement the phonograph with the standard teaching techniques. New models may be used to emphasize specific needs. We have found that a fair trial of this method yields astonishing results in a short time. It is particularly profitable in the case of the fairly advanced student, for whom it becomes a corrective measure.

We have a variety of oscillographs and oscilloscopes which make the form of the sound wave visible. The presence of each and every partial in the tone is indicated by a characteristic deflection in the sound wave. But we must recall that the intricacy and the contour of the sound wave not only is as complex as the structure of the tone but is complicated by other factors so that it is not easy to identify each partial by immediate inspection of the oscil'ogram. To yield such complete details, it must be submitted to harmonic analysis. Yet it is quite possible and profitable to set up a sound wave from a singer or an instrument as a standard tone so that when the singer or player performs in front of the microphone he can compare his sound waves with the norm, the object being to approximate the sound wave of the norm. Thus the student continues to hear the model tone but uses the picture of the sound wave to magnify, as it were, and objectify the differences which might not be heard without the visual aid.

With instruments now available, reasonable in cost and comparatively simple to operate, one can instantly recognize the different vowel patterns, degrees in richness of tone, characteristic brightness or roughness, and various types of tone placement. A student's oscilloscope is a most effective instrument for aid in musical practice. If the object is to correct a particular fault, the pattern can be set in such a way as to accentuate that fault by contrast with the desirable tone. The fundamental goal in training with the oscilloscope is the refinement of artistic hearing by identification of specific factors which modify it, such as changing the amount of energy in a given overtone, changing the position of formants, or modifying the richness of tone.

The possibilities for developing creative exercises with the aid of these instruments are practically unlimited. Suffice it to say that if a student is given a chance to use these aids and has natural ability, he will recognize the possibilities of their use for the acquisition of a high order of skill in a minimum time.

We are so familiar with the extraordinary expansion of the musical world which the phonograph and radio have brought about that we grossly underestimate the step that has been taken. The thing now needed in training voice and instrument teachers is to convince them that corresponding improvements in musical training can be made if they are willing to accept instrumental aids for scientific analysis of the learning situation. The recommendations here made are in the nature of a prediction, but they emerge from sound scientific bases. The situation is so new that it has not come to the attention of many music educators. But time works wonders.

Chapter 29

MUSIC AS PLAY

WHAT IS THE ROLE of play in music? Let me put the burden of original thought upon the reader in answering this question. Here is a realistic description of the nature of play and its role in daily life, based on experimental evidence from many sources. Let the reader, be he educator, auditor, artist, composer, scientist, or philosopher in music, check this description *item for item* and, after deliberation, answer this question: *In what respects do these aspects of play apply to music?*

PLAY IS PREPARATION FOR LIFE

Children seldom play with the intention of fitting themselves for life, nor are adults ordinarily conscious of serving this purpose in play. Children play, as do the rest of us, because it satisfies certain cravings and seems to be the natural thing to do. It is only in the larger, retrospective view that we realize how nature has wrought marvels of development through the operation of the play instincts.

The senses develop largely through the play which their exercise invites. By play the infant discovers his ears, investigates his nose, "pat-a-cakes" with his hands, splashes, fumbles, rubs, scratches, gropes, and grasps to feel himself and the objects about him. This semirandom play refines the sense of touch, develops ability in locating tactual impressions, and gives meaning to these experiences by establishing and enriching associations. At the same time play furnishes amusement and develops curiosity.

Adapted from the author's *Psychology in Daily Life,* D. Appleton & Co., New York, 1913, Chapter I.

All sorts of ringing, rapping, shouting, sizzling, rattling, cracking, and jingling sounds appeal to the ear of the infant. Through such exercise the auditory interest, comprehension, and appreciation are gradually refined into a liking for higher forms of rhythm, accent, modulation, tone quality, pitch, melody, and harmony. The child is first attracted by the louder sounds; through the mastery of these he acquires the power of finer discrimination. At first all sounds are alike to him; their distinctive qualities are learned through play.

The playful production of sounds runs parallel with the growing appreciation of sounds. The ability to make sounds is a continual source of pleasure and profit. There is a close connection and a gradual transition from the youngster's howl to the set and studied piano exercise and the lesson in voice culture. The mastery of the voice is acquired far more by play than by conscious and purposeful effort.

A child's occupation, it is safe to say, is mostly in the overcoming of some difficulty. From the random and instinctive movements of infancy the child gradually develops a hierarchy of achievements—sitting, creeping, walking, jumping, balancing, swimming, skating, dancing, gymnastics, physical sports, tricks of contortion, and sleight of hand. Each is the outgrowth of some previous skill with a place in the series, each successful only after persistent practice, each a victory in the child's absorbing struggle for the acquisition of power.

Similarly, play develops the capacity for using tools and for moving objects other than one's own body. Handling is conspicuous in children, as the picking, tearing, lifting, shaking, and throwing movements of the little boy prove. When he leads the dog, the horse, the kite, or his own playmates, he enjoys this extension of his own personality. In this process he begins by dropping his playthings and throwing everything helter-skelter. Later he enters into competition to extend his sphere of influence. He learns to project himself by a blow or a throw, as in handball, football, baseball, tennis, golf, croquet, skipping stones on the water, using a slingshot, and shooting a bow and arrow or firearm. He projects his skill to the behavior of its object. Then there are reciprocal movements, reacting to those of another agent, as in catching, dodging, and parrying. Motor skill, when established, is motor automatism. It comes only through practice, and, in the child, most practice is play. This play forms an endless chain, as the craving for it is stimulated by play itself.

Curiosity, the primary drive in childish activity, may assume either a destructive or a constructive form. The child whose curiosity moves him to take things apart in order to see what is inside may develop into a scientific experimenter, artist, or philosopher. Constructive curiosity results in inventions, plans, designs, and the shaping of material to these ends. The sandpile is modeled into mountains, houses, rivers, lakes, beasts, and living folk. Collecting represents an allied impulse. The little urchin who stuffs his pockets with pebbles, bugs, nuts, paper, doughnuts, pennies, or what not is moved by an impulse related to that which, in its more studied and critical form, fills our museums, art galleries, and churches.

The higher mental powers normally develop in close connection with the use of the senses and the muscles. Children's games characteristically involve the expression of the whole being; in this lies one of the charms of child play. The child is ever responsive. He is alive to the total environment; and play is the main channel for the free outpouring of his mind in action. His memory is not as yet selective, but indiscriminate. His imagination is not yet schooled; possibilities are not yet distinguished from desires; all he sees is his, the impossible is easy, while the easy may seem impossible, and inanimate nature is animate. He is not yet bound down to systematic thinking in a prescribed channel; his wonder goes out equally to heaven and earth, to his origin and his destiny, to the most trivial details or the riddle of the universe, and his inventions and solutions keep pace with his imagination. His feelings are as yet neither blunted nor refined; he lavishes his tenderest affection upon mud puddles, hobbyhorses, and cats, as well as upon members of the family; he tortures and abuses the worm, his playmate, or his mother. His instincts have not yet been suppressed; he lives the animal life of his species and is sympathetic with the elemental forces of nature. He is not yet bound to a trade or a profession; his fancy finds expression, his ingenuity is exercised, and his attention is strained in the effort to copy the patterns of nature, and particularly those set by other human beings. He has not yet developed an organized system of habits; his will is ever free to act out its motives. And in the resulting free action he is strenuous, persistent, indefatigable; he is overcoming difficulties in play.

Growth through play is evident in the development of the social nature of the child, and is especially marked in the development of his consciousness of kinship with a group. The child comes into the world socially inclined, with tendencies toward altruistic as well as toward self-protecting and self-enhancing actions; but the altruistic nature needs enforcement and direction. Child play reproduces on its own level the struggles and achievements of developed social life. Warfare and love, obedience and defiance, comedy and tragedy, regeneration and degeneration, domestic occupation and the spirit of adventure—all these the child experiences at his own level. Gradually he approaches stern adult realities, taught and trained, hardened and softened, warmed and cooled, roused and rationalized, through these very engagements in play which, without break or loss of their original character, gradually blend into the duties, responsibilities, opportunities, and achievements of adult life.

This conception shows how both mind and body develop more through play than through work. Sensory experience gradually acquires associations and responses, comes under the control of voluntary attention, and becomes differentiated and serviceable through play. Memory, imagination, conception, judgment, and reasoning are whetted, strengthened, and enriched through their exercise in play; the affective life becomes sensitive, adapted, balanced, and serviceable through play; habits are formed, urges developed, impulses trained and brought under control, streams of subconscious activities crystallized, and the power of attention disciplined through play. In short, play is the principal instrument of growth. It is safe to conclude that, without play, there would be no normal adult cognitive life; without play, no healthful development of affective life; without play, no full development of the will.

Such a statement does not deny the value of work and of tasks deliberately undertaken for immediate ends other than pleasure. It does not deny the place of drudgery, of dull routine, of obligatory exercise of mind and body. But it emphasizes the fact that, in mental development as a biological process, spontaneous self-expression, characteristic of play rather than of work, is the larger influence. From the earliest years the child should be made to feel useful, to feel that he has duties to perform for himself and for others, thus cultivating a sense of satisfaction in service. Such work sharpens the appetite for play. It is good pedagogy not to make play the avowed object of childhood. If the labor is not unduly strenuous, and if it offers sufficient variety of exercise, useful occupation of the child should balance his play life. The child's occupation should be viewed with reference to the making of a useful individual. Lessons at school should be assigned as work for a definite end; and they should be so regarded by the child. Yet such tasks may well occupy but a portion of his time; the school hours might well be more intensive and shorter than at present. Although tasks are done for themselves, the activity involved may include many of the essential elements of the play attitude and play impulses. This is true at least insofar as the child pursues them in a natural way. Tasks well done become a part of a larger play, for the play of life is the child's occupation. He fits himself for life by living it at his own level. The training of play is most effective because, to the player, it is not training, imitation, or pastime, but is part of life. Nature has made the period of infancy and childhood long in order that the fruits of child play might be correspondingly great. It is well for the adult director of the child's activities to realize the size of the child's task; to realize that normal life may be crushed by depriving youth of the rights and opportunities of play; to realize the necessity of encouragement in defeat, of applause in victory, of approval in success; and to exercise sympathetic and prudent selection in shaping the innate childish impulses toward the making of the man.

PLAY CONTINUES THROUGHOUT NORMAL LIFE

The stimulation of the senses is a source of play. Basking in the sun is a temperature play. Sweetmeats are frequently eaten not for their food value but for the agreeable stimulation of the sense of taste; even bitter and sour substances are played with. Color in nature, in pictures, in dress, and in ornaments is part of the enjoyment of life; so also is form, both in real objects and in drawing, painting, sculpture, and architecture. The music lesson may become work, but the artist in music "plays" and reaches his highest mastery through play. The racial development of music and poetry is largely the spontaneous result of play; when genuine and a true expression of impulse, art ever carries the quality of play.

The exercise of memory is a variety of play. The power of reminiscence is one of the charms of life. Primitive man was a storyteller. We memorize a great deal for the mere pleasure of memorizing. Recognition gives a feeling of warmth and possession, as in the appreciation of the drama or the interpretation of historical events. The exercise of the imagination is a form of mental play. The effective novelist lives with his characters. It is the play illusion that makes the writing artistic; and the same spirit is transferred to the reading of fiction and poetry. The theater is by nature as well as by name a play-house. The imagination invites play, even the shocking and the grotesque. Imaginative play constitutes the charm of reverie, of mental romance, of musings and idlings. The child plays with sticks and toys; the adult plays more in images. A score of men engage in action on the football field, while thousands replay the game in the grandstand.

The exercise of the most distinctive mental process, reasoning, may also be play or its close parallel, a game. The guessing of riddles, the flash of wit, the art of conversation, and chess are all plays of thought. The emotions enter distinctively into mental play, in that their very presence reflects the enjoyment of the play impulse. Even the despondent misanthrope plays with a morbid craving for bad news, tragedy, and misfortune. Indeed, we enjoy or appreciate most the tragedy that is the truest picture of great misery. If it were not printed on the program that the crucifixion scene in the Passion Play at Oberammergau is a trick illusion, many in the audience would be overwhelmed at the sight of it; yet people travel far for the emotional play which this spectacle represents.

Action is constantly stimulated and directed by the play impulse. The plays of adult life take the form of sport, artistic expression, fellowship, and recreation. Sport is the scientific play of the adult. The sportsman has a theory of the game and makes deliberate efforts to elaborate on it and apply it. Hunting, racing, fencing, flying, gambling, and such are serious and strenuous affairs, carried on with intense interest and application of knowledge, forethought, and designed action; yet insofar as they are sports, they are play, first and foremost. Music, poetry, fiction, sketching, painting, and experimenting furnish a most valuable outlet for the creative impulses, enlarging vision, developing feeling, giving form and reality to natural strivings, and conveying ideas from mind to mind. They do this in more or less of a play attitude. Dancing, conversation, physical bouts, mental contests, cards, and chess serve the purpose of developing social bonds in man, making him something more than a self-centered, self-asserting individual. Fishing, sailing, skating, riding, walking, tennis, cricket, and golf serve as recreation, engaging the parts of the mind and body that have not been exercised in labor. Loafing, basking on the beach, bathing in the open water, listening to music, and watching games are forms of rest; they bring equilibrium through the luxury of abandonment to free associations and casual mental imagery.

Adult play, though not to the same extent as child play, is progressive preparation for life. Sport holds its sway only as long as there is room for advancing achievement; one sport follows another in answer to the needs of the maturing man. Plays, like serious occupations and associations, change with the growth of the individual. Recreation, to be effective, must possess an engaging charm in the form of fresh impressions, novel associations, and new outlets for activity. Even rest serves its purpose only insofar as its form is progressively adapted to the changing needs of the constitution. In all these respects play fits the individual for the larger life to the extent that he retains plasticity and interest in growth. As long as one is alive there is something to learn. There are visions to be seen, inspirations to be received, ideals to be set aglow, sympathies to be cultivated, emotions to be refined, dreams of achievement to be enjoyed, riddles of life to be solved. While adult man pursues these objects through systematic effort, much of his learning and adaptation comes through living in the play attitude. The man or the woman who has ceased to play is to be pitied.

PLAY IS ONE OF THE CHIEF REALIZATIONS OF LIFE

Primitive man lived relatively free from thoughtful care; the child, though endowed with a keen imagination, is disposed to tread in the footsteps of his distant ancestors. Civilization has modified this tendency in two ways: it has established a sense of responsibility, a prudent forethought in the division of labor, and a mutual effort to advance; on the other hand, it has opened up vast avenues of possibilities, not only for playful expression in art, science, and religion, but also in the increase of means and avenues for pure play. While primitive man was essentially a playing animal, cultured man has vastly more play interests than had his remote ancestor. Indeed, play goes with greatness and with a strenuous life. To Theodore Roosevelt the wilds of Africa and the courts of Europe formed a continuous, fascinating playground in which he played with all his heart, and the world proclaimed him a leader in political thought and action.

A vital element in self-realization is the experience of growth, a consciousness not merely of success in work or play, but the recognition of new power and capacity. It appears in the child's satisfaction with his increase of strength, speed, imagery, and self-control. As there is a conscious satisfaction in knowing the history lesson or the music lesson, so there is a general state of well-being which comes from a sense of equilibrium or adjustment. This the psychologist traces to the mastery of nature's lessons, which, indeed, are so important that they are not always left to the free initiative of the individual, but are provided for in the traditions of the race.

Man has an urge to do everything that he can do. The possession of capacity carries with it the tendency to use that capacity; with the possession of wings goes the tendency to fly, with the possession of the capacity for reflection goes the tendency to reason. Work and the necessities of life develop but a relatively small part of our instinctive resources. Groups of instinctive capacities would be lost were it not for the liberal education of play. It develops those traits which have not been called for by the spur of necessity. It elevates even as it levels. Our artificial life is narrow, specialized, and intensive, and this is indeed a condition for great achievements; but play develops the possible man, rather than the man of choice and condition. Dr. Woods Hutchinson says that we are all of about the same age—at least twelve million years. We have been millions of years in the making. Instinct is the conservator of the product of these millions of years, and play is its agent.

The racial life is a reversion to type. When the tired wage earner comes home from business, he sheds his coat and rolls and romps on the floor—a child with the little children. When vacation comes, we break for forest and stream, mountain and field, and live the simple life. When we join in celebration, we shout and sing with abandon. The tendency in play is to fall back upon the elemental. Whatever artifices of war may be devised, fighting games will always gravitate back toward the simple form of direct bodily contact, be it with fellow men, beasts, or the forces of nature. It is not plausible to assume that boys climb trees and swim in response to survivals of these specific activities from a distant arboreal or aquatic ancestry. Boys come into this world with limbs fitted for climbing and swimming; trees are common and inviting for climbing, and the water is a natural temptation. But the tree and the water arouse curiosity, bravery, and excitement. A strong arm, a brain capable of both voluntary and automatic control of that arm, a mental capacity for impulses, images, ideas, and feelings, in response to the environment—these the child inherits. If free to play, the arm will be put to all manner of tests from simple and gross to complex and refined movements. The child appropriates the available. I was telling stories to the children of the neighborhood one evening—stories of my adventures in riding. I told of my riding on elephants, camels, wild broncos, steers, goats, rams, and dogs. The interest was intense; and to satisfy a last appeal came the story of my first ride—a ride on a broomstick. That ended the stories, because the children rushed to find brooms and, for that evening and several days following, the community was invaded by a broomstick cavalry. Had elephants been available, elephant rides would have been preferred, because they would have been more imposing.

The realization of a sense of freedom is an essential and distinctive trait of play. In the very desire for mastery, freedom is the goal. With power, as with duty, come restrictions and strains to millionaire, ruler, or servant. Therefore all turn to play for diversion, and for the expression of their cravings. Whether in sport, art, invention, adventure, social contact, recreation, or rest, the sense of freedom which play generates is an enduring value.

Play fascinates by the very satisfaction which it engenders and which supports it. The dance, when it is real play and not mere social labor or conformity, carries the dancer away, so that he may fall into a state of dreamy consciousness, intoxicated by the sense of pleasure, lulled by the automatic rhythmic movements, and soothed by the melodious and measured flow of the music. This element of fascination or elation is present in some degree in all play—in the romping of the infant, the love play of the adolescent, the sport and adventure of youth, or the recreation of the adult. Indeed, in this fascination lies a grave danger of play—the danger of overindulgence.

The satisfaction of being a cause is one of the compelling motives in play as well as one of its direct rewards. Closely related to this is the feeling of extension of personality. This is well illustrated in games of competition. The boy who flies the kite the highest is the champion of the group. He who in the flash of wit parries best and thrusts most keenly is master for the moment. The adventurer is a hero in proportion to his success in thrilling deeds. Insofar as achievement expresses and reflects our freest ambition, fancy, or ideal, it is rated as a part of ourselves.

Play is essentially social; it is therefore natural that one of its aims and rewards should be a sense of fellowship. Laying aside petty differences, interests, and points of vantage, the playing group fuses into a common consciousness with common means, common interests, and common enjoyments. Play is the making of social man, welding the bonds of fellowship in the social group. We become like those with whom we play. A sense of fellowship with those among whom we live is one of the truest rewards of life.

Play is satisfying because it is positive, even aggressive. It stands for acquisition, seriousness, and optimism, as may be observed by comparing the child who is busy at play with the child who does not play, or the adult who is young at heart and finds self-expression in play with the youth who has lost this plasticity. Strong proof of this is found in the fact that the feeble-minded play comparatively little.

Play is an expression of the joy of life. This joy is expressed most characteristically not so much in deliberate, systematic play as in the entry of the play attitude into work. Indeed, everything in life presents aspects of play to the eyes of the mentally alert. The play attitude is the most universal medium for the manifestation of a sense of freedom and conviction of the worth of life when these exist.

The spontaneity of play results in a strenuous and whole-hearted exertion. When we work, we walk or plod; when we play, we skip or run. When performing a duty, we do as much as is required; but when we play, we do all we can. Work seldom leads to overdoing, but play offers great temptation in that direction. If football players worked as hard at their mental tasks as on the football field, there would be fewer failures in the classroom. Extreme exertion attracts, especially when it is joyous as in play.

The seriousness of play is one of its fascinations. If we join in a game and are not serious or zealous about it, we are not playing. To play means to be in the game. It is engrossing absorption that drives care away. It is not the golf ball but its pursuit that compels the attention of mature men to the complete exclusion of business and professional cares.

The final secret of the success of play is its fictitious nature; it rests upon make-believe. Liberated from realities, it accepts the ideal and lives it as real. Each game has its distinctive charm. There is the attraction of variety in the very choice of games, and in changes from day to day and from season to season.

Our moments of greatest satisfaction come during activities which are most conspicuously characterized by play attitudes— either from play pure and simple, or from work in which play motives dominate. We all have our work, our set tasks and duties; but those of us who get the most out of life are those whose work would be their preferred play, quite apart from its pursuit as a means of livelihood. Conversely, the most fortunate are those who obtain their relaxation, rest, recreation, stimulation, and self-expression without making tasks of them. The things we do for pleasure are the rewards of life; they are an expression of the freed self, a channel of release from the routine of necessity, the source of inspiration, power, and satisfaction.

* * * *

If the directions for the giving of the experiments have been followed, the reader will have gained a deepened analytical insight into the nature and prevalence of some esthetic laws in art and their role in the appreciation and understanding of music as a form of play.

Chapter 30

WORDS IN MUSIC: BEAUTY IN DICTION

THERE IS A BOOK dealing with words in music called *The Neglected Half*. That title is a very apt description of the present role of words in music. Notorious are the neglect by music schools of training in phonetics, acoustics, and articulation; the ignorance of singers about how the composer fits music to words and how the poet fits words to music; the indifference of singers to the message the words convey; the slovenliness in articulation and phrasing in so-called artistic performance; and the lack of development of the good speaking voice. Strangely enough, there are not many who are concerned about these facts. Witness the very subordinate position given to the subject in manuals of music. Witness the public applause accorded to singers despite gross neglect or abuse of this phase of song.

While there is abundant laboratory material for a technical chapter on this subject, diction in music is at such a primitive stage that a greater service can be rendered to esthetics by using the allotted space to describe as realistically as possible the significance, rights, relationships, and esthetic values of words in music. There are two main aspects of this subject: first, diction, or the artistic articulation and phrasing of words; and, second, the message conveyed by the words.

The present generation is becoming voice-conscious, speech-conscious, and ear-minded. We hear the morning news, the song, the drama, the comedy on the radio. The various arts of speech are now taught from the kindergarten up through the public schools, and have acquired academic status in colleges and universities. The traditional conservatory is passing out.

See section on "Religious Music in Public School Choruses," in *Music Educators Journal,* October 1941.

New demands are being placed upon the musical artist, one of them being proficiency in the art of diction.

ARTISTIC DICTION

The composer who writes the music for poetry already available—lyric, comic, heroic, dramatic—aims to adapt his composition so as to fortify and enhance the meaning of the words. The poet who writes words for music already existing applies dramatic art to the finding and fitting of words to every aspect of the music. Knowledge of phonetic art is a relatively new demand upon poets and composers as a whole, although beautiful illustrations of the principles have always abounded in great music. It opens up a distinctive division in experimental acoustics, which will lay scientific foundations for this aspect of musical esthetics.

It is a common error to assume that artistic phrasing in the vocal art pertains only to the music. What we are coming to recognize now is that artistic phrasing and dramatic movement in song are determined as much by the words or meanings to be conveyed as they are by the music. The performer not only becomes an interpreter of the musical phrasing as illustrated in a song without words, but assumes a double duty in the artistic enunciation of the words and the phrasing for emphasis and meaning.

In this there is room for artistic license, as in the choice of vowel quality, the relative duration of vowels and consonants, and various types of pauses which might not occur in speech by itself. This is, of course, a legitimate phase of art. But even when the words are merely an occasion for vocalizing and are of no consequence in themselves, the demand for adequate articulation still obtains.

The problem of foreign language, so conspicuous in great music, comes to the front anew. The primary aim is not to convey meaning, since the language is not understood by all its hearers, musical art demands clear articulation for enhancement of tone. Indeed, one reason for using a given foreign language, such as Italian, is that it lends itself so well to artistic vocalization; but the main reason is that the poetry and the music fit together better in the original than in most translations. However, given a good translation, song would be more effective if the music were accompanied by words that were understood.

The first step in education for good diction is to emphasize the existence and significance of these demands, and to condemn professionally slovenliness and muddling confusion in the conveying of words in song. Science in the art of speech sets the pace for training in the art of diction for music. The singer must first learn to speak beautifully. The pedagogy of music must draw its first lesson from experimental phonetics in speech. Singing teachers must learn a new lesson—one which can be acquired only by thorough and scientifically organized training.

Let us approach diction in music by studying diction in speech. If the reader will remember throughout the following section that he can substitute the words *beauty in musical diction* wherever the idea of beauty in speech occurs, he may find it helpful in discovering the relation between diction in music and diction in speech. If beautiful diction is mastered in speech, it also will express itself in song.

BEAUTY IN SPEECH

It is appropriate to call attention in this volume to the analogy between beauty in speech and beauty in music. In the University of Iowa, research work on speech has been an outgrowth from research in the psychology of music. The research staff and the achievements through research in the department of speech and related departments of our school of fine arts compare favorably with the staff and the achievements in the department of psychology of music.

I have abundant material for a technical volume *In Search of Beauty in Speech* as a companion piece to the present volume. The scope of such an undertaking is indicated by the introductory paragraph of the section on "Research in Speech" in Chapter IV of my *Pioneering in Psychology,* as follows:

> Under the general head of speech, we may group a number of new approaches to the science of fine arts which had a com-

mon origin in the psychological laboratory. Some of these have developed into highly organized divisions through acoustics, phonetics, dramatics, poetry, linguistics, and education, together with clinical principles and services. The points I wish to emphasize are: (1) the taproot of all these scientific findings and approaches is found in the psychological laboratory; (2) the central psychological laboratory is shared by all engaged in research in these fields from a scientific point of view; (3) the personnel of the staff is intimately interrelated with the personnel in psychology and the differentiated fields; (4) while the applied side of the work is obvious, the spirit and attitude of the approach rests upon pure science and builds on research; (5) success on the practical side is due largely to rigid adherence to the principles of experimental psychology; (6) psychology has been greatly enriched through the generous response of the representatives devoted entirely to the art side; (7) the adoption of the scientific approach to this subject explains in large part the generous support obtained from outside foundations and the great influx of advanced students who carry much of the burden of work as apprentices; (8) both on the theoretical and the practical sides, music and speech have common origins, problems, techniques, and goals.

Instead of delving into this technical material, I shall take the liberty of presenting my point of view, gained from my intimate association with research in this field, by reproducing here a brief presentation, originally prepared for radio.

When you meet a young man and, after five minutes of visiting with him say, "I like him," what is it that you are most likely to go by? Is it the fact that he is six feet tall, weighs two hundred pounds, has a good complexion, stands up straight, has an eagle nose, a well-trimmed mustache, and curly hair? These may all, indeed, contribute toward a favorable impression, but they are all static. They tell you very little about the character and life of the individual—what he is and might be to you.

The real basis of your liking lies largely in his speech. He speaks plainly, easily, and clearly, and certifies his truthfulness by convincing smiles. His speech is like a song, agreeable to the ear. His speech reveals his personality, his inmost character.

It is a mark of culture and charm, far outweighing any of the physical features which we ordinarily group under the heading of appearance. On the other hand, if you arrive at the decision that you dislike him, your decision is likely to be based on the same principles of self-expression through speech. Should your acquaintance be a young lady, the role of speech would be even more outstanding.

Let me stress four fundamental facts: (1) Speech is the principal medium of personal communication, so that success or failure in life depend in large part upon it. (2) Speech impresses us as either beautiful or ugly. We are attracted to those who have beautiful speech, and withdraw from those who have ugly speech. (3) Speech is an index to a person's real character and therefore is an influence in the building of character. (4) The development of beautiful and effective speech should be one of the primary objectives of education in the home, in school, and in society.

The effectiveness of speech. Take the simple case of saying "Good morning." What countless possibilities there are for success or failure! The speaker may convey to you the idea that this is a good morning, or he may express himself so ineffectively as to make you feel that a good morning is bad.

We think at once of the effectiveness of the speech of the orator, the teacher, and other public speakers. Before a large group the voice must carry; the enunciation must be clear and adequate. When the orator or teacher feels that he has not made himself effectively heard by a large portion of his audience, he feels crushed and humiliated. Both he and his audience suffer.

This is even more true in conversation. The person whose speech is ineffective has a continual feeling of failure in the delivery of a message. This works in a vicious circle, often leading to an inferiority complex of far-reaching character.

There is therefore a double aspect to the problem of speech inefficiency: the ineffectiveness in the conveying of ideas and the consequent loss of power, and the development of progressive inferiority complexes, not only in speech itself, but in countless activities more or less remotely associated with speech.

Beauty or ugliness. Consider the significance of beauty or ugliness in speech. Persons appeal to us primarily either through the eye or the ear. It is only remotely that we like or dislike a person as a result of touch, taste, or smell. A beautiful face, commanding stature, and bodily carriage have a universal appeal; but beautiful speech plays a deeper role in our likes and dislikes. A person with a good voice, well placed and well modulated, has charm and arouses admiration. And, conversely, loud, rasping, inflexible, slovenly speech is repulsive to us and often makes us feel sorry for a person who in other respects has great personal charm.

A pleasing voice is one of the fundamental forms of beauty and power in personality. Ugliness of speech is most repulsive when associated with beauty in other respects, such as beautiful features or form, or a good singing voice.

An index to character. Consider the significance of the fact that speech is an index to character. Here, I use speech in a broad sense, including gesture, laughter, smile, attitude, and the countless reflexes which convey ideas. Modesty, sincerity, courage, trustworthiness, truthfulness, and numerous other evidences of character are revealed through speech, not only in the ideas that are conveyed, but in very large and essential part through manner of speech. A good judge of human nature quickly reads personality through speech, even in incidental or ordinary conversation.

A rogue may have a cultivated voice, but we have developed the ability to detect quickly the sincerity or on the other hand the make-believe and artificiality which veneers the genuine character of the person. Imitation is easily detected. Indeed, an appealing and winsome voice on the part of the rogue makes him all the more repulsive to us.

Here, as in the case of efficiency and beauty of voice, the character value of voice is far-reaching in its effect upon the individual. If he acquires the power to avoid ugliness in speech, such as harshness, slovenliness, ineffectiveness, impulsiveness, and hesitation, he becomes conscious of this power and it influences all his behavior. Thus, clear speech immediately becomes a persistent stimulus to avoid slovenliness in all other activities. The consciousness of the power to avoid harshness in speech becomes a constant reminder of the desirability of avoiding harshness in every other activity.

We soon learn to distinguish between what a person says and what he does. In other words, speech is not merely efficient and beautiful or inefficient and ugly, but it is a label for or an index to what a person really is. As a result, the effort to express the truth operates constantly as a motive for being true, for being what he professes to be. Thus, we not only judge character in terms of a person's speech, but his speech tends to form and stabilize his character.

I have stated this from the point of view of *good* speech. The principle applies equally to *bad* speech, and is more strikingly evident to the casual observer. As Demosthenes says:

> As a vessel is known by the sound, whether it be cracked or not; so men are proved by their speeches.

And as Ruskin says:

> There is nothing that I can tell you with more eager desire that you should believe, nothing with wider grounds in my experience for requiring you to believe, than this, that you never will love art well till you love what she mirrors better.

Training for good speech. A new profession has arrived, that of the expert to whom actors, musicians, business people, doctors, lawyers, preachers, and teachers may turn for corrective training in speech. Training for good speech should be and in the future will be one of the primary objectives in the early education of children, both in the home and in the schools. We cannot change our facial features much, except by face lifting or superficially covering up with powder and paint, but we can change our voices. Indeed, every aspect of our speech can be completely changed through early and well-ordered training.

Let me outline briefly the program for speech education as I think it should develop in the near future. The first step would consist in making people speech-conscious by teaching them the significance and the possibilities of good speech. We must begin by educating parents to a full realization of the value and beauty of good speech. They must learn that the young child has natural possibilities for good speech; that it is possible to create good speech; and that they are responsible for preventing speech backwardness in the child. Then we must appeal to the child himself, giving recognition to existing good qualities in his speech, encouraging improvement, and making him conscious of progress and of the value of achievement. And let us not forget that good speech is acquired mainly through imitation.

The teachers of today are also in need of this education. As a rule they have neither effective nor beautiful speech and give the matter little or no attention in the progressive training of the child. We must have an awakening among the leading educators, who set up the goals of education, in order that training in effective and beautiful speech may become a standard objective in the educational organization. It is distressing to find that large numbers of graduate students, who go out with advanced degrees, are seriously handicapped by ineffective and unattractive speech which may detract very seriously from their success in a career.

In order to make people speech-conscious, I have a proposal that picture producers organize a five-minute serial in which very attractive children and those around them engage in little plays exhibiting beautiful speech in its growth from early childhood upward, showing at the same time how beautiful speech is associated with beautiful action—even beautiful thinking and feeling. Think of the value of hearing such a group from week to week and watching the children grow! This project presents great possibilities, both for education and for entertainment. Radio, also, is modifying the speech of our youth to a surprising degree. Witness the good diction in "This is the Army."

When we once become thoroughly speech-conscious, the training will in large part take care of itself; but it must begin early, because the speech habits are set in the home and on the playground before the child reaches school, and stress upon formal training should be made in the early grades.

The training should always have two aspects: first, a positive aim for the cultivation of good speech; and, second, a protective suppression of bad speech habits. Scientific study of the subject has now demonstrated that we can isolate each one of the factors of voice, and train or re-train with excellent results.

The cultivation of good speech is intimately associated with other forms of self-expression, such as the smile, the frown, gestures, posture, ideas, ideals—in short, good taste and gracious action. Training in speech will therefore always involve the refinement of these, and it is largely in the exhibition of the harmonious development of all means of self-expression that we find the charm of effective and cultivated personality.

The mind must first be trained in the perception of beautiful speech, but this is only a step in the learning process. Good speech must become a habit which functions automatically before it can serve adequately for both efficiency and beauty. As Elbert Hubbard once said:

> The best way to cultivate the voice is not to think about it. Actions become regal only when they are unconscious. The voice that holds us captive and lures us on, is used by its owner unconsciously. Fix your mind on the thought and the voice will follow. If you fear you will not be understood, you are losing the thought—you are thinking about the voice. If the voice is allowed to come naturally, easily, and gently, it will take on every tint and emotion of the soul.

THE MESSAGE

The singer has something to say; music adds to the effectiveness and beauty of the saying. Song is words *and* music: the words are the message, the music is the form and accompaniment. To be beautiful, the message should be true, good, and beautiful in itself, and should have beneficent sentimental and emotional values. The opposite of this can be accepted only for contrast, as in comic effect and other artistic devices. Relative importance of the role given to the words differs, the crooner or ballad singer going to one extreme and making the most of the words, whereas the opera singer goes to the other, making the most of the music.

RELIGIOUS MUSIC IN PUBLIC SCHOOL CHORUSES

Religious music for use in the public schools is usually selected for the beauty and dignity of the music, and little attention is given to the words. Directors often fail to recognize the fact that the words which are sung should arouse a deep feeling for the truths which are expressed through beautiful music. Unfortunately, much of the religious music available for choruses is at fault in this respect, and youths in the public schools are taught to sing religious doctrines which they do not and perhaps should not believe.

The words in religious music take three forms: the dramatization of a religious epoch, such as that of the saints and martyrs; the inculcation of denominational doctrines; and the poetic expression of universal sentiments of truth, goodness, and beauty in the spiritual life. It is the third form which belongs in the public schools and which can be of service to the individual and society today. The first two have a great dramatic value; but they carry the conviction that religious thought and life are matters of the past.

It is unfortunate that the bulk of the beautiful religious music available is accompanied by words which express denominational dogmatism and outmoded religious doctrines which do not stir the hearts of young people toward self-expression in beautiful religious thought. Angels, the virgin birth, baptism, blood, pietism, and warring characters in religious doctrines do not express the young people's need as a nondenominational religious group. Heaven and hell may be of interest to many, but not of vital importance for the awakening of religious sentiment through beautiful music. The music is effective in generating genuine response, but the words too often are jarring and are frequently accepted as a necessary evil.

The alibi often given by the director is that the words are legends, symbols, or examples of the way religious people used to think. There is a place for oratorios, anthems, and rituals which dramatize historical doctrine. Such music has a place on the stage, where we do not hesitate to applaud its good performance. But to the main body of public school youth, it conveys the idea that religion is a thing of the past and is therefore of negative value for those outside the doctrinal faith represented.

Universal religious truths constitute one of the finest channels for beautiful poetry in association with beautiful music. But the American people are living now in an age of social and religious reconstruction in which music is going to play a vital and stirring role, if rightly conceived. The religious emphasis which appeals to all thinking people is upon the truth, goodness, and beauty of religious life. To be effective it must steer away from factional dogma, outmoded doctrines, and unbelievable religious fictions.

It has been argued that it is not the function of the public schools to give religious training. To this we can say that respect for spiritual life and appreciation of its beauty *are* functions of public education. It is certainly not a function of American education to promulgate negative religious influences.

This presents a problem to the directors of our public school music, because the words in much of the beautiful religious music of the past do not answer the director's purpose. We must appeal to poets and composers to create for us a new body of beautiful religious poetry associated with beautiful music if the spiritual influences in music are to serve their function in the reconstruction of the social order. We must ask the musicians in the public schools who really believe in the vitality of music for social regeneration and a finer esthetic life to take this fact into account when making their programs.

Music is now in the air, literally and figuratively, as never before. Composers of songs have found a money-making career, but the songs are nearly all of a nonreligious character, which is to be expected. In this unprecedented song-composing movement the religious theme is conspicuously absent, largely because composers do not believe in much of the poetry of the religious music of the past and because of the absence of financial inducements. The outlet for publication is very limited.

We must therefore appeal to the religious leaders in poetry and music to seek their reward at a higher level. Many preachers whose sermons are unknown or forgotten live vibrantly in the beautiful poetry they wrote for music. In the same way many composers will be immortalized by writing beautiful music to beautiful poetry now extant. The public school constituency which has responded so heartily to the cultivation of beautiful music will welcome with it beautiful and vital truths. Directors of music in our public schools are facing new opportunities and new responsibilities for leadership in this movement.

THE WORDS IN CHURCH MUSIC

Leaders in the imminent reconstruction of the world order after the war are quite unanimous in emphasizing the importance of the spiritual life as a guiding force. In this movement religious music may play an important role by vitalizing our worship through dignified music and poetic truth which will inspire followers and serve as a genuine medium for our honest personal communion with God.

Marked progress has been made in recent years in the improvement of Protestant hymnals. Some progress has been achieved in anthems and solo music from the point of view of the religious message conveyed. But there are still many controversial doctrines and outmoded creeds which limit the usefulness of this form of worship for the constantly growing body of religious thinkers.

There is a gratifying movement for emphasis upon those aspects of religious life which are central to all religions and hinge upon the progressive development of truth, goodness, and beauty in the life of the individual and in the church body. There is no shortage of themes; there is no difference of opinion as to emphasis upon truth, goodness, and beauty—individual and social—which are the three great spiritual powers in human life.

Yet in many Protestant churches we are still called upon to give utterance in our musical worship to a great many falsehoods and dead doctrinal assertions to which we would not give utterance in our modern way of thinking and in our common-sense statements of what we believe. A great many Protestant churches are deserted by some of their best constituents because thinking people cannot tolerate the singing of outmoded doctrines in either hymns or anthems. For religious solidarity and the finest type of leadership in the Christian church we should bring these people back into congenial fellowship.

Church music which emphasizes doctrinal specifications that vary from group to group and age to age has a disruptive influence and serves to cultivate factions and strife; whereas music which emphasizes those truths common to all people who try to lead a religious life forms a common bond and tends to generate the broadest and deepest sense of fellowship and co-operation in the higher life.

I recently listed scores of themes taken from the Bible which would make vital subjects for religious solos or anthems. They would not convey factional dogma but could be sung with universal approval by Catholic, Jew, or Protestant. Such must be the music that is to be a power for the incoming social and spiritual awakening! It must be music that can be heard and sung with inspiring conviction by the largest possible group. We should charge our directors of church music with responsibility for selecting those universal or fairly generally accepted truths which we shall sing or hear sung.

I fully realize that religious music must take the form of worship, meditation, and prayer; that the words must have the merit of beautiful poetry; that good poetry makes generous use of poetic license; that a certain amount of hyperbole is permitted; that figures of speech may be bold and concrete; and that historical values must be conserved. None of these features should be sacrificed in the progress we seek. But let us have religious music for our day.

What do these arguments have to do with musical esthetics? A great deal! Truth is beautiful, and in music words should acclaim truth—the more profound the more beautiful. Error is ugly, and the more it affects the higher life the uglier it is. Esthetics as a normative science must cultivate the true and abhor the false. When falsehood is clothed in beautiful music, the music becomes the vendor of spoiled goods. Music lends beauty to poetry, and poetry enhances the beauty of music. Together they generate esthetic emotions and sentiments. If music is ugly, the poetry will suffer; if poetry is repulsive, the music will suffer. Good singing is at its best when a singer has a truth of emotional value to proclaim.[1]

---

[1] This issue regarding the religion of today concerns not only *music* and *religion*; it is at the very heart of *world politics* as a substitute for the atom threat. If religion is to be our "last stand" for global peace, it must be sane and universally acceptable in terms of the ethical aspects of the great religions, built around the idea that it is an attitude which results in progressive realization of truth, goodness and beauty in the life of the individual and of nations. I have tried to implement this idea in a recent article "One World, One Religion" in *School and Society,* September 7, 1946, Vol. 64, No. 1654.

Chapter 31

COLOR IN MUSIC

A PSYCHOLOGICAL MONOGRAPH reporting experiments on color music has led to much discussion in psychology and music,[1] especially in connection with the present association of color with music in motion pictures and color organs. The author of this monograph found that "A preliminary survey of 274 college students revealed 165, or 60 per cent, who showed some tendency to associate color with short musical selections."

This is perhaps a correct statement of fact, but it is misleading when taken to mean that more than half of the listeners have colored hearing. The statement is likely to lead to wild theories and speculations in music and psychology. I therefore wish to state my interpretation of the underlying psychological facts.

Synesthesia is the experience of an associated sensation when a particular sense is stimulated. This may occur in any combination of the senses. *Chromesthesia* is the experience of color when any sense organ other than the eye is stimulated. *Colored hearing* is the seeing of color when the ear is stimulated. Certain persons invariably see a color when they hear a particular tone. The color may vary with pitch, intensity, or timbre, but it is fairly constant for a fair sample of representative tones. The literature on the subject is unreliable because the earlier experiments were made without critical psychological control. An excellent historical treatment of the subject has just been published.[2] Colored hearing varies in degree and stability, but I venture to predict that critical repetition of the historical experiments on this subject will show that true colored hearing is limited to less than one per cent of the population and yet

---

[1] *A Review of Color Music,* by Theodore F. Karwoski and Henry S. Odbert, Psychological Monog., *Psychological Review,* Ohio State University, Columbus.
[2] Alfred G. Engleman, "In Defense of Synaesthesia in Literature," *Philological Quarterly,* University of Iowa Press, XXV, 1946, 1–19.

is a concrete and striking phenomenon. It is usually associated with high-strung temperament and sometimes with hysteria.

How then shall we account for findings like those just cited? In general, I think they may be classified under three heads: entoptic phenomena, visual imagery, and association by analogy.

ENTOPTIC PHENOMENA

Try this experiment. Close your eyes, cover them with your hands, and then observe what a gorgeous display of color in action you see. This is the stuff that dreams are made of, because these colors are most prominent in the dark. After a little training and observation, you will be able to see these colors under various degrees of light and darkness. Indeed, the phenomenon is present every moment in our life and it modifies the actual colors of objects that we see. Therefore, when the class tested was listening, a large portion of the good observers saw these colors and reported that they saw them when they listened to the phrasing.

VISUAL IMAGERY

Wagner, for example, tried to portray fascinating scenes in the mountains. At the time of composition, the scene probably played upon the mind of the composer through all the senses, and so it does to a large portion of intelligent musical listeners. If a movement suggests a scene, the listener is likely to see that scene in color, movement, and perspective, and to experience it through each of the other senses represented. Think of an apple, for example, and it will be seen in size and color, form and taste, touch and weight; and to a good visualizer, the color display will be conspicuous, and yet you merely thought of an apple. Therefore, when one says, "Listen to this phrase," which may suggest moonlight, you not only hear something but you see it. In the citation just made, probably certain phrases suggested certain events or objects which could be seen in color by good visualizers.

ASSOCIATION BY ANALOGY

A bright tone, a quick tempo, or a brilliant movement may make the listener think of a bright color; and if he is a visualizer, he sees it. A phrase displaying excitement may bring up visions of murder or fight and with it the thought of blood; and one sees red. Then there is a great variety of musical moods which tend to be associated with corresponding moods in color scenes; for example, tranquility, fear, anger. This is the way we get meanings out of program music.

Hence, I should say that it is not overstating a psychological fact when more than half of a class in psychology reports seeing colors when they hear music. Most of these experiments may be related through three fixed features in perception: the continuous color activity of the retina which normally goes unobserved but can be seen whenever attention is directed to it; the normal tendency of associating musical sounds with objective situations in which color may play a vivid role; and a wide range of normal habits of association by analogy in which one sense experience suggests another.

Is there then any psychological basis for the current interests in tying up actual color with actual music? The answer is yes, but not through the phenomenon of colored hearing, which is so rare that there is no object in taking it into account; and there is no foundation for the often-claimed theory that there is a physical relationship in vibration frequency for sound and for color which can be utilized. Nor is there any constant tendency wherein two individuals associate the same color with a given tone or phrase for any considerable time.

The success of color music thus depends primarily on the association of general feelings of pleasantness and unpleasantness, agreeableness and disagreeableness, harmony and discord.

Chapter 32

WHY NO GREAT WOMEN COMPOSERS?

How MANY NAMES of women composers have appeared on programs of great and lasting music? Their absence is conspicuous. David Ewen in his recent volume, *Twentieth Century Composers,* presents biographies of seventeen of the world's outstanding composers of the last century, and among these there is not one woman. Claire Reis, in the 1932 edition of *Composers in America,* sketches the lives of 200 composers who have written "in the larger form" and of these only 5.5 per cent are women. The same author gives a supplementary list of 274 composers, presumably of the second order; of these, 11 per cent are women.

Many explanations of this disparity have been offered and argued vigorously. There is no single or simple explanation that holds universally; history, science, sociology, anthropology, and the arts are involved. The problem is, however, fundamentally a psychological one and calls for analysis, although as a psychologist I cannot offer a full or authoritative explanation. Let me list without elaboration some of the issues involved, proceeding by a process of elimination.

NATIVE TALENT

Great composers must be born with musical talent. Nature is prolific in this respect, but individuals, society, and environment are wasteful with such resources. It is only rarely that such seed which nature has implanted comes to full fruition in creative music. Indeed such fruition is especially rare among women. But from all evidence now available it appears that boys and girls inherit musical talent in approximately the same degree, of the same kind, and equally diversified. Therefore, we cannot attribute differences in the inheritance of musical talent to the sex difference.

INTELLIGENCE

Of all musical pursuits, composition demands the highest order of intelligence—both native capacity and cultivated power. This intelligence is fundamentally of the same order as scientific, philosophical, or esthetic intelligence in general, but its content is dominantly musical. Given artistic talent and a musical constitution, a good general intelligence may become a great musical intelligence. Girls tend to average better than boys in public school subjects. While inheritance may be developed in diversified types, present evidence indicates that boys and girls are approximately equal in this endowment. Therefore, the explanation cannot lie in the lack of native resources for musical intelligence.

MUSICAL TEMPERAMENT

Great composers are born with certain mental and nervous, often psychotic and neurotic, dispositions which, when cultivated, take on marked forms of artistic license, sometimes beneficent, sometimes noxious. To favor creative work, the composer must cultivate the beneficent aspect of temperament. It is now generally recognized that artistic temperaments—the musical in particular—are inherited approximately in the same way and to the same extent by boys and girls. Women therefore cannot find an alibi in the supposed lack of this endowment.

CREATIVE IMAGINATION

Composition is an act of invention or creative imagination on a large scale and in diverse forms. It is admitted that women have rich and free imagination, but it is said to be of a less sustained order, while men's achievement in creative work is often attributed to greater native capacity for creative power. For this there is no clear support in genetics. The difference is probably due to environmental influences and should not be attributed to heredity.

MUSICAL PRECOCITY

The great composers as a rule have been precocious, often musical prodigies. Countless potential musical prodigies have been born, probably boys and girls in equal number, but only the "ships that come in" count for much in history and tradition. Since the great musicians as a rule have been men, memories and records of their childhood tend to live. The girl prodigies are forgotten.

EDUCATION

Composition in the larger forms demands a high and intensive order of education. But most of the great composers have been self-educated, often, especially at the higher levels, in the face of most adverse circumstances. The power of genius for outstanding achievement cannot be taught. Teachers of great composers take but little credit for their prodigies. Throughout modern history music has been considered a feminine accomplishment. Many more girls than boys study music. As compared with the useful arts, the fine arts have for the most part been a realm open to women. Musical environment, criticism, and admirers are among the most formative musical influences. These have been equally available for women and for men.

RECENT EMANCIPATION OF WOMEN

It is often said that until recently women have not had a chance; that they have not been free; that modern women will come to the front in this field. Yet, in the Victorian period and later, women were the influential patronesses and promoters of music. They were in search of genius wherever it could be found. The salon was open to men and women on equal terms, and the outcropping of genius is above social considerations. Will the emancipated woman who smokes, dons mannish attire and manners, takes marital obligations lightly, is athletic, and competes freely with men in business, politics, and professions, pave the way for great composers?

MARRIAGE

In the graduate school I have observed that when a woman of marked achievement and fine personality is invested with the doctor's hood, there is a young man around the corner: we hear the wedding march, love's goal is reached, and the promising Ph.D. settles down and gets fat. We find no fault with that; but to the career-minded woman, it is often a tragedy. Yet it need not be and should offer no true alibi. The bearing of one or more children should add to normal development of a woman, and marriage under favorable circumstances occasionally brings to the wife more freedom for self-expression in achievement than the husband—the breadwinner—enjoys. A woman skilled in music is, as a rule, especially admired and sought in marriage; and marriage, as a career in itself, then invites music as an avocation and not as a fierce, all-demanding, time-consuming goal of composition. Seldom is either the husband or the woman willing to make marriage the secondary career. Married women may not have produced great compositions, but they have produced great composers.

ENDURANCE

The achievements of great geniuses came from work, work, work, according to Edison. It often involves excessive, even pathological strain. When we speak of the male as the stronger sex, we usually refer to muscular strength. The passionate intellectual and emotional drain and suffering undergone by the great composers is of a different order. Women can bear, suffer, and sacrifice in such respects fully as much as men.

Summing up the above observations, we may say that the real explanation for the absence of women from the higher fields of achievement in creative music does not lie in any form of limitation by heredity, nor does it lie to any great extent in present limitations of opportunity, environment, or woman's peculiar obligations. Woman is born with many distinctive feminine traits, but it is doubtful if we shall find any of these of critical significance in the present issue. Environmental factors of all sorts often determine types of development and achievement, but each of these may be laid to some other and more fundamental cause.

THEORIES OF URGES

Woman's fundamental urge is to be beautiful, loved, and adored as a person; man's urge is to provide and achieve in a career. There are exceptions; but from these two theories arise the countless forms of differential selection in the choice and pursuit of a goal for life. Education, environment, motivation, obligations, and utilization of resources, often regarded as determinants in themselves, are but incidental modes for the outcropping of these two distinctive male and female urges. They make the eternal feminine and the persistent masculine type. It is the goal that accounts for the difference. Men and women both have their choice and both can take pride in their achievements.

Chapter 33

THE FUTURE OF MUSICAL INSTRUMENTS

ARE WE NEARING THE END of the "horse-and-buggy" stage of musical instruments? Can the possibilities for revolutionary procedures now looming up in the construction of musical instruments be as strategic for music as were the principles embodied in the coming of the automobile and the airplane for transportation? Those of us who remember that faithful servant of man, the horse, and the conveyances he served, look back with fond appreciation upon what amounted to a sort of fellowship with a fine-performing animal and the luxury of being conveyed by him in saddle or on wheels. So future generations may look back upon the past in fond memories of the companionship they have enjoyed with their favorite instruments, which may be destined to a niche in the historical museum. But in spite of competition, the horse has survived, and so probably will the fiddle and some of its companion instruments.

It is now safe to predict that the future instrument maker will be able to produce any sound now known in nature or in art that may possibly have musical significance. We already have at hand the means by which any such sound can be adequately defined, described, specified, measured, analyzed, and reconstructed. And there is reason to think that with the conquest of new and marvelous resources for musical media, musical composition will move with strides in step with instrument building.

The musical devotee is therefore facing new issues, thrilling and possibly heart-rending. Can a musician adapt himself to

---

Extracts from Chapter 7 of the author's *Why We Love Music,* Oliver Ditson Company, Philadelphia.

these changes? Will he tolerate modifications of old instruments, radically new instruments, revolutionary types of ensembles, and fundamental innovations in musical creation? Can musicians adapt themselves to these new musical media and musical forms as rapidly and completely as we have adapted ourselves to the transition from horse and buggy to automobile and airplane within the span of less than half a cenutury? The answer is probably "no," for good reasons. Yet, sooner or later, the transition will come in the form of new musical media, new musical composition, and new types of musical appreciation and attachment.

POSSIBLE LINES OF DEVELOPMENT

We can now foresee that musical instruments will be submitted to critical analysis, with improvements even on the very best; that substitute forms in great variety may be developed for any now available musical instrument; that new instruments will be designed for the production of new tone qualities and other musical effects; that new ensembles may be built for any number or kind of instrument. It is within the bounds of possibility that the entire performance of the symphony orchestra, the symphonic band, and the grand opera may be performed through a single instrument operated by less than a half a dozen persons. The transmission of music by remote control of the instrument has extraordinary possibilities; a vastly superior control of tone for precision and modulation can be realized. The cost of musical instruments may be greatly reduced. The number of players needed in ensemble performance may be reduced, since, on the analogy of the pipe-organ player, one individual may perform for an entire orchestra. Current music which has been hampered by limitations of the instrument may be perfected and new types of music may be introduced. The musical instrument may become a medium for the production as well as the reproduction of song and speech and the musical tone may be associated with other esthetic appeals, such as visual presentation of color, relief, and dramatic action. All of these are within the realm of possible predictability.

NEW MUSIC

The improvement of old instruments and the introduction of new ones will call for an unprecedented revision of existing music and a creation of new forms. When music was written for the well-tempered clavichord, it was limited to the resources of that instrument. The same is true of music for all instruments. Music has been adapted to the limited resources of the instrument. It is reasonable to suppose that composers will respond from time to time with adaptations and compositions embodying the improved range of pitch and loudness and new resources for variety in harmony and richness of tone. It is equally conceivable that the composer may set up new demands to which the inventor and instrument maker may respond. It is difficult to realize what extraordinary musical enrichment may develop under the impetus of instrumental advances. There will be fresh treatments of scales and intervals, since the pitch control will be far more flexible than it has been. Perhaps one of the largest innovations will be in the freer use of intonation not built on any particular scale but soaring with the greatest freedom on an instrument as, for example, we now hear it in the singing of Negro spirituals. Performance scores show that these natural singers defy scales, but produce beautiful effects through their free and soaring pitch inflection. Stringed instruments have been hampered by accompaniment and by tradition and theory. We can anticipate significant developments outside of our diatonic scale which has come to be a sort of straitjacket, at least theoretically. It has been shown, for example, that a quarter-tone instrument is not of much use unless music is written not only for these intervals but in modes, themes, and atmosphere adapted to such purpose. The pitch range of the composition will be extended, so also will the dynamic range. Countless new features can be introduced for enrichment of tone and variety of harmony. Nomenclature will develop so that the composer may not only think in definable terms but may be able to inject new elements of terminology into the score. For various types of ensembles the music will, of course, have to be written or adapted specifically. Stunt music will find here unlimited opportunities for novelty and escape from conventional tone. This may give us relief from the limitations of jazz and swing which have been so boring in recent years. There will undoubtedly be great bewilderment as to the limits of tolerance for new media and new forms for musical creations. History has revealed clearly that the adaptation of taste and tolerance requires time, and conservatism is often a beneficent safeguard.

Chapter 34

THINGS ARE NOT WHAT THEY SEEM

In the psychological approach to musical esthetics, we draw heavily and basically on the concept of normal illusion, as has been shown in Chapter 6, under the title "The Principle of Artistic Deviations From the Regular" and implemented in all succeeding chapters. This conception of illusion as a normal process in perception may best be reinforced for music by an appeal to a sister art in the field of vision.

LAW IN NORMAL ILLUSIONS

To consider a specific principle in graphic and plastic arts, let us take the principle of "deviation from the regular" into the visual field and see how science deals with it as an explanatory principle. As an example, the *illusion of the vertical* may be considered. To get the vital significance of this illusion and its meaning for music, it is essential that the reader shall digress from further reading in this chapter for the present and *actually perform some experiments*. Here are the directions for four very simple but fundamental experiments:

Subject: *The normal illusion of the vertical*

Exper. I: Before reading beyond the present paragraph, draw a horizontal line about the full length of a lead pencil, and, at one end of this line, erect a vertical line to such height that the two lines will look equal in length. Trust your unaided eye and do not measure or move the sheet until you are told to do so!

Exper. II: Draw a similar horizontal line on another sheet of paper and, at the middle of this line, erect a vertical line to a height that looks to you equal to the horizontal line in length.

Exper. III: Without verifying previous results, repeat experiments I and II half a dozen times or more on fresh sheets of paper.

Exper. IV: Without any warning or discussions on the presence of an illusion, repeat these three experiments on as many other normal people as you can find time for.

Now measure the result for all trials and reduce the amount of error to percentage of the longer line.

If you are a good observer, if you have followed the directions and have not made any conscious allowances on the ground of previous knowledge of the illusion, training, prejudice, theory or attempt to beat the experimentor by any aid, you will find the following results: The average errors (a) will be in the same direction in every trial; (b) they will amount to more than 6 per cent in Experiment I; (c) they will amount to more than 12 per cent in Experiment II; (d) they will persist in Experiment III and will vary no more from trial to trial than would normally occur where no illusion is involved in' the judgment of length of lines; (e) they will tend to be somewhat larger in Experiment IV than in the other three experiments on account of the absence of the forewarning. These results are measures of the *power of prediction* which is one of the ultimate evidences of scientific procedure and normality.

These experiments are samples of procedure in the psychological laboratories, and they might be multiplied indefinitely by fractionating the problem and answering one question at a time. Experiment I sets the illusion in its simplest form in that it is free from marked influence of co-operating or negating motives for illusion. Instead of lines, however, we might have taken simply three dots to indicate position and distance. Experiment II shows the effect of varying a single factor, the position of the vertical line. Such variation might be found in thousands of cases, for example, by increasing the complexity of the figure, by adding volume and perspective, or by turning to natural objects such as trees or animals or any parts or proportions of these. Experiment III reveals the persistence of the illusion which might be verified in all common-sense perception of the relations of the vertical to the horizontal in situations of sensory experiences in daily life. Experiment IV shows how we can discover the causes of the variations in the illusions with subjective factors. All such variables are measurable, and they constitute normal perception to the extent that they are predicted.

The illusion of the vertical varies with training, age, sex, intelligence, taste, mental effort, and scores of other ascertainable subjective factors. It varies with the complexity, size, distance, and hundreds of other recordable objective factors. In short, it is present wherever our eyes fall upon one, two, or three dimensions of space involving the vertical.

Like plants and animals, the normal illusion of the vertical may be classified into families, genera, species, varieties, etc., thus enabling us to consolidate in a skeleton classification all we know about an infinite number of cases. Therefore, the classification furnishes a basis for definition, description, explanation, prediction, and control or correction of the illusion.

The *small angle illusion* is another of the score or more of basic families of the normal visual illusions which can be isolated, measured, and classified. The rule is that small angles are always overestimated, that is, they seem larger than they really are. The small angle illusion is as universal and normal as the illusion of the vertical. Many of the established general laws hold for one as for the other. Comparable definitions, classifications, interpretative principles, and explanations may be the same in one as in the other. In short, in our visual world things are not what they seem; but it is what they seem to be that counts most significantly in normal daily life.

Who can question the principle of law in illusion in graphic and plastic arts? Who can fail to see its application to musical esthetics? In the expression of beauty, it is the mind's eye and the mind's ear that count most. Beauty lies not so much in the functioning of the eye or ear as upon the mental impression derived from these senses.

These illustrations from the field of visual experience have given support to four aphorisms which operate in music: there is nothing new under the sun; there is nothing useless in the operations of normal illusions in nature or art; beauty is everywhere for him who can respond to it. All these are overstatements but each conveys a profound truth applicable to all art.

THE DISCOVERY OF A NORMAL ILLUSION OF HEARING

Working in the Yale Laboratory in the early nineties, I made the interesting discovery that I could produce a phantom sound and locate it in any direction from the center of the head with precision in terms of the relative loudness or the difference in the wave phase for the two ears. For years it did not occur to me that this sound could be of other value than the joy of mastering the control of a beautiful, normal illusion [1] in scientific terms. But I proceeded to organize numerous series of experiments which came to a climax at the opening of World War I.

Five or six years after the discovery I found a footnote in one of Lord Rayleigh's treatises in which he reported having made exactly the same observation and presumably treated it as an original discovery, but probably useless. Then, in 1904, while working on this illusion, I came across a reference to exactly the same thing reported just 100 years before as a news item in the *Berlinische Wochenschrift*. Undoubtedly other experimenters must have made similar observations but perhaps regarded them as mere curiosities. Now, who really discovered that illusion? Such experiences of independent origins are relatively frequent in the progress of science and show how deep the taproots of a discovery or invention may run. It is indeed difficult to assign credit and predict a future role for such a discovery.

For one step in my discovery I can claim credit, namely, that I immediately proceeded to organize experiments to give the observed fact a respectable status in science in spite of the fact that at the time I did not foresee any practical use for this newborn idea. I treated it as a beautiful operation of natural law and order in normal illusions, offering theoretical insight into this phase of human experience and behavior.

[1] The term *normal illusion* should be outmoded because it carries the meaning of misguiding and exceptional experience, whereas we now recognize that it is a guiding element in all perception. The nearest we have come to such a word is the word *apperception*, which passed out with the fading of structural psychology. Each school has its own terminology.

THE "USELESS" ILLUSION BECOMES A LIFE-SAVING
WEAPON IN WORLD WAR I

When physicists were confronted with responsibility for locating undersea weapons of war, they hit upon this phenomenon of sound location through binaural hearing and developed instruments for a practical utilization of it, leading the sound into each ear in a different wave phase. The sound of the menacing boat was heard as coming from a specific direction, but this was not the true direction of the source. A conversion table had to be used so that the apparent direction of the sound could be referred to the true direction in accordance with a law of this illusion of binaural hearing.

As chairman of the committee of acoustical problems in the psychological war service, it became my duty and privilege to demonstrate how accuracy in this locating of sound could be increased by the selection of listeners who were ear-minded and had high innate capacity for the location of sound. This greatly increased the accuracy in locating the craft. It was demonstrated, for example, that while one gifted observer could locate with an accuracy of plus or minus one degree, another equally intelligent observer might have an error of plus or minus five degrees or more. A difference of four or more degrees at that time may have meant the loss or saving of millions of dollars in property and hundreds of thousands of lives of men. Just before the Armistice, however, the Navy physicists developed a photographic process to take the place of the listening ear, but, up to that time, the determination of the direction of submarines had been made by means of knowledge of the laws of this illusion in binaural hearing which had been discovered at least three times and was regarded as useless but scientifically interesting. Today it is recognized as the forerunner of radar!

THE ROLE OF NORMAL ILLUSION IN MUSICAL ESTHETICS

The late Colonel Fabian was a millionaire who had made his fortune in wholesale handling of rags for paper. He was the chief promoter of the Baconian cypher which attempted to

prove that Shakespeare did not write *Hamlet*. He was the leading figure in the large staff of cryptographers in World War I,
a mechanical genius and most delightful gentleman who after
the war turned for avocation to the entertainment of scientists.

I had the very great pleasure of spending a week as guest
in his four-story guest house. When I woke up the first morning I heard soft organ tones gradually swelling into exquisite
harmonies, ending with full organ of enchanting beauty. This
was his alarm clock for guests to notify them that he was coming in for breakfast with them. Upon request to see his organ,
he led me through the building and pointed to resonating pipes
and horns scattered all around on the walls and ceilings of the
rooms and halls and then said with some pride, "Here is your
illusion at work." There were several loud-speakers of the same
note in pitch on different floors, but when two or more were
sounded by the organist seated at an isolated console only one
was heard, and the location of that one could be predicted if one
knew the location of each of the contributing speakers. That
location was just as definite as if there had been only one source
of sound. That principle was applied to all notes in the compass
of the organ and the result was a marvelous revelation as if
each note had been played from one specific point. He called
it the harmony of spheres.

Such an organ, the "choralcello," had been exhibited in the
New York Museum of Natural History several years before.
The organist sat at a manual six miles downtown and by the
distribution of a number of loud-speakers for each note
throughout the museum, a magic musical effect was produced.

A few years ago the musical world was startled by the Bell
Telephone demonstration of the function of a whole battery of
normal illusions of this sort when the Philadelphia Symphony
Orchestra, playing on a stage in Philadelphia, with Stokowski
seated at a small console in Washington, D. C., performed for
the entertainment of scientists and musicians under the auspices
of the National Academy. Utilizing a number of the laws of
normal illusion, the engineers were able to produce a realistic
illusion of the third dimension of space by which the Washington listeners could locate instruments on the Philadelphia stage.

Chapter 35

WHY WE LOVE MUSIC

IN COMMENTING on my book *The Psychology of Music,* the magazine *Time* (August 8, 1938) spoke approvingly of the scientific contribution to music but gibed that psychologists have not explained why we love music. I think psychology does offer an adequate explanation for this. It is, of course, immensely intricate, but in high lights I would say that love of music, for those who really do love it, rests upon five fundamental grounds: the physiological, the perceptual, the esthetic, the social, and the creative.

A PSYCHOLOGICAL ANSWER [*]

We love music because we have a physiological organism which registers music and responds to it, somewhat like a resonator. The whole organism responds, involving the central and peripheral nervous system, all the muscles, all the internal organs, and especially the autonomic system with its endocrines, which furnishes a physical basis of emotion. Musical sounds affect nervous control, circulation, digestion, metabolism, body temperature, posture and balance, hunger and thirst, erotic drives and pain, and indeed reverberate in both voluntary and involuntary action. Impressions from the environment are generally classified as good or bad for the organism, beneficent or noxious, attractive or repulsive, sources of pleasure or pain. The response to music is beneficent, bringing about a feeling of well-being and body glow which results in the physiological attitude of attraction and pleasure. Without this there could be no emotional love of music.

---

[*] From *Music Educators Journal,* March 1940.

Like flowers and human faces, sounds in themselves may be beautiful. A single sound in nature or art is capable of appearing in endless variety in terms of pitch, dynamic value, duration, and tonal quality. It may be an object of beauty in itself in thousands of ways quite apart from its utility in music. The tonal world is full of beautiful sounds, and we love them because we are intellectually capable of recognizing elements of beauty and of feeling the beneficent physiological response which they elicit as individual sounds. But they may be beautiful to the untutored mind as well, because they arouse an immediate pleasurable feeling in the same way that a flower may seem beautiful to a child.

When beautiful sounds are woven into beautiful structures, we have music. We admire the harmonic structure, the melodic progressions, the rhythmic patterns, the qualitative modulations in the flow of beautiful sounds. Harmony, balance, symmetry, and contrast become embodied in musical form. Here, the object of our affections is the artistic creation. This is analogous to the astronomer's feeling of the sublime as he looks into the heavens with the insight of his knowledge of the nature and the movements of heavenly bodies. Appreciation of musical art is the expression of our esthetic emotions at their highest. Yet again, the untutored and relatively unmusical tend to experience an immediate feeling of pleasure in the art forms, even though they lack any capacity for knowing wherein the beauty of the music lies. Indeed, often the musically trained, both in performance and in listening, launch themselves in unanalyzed feeling without awareness of technique, theory, or deliberate effort. One of the marvels of true art is that, within certain limitations, it speaks directly to the feelings instead of to the intellect.

Music is a language of emotion. Through it the composer and the performer convey their own emotions to the listener. It is a message, a means of communication which enables the performer and the listener to live for moments in the same tonal world of pleasure. For this reason music has acquired a great social value. It promotes common fellowship and feeling. It is a language in which the worshiper speaks to God, the lover pleads with his sweetheart, the friend expresses his sympathy, and the entertainer spreads good cheer. We love music for its social values.

But there is still another reason why we love music: it furnishes a medium of self-expression for the mere joy of expression and without ulterior purpose; this is play. Music becomes a companion in solitude, a medium through which we can play with the rest of the world. Through it we express our love, our fears, our sympathy, our aspirations, our feelings of fellowship, our communion with the Divine.

Chapter 36

LOOKING AHEAD

As a result of the dawn of the scientific view in music, a radical new vantage ground in the field of esthetics has been established. The learned tomes on esthetics with long historic lineage are massive speculations from the armchair of the musician or the philosopher. We are now in a position to challenge the promoters of these speculative points of view and demand that workers in this field utilize all these new tools for investigation for the discovery of new points of view and the establishment of series of verifiable facts about the nature of beauty in music.

The great search in ages past has been for a theory of what constitutes beauty in music and the answer has been sought in some all-embracing formula with a series of corollaries. These usually manifest a lack of scientific interest and insight into the analyzable and measurable aspects of musical phenomena. Now that we can analyze in the minutest detail the structure of tonal beauty into its thousands of aspects, can measure the reactions of the listener in hearing and appreciation, can submit any specific theory of beauty to critical laboratory analysis, and can establish norms of tolerance for each, we have the basis for the building of a new structure for musical esthetics. It will not be a wholesale solution. It will suffer from the sacrifice science makes by fractionating the issue, and will be an endless job. It will show that what is regarded as beautiful to one person is not necessarily so to another under establishable conditions. It will depict the evolution of musical values in the rise of man which had its groundwork in some of the lower animals. It will rationalize the teaching of music. It will lay a foundation for the blending of instruments and furnish blueprints for the construction of new types of instruments. It will be sympathetic to philosophical or artistic speculation, but will chasten them by verifying or condemning them by critical analysis.

INDEX